THE BEER DIRECTORY

AN INTERNATIONAL GUIDE

Compiled by Heather Wood

A Storey Publishing Book

Storey Communications, Inc.
Schoolhouse Road
Pownal, Vermont 05261

*The mission of Storey Communications is to serve our customers
by publishing practical information that encourages personal independence
in harmony with the environment.*

Edited by Pamela Lappies
Cover design by Cindy McFarland
Cover photograph/illustration by Meredith Maker
Text design and production by Cindy McFarland and Susan Bernier

The information in this book is true and complete to the best of our knowledge. All recommendations are made without guarantee on the part of the author or Storey Communications, Inc. The author and publisher disclaim any liability in connection with the use of this information. For additional information please contact Storey Communications, Inc., Schoolhouse Road, Pownal, Vermont 05261.

Printed in the United States by R.R. Donnelley
First Printing, June 1995

Library of Congress Cataloging-in-Publication Data

The beer directory : an international guide / edited by Heather Wood.
     p.   cm.
  Includes index.
  ISBN 0-88266-903-6
  1. Beer — Directories. I. Wood, Heather.
TP577.B413   1995
641.2'3'09—dc20

                          95-13099
                            CIP

Table of Contents

Thanks
and
Acknowledgments

To Michael Jackson, at one of whose beer tasting dinners
in New York the idea of this directory was born.

To Alan Eames, who put his vast resources at our disposal.

To John Melby, of Texas, for his amazing computer printout.

To Steve Cox, Roger Protz, and CAMRA, who "have lighted
a fire in England that may never be put out."

To Richard Factor, without whom none of this
would have been possible.

To all the people around the world, from breweries, embassies,
chambers of commerce, etc., who tolerated our visits and
answered our letters, faxes, and phone calls.

And to those who didn't answer, perhaps next time.

Introduction

What This Directory Is Not

It is not a guide to the beers of the world. There are no tasting notes, comments on aroma, nose, color, etc., or recipes for making identical brews at home. Indeed, homebrewing as a topic is mentioned only fleetingly — it is too vast an area.

What This Directory Is

It is, as its name states, a directory. Whatever your interest in the world of beer, you will find something among these pages. If you travel, you'll find the addresses of people to contact and places to go: places to drink, learn, or simply visit, all over the globe.

As more and more people of all nations become conscious of the delights of a well-brewed beer as something to be savored instead of simply something to quench the thirst, there is a growing camaraderie that cuts across national and class borders. Whereas only the very rich can afford the best wines, almost anyone can afford a good beer. So grab a pint, or a liter, or whatever, and read on in good health.

—— How to Use this Book ——

We have attempted to provide the most up-to-date and correct information in all our listings. However, we are well aware that errors are unavoidable. Organizations — and even countries — fold up their tents and steal away into the night, and new ones spring up like mushrooms. People change.

We neither endorse by inclusion nor condemn by exclusion any persons, companies, or organizations. If we haven't included your particular favorite brewer or pub, or you know of changes in existing listings, please write to the Editorial Department, Storey Communications, Inc., Schoolhouse Road, Pownal, Vermont 05261. We reserve the right to select listings for subsequent additions.

Other Directories

Many areas of the international beer scene have been very adequately covered by other publications and directories. We have not attempted to duplicate their efforts, but have listed such directories instead.

The online subscriber services and the Internet are excellent places to browse for information about beer. Most seem to be about homebrewing, which this directory does not attempt to address thoroughly, but some groups discuss beer in a more general manner. The time you spend searching for online beer companions will without a doubt be well spent—particularly if you enjoy one of your favorite brews at the same time.

Order of Listings

State or regional listings are alphabetical by city under type.

International Listings

We have tried to make international addresses conform with the customs of each country.

UNITED STATES

National Organizations

Mail Order Beer Clubs

Cider Manufacturers

Importers of Beer and Cider

Collectibles and Other Stuff: Organizations

Collectibles: Sources

Courses of Instruction

Magazines, Newsletters, Journals: Consumer

Magazines and Newsletters: Trade

Books and Publishers

Beer People

Responsible Drinking Programs

Travel Services

Homebrewing Supplies — U.S. Retail Catalogs

State by State (alphabetical by city)
   Breweries, Large, Regional and Micro
   Brewpubs
   Places to Enjoy Beer
   Retail Stores
   Festivals and Events
   Of Historic Interest

Marshall Islands, Puerto Rico, and U.S. Virgin
Islands are listed at the end of the U.S. Listings
by State section.

National Organizations

American Breweriana Association
See Collectibles and Other Stuff.

American Society of Brewing Chemists
3340 Pilot Knob Rd.
St. Paul, MN 55121
(612) 454-7250

American Brewers' Guild
2110 Regis Dr. #B
Davis, CA 95616
(916) 753-0497
Fax (916) 753-0176
Education and training for the craftbrewing industry.

American Beer Association and Gourmet Beer Society
Box 1387
Temecula, CA 92593
(909) 676-2337
Fax (909) 699-3477
Contact: John S Thomas. E-mail Brewbaron@aol.com.
Works to foster American brews, modernize federal and state regulation of brewing and selling beer.

Association of Brewers
P.O. Box 1679
Boulder, CO 80306-1679
(303) 546-6514
Fax (303) 447-2825

Beer Drinkers of America
5151 Golden Foothill Pkwy., #100
El Dorado Hills, CA 95630
(800) 441-BEER
Magazine: *Heads Up*

The Beer Institute
1225 Eye St. NW
Washington, DC 20005
Lobbying organization.

Brewers' Association of America
P.O. Box 876
Belmar, NJ 07719-0876
(908) 280-9153
Contact: Henry B. King

Bureau of Alcohol Tobacco and Firearms
650 Massachusetts Ave. NW
Washington, DC 20001
(202) 927-7777
Government regulatory body.

Hop Growers of America
P.O. Box 9218
Yakima, WA 98909
(509) 248-7043
Fax (509) 248-7044

Institute for Brewing Studies
P.O. Box 1679
Boulder, CO 80306-1679
(303) 447-0816
Fax (303) 447-2825
Nonprofit trade association devoted to the promotion of quality in beer and brewing. Publications, conferences, and more.

National Beverage Retailers Association
5101 River Rd., #108
Bethesda, MD 20816
(301) 656-1494

National Licensed Beverages Association
4214 King St.
Alexandria, VA 22302
(703) 671-7575

National Beer Wholesalers Association
1100 S Washington
Alexandria, VA 22314
(703) 683-4300

National Association of Beverage Importers
1025 Vermont Ave. NW, #1205
Washington, DC 20005
(202) 638-1617

NABA
See section on Collectibles.

North American Guild of Beer Writers
Reilly Rd.
La Grangeville, NY 12540
or
P.O. Box 747
Poughquag, NY 12570
(914) 223-3269
Fax (914) 227-5520
Contact: Rob Haiber
Association of media professionals whose objective is to increase informed media coverage of beer and brewing and to enhance public knowledge and appreciation. Annual awards (open to non-members).

Mail Order Beer Clubs

Members receive monthly shipments of selected brews.

American Beer Club
6399 142nd Ave. N, #117
Clearwater, FL 34620
(800) 953-BEER
Two six-packs per month.

Beer Across America
150 Hilltop Ave.
Barrington, IL 60011-0728
(800) 854-BEER
The original microbrewery beer of the month club.

Premium Beer Club
(800) 671-BREW
Two microbrew four- or six-packs per month. Newsletter.

The Beer Exchange
Chicago, IL
(800) 454-BEER

Beer of the Month Club
(800) 854-2337
Fax (312) 549-0114
Delivers two choice selections each month of beers from around the world.

Beers 2 You
Milwaukee, WI
(800) 323-BEER

Brew-to-You
Box 381
Streamwood, IL 60107
(800) 800-BREW

Great American Beer Club
480C Scotland Rd.
Lakemoor, IL 60050
(800) 879-2747 or
(800) 995-3991
Newsletter, t-shirt.
A twelve-pack per month.

Micro Brew Express
2246 Calle del Mundo
Santa Clara, CA 95054
(408) 748-9090
Fax (408) 748-9099
Club offering two microbrews per month.

Cider Manufacturers

American Hard Cider Co.
Boston, MA
(617) 266-6035
Cider Jack Hard Cider.

Joseph Cerniglia Winery
Cavendish, VT 05153
(800) 654-6382
Woodchuck cider (excellent). T-shirts, mugs. Call to find your local stockist.

Selkirk Cider Co.
Sandpoint, ID 83864
(208) 265-4644
Seven Sisters Apple Cider.

Importers of Beer and Cider

Acme Food Specialties
P.O. Box 4445
Santa Fe Springs, CA
   90670-1457
(310) 946-9494
Fax (310) 944-6809
Ritterbrau, Einbecker UrBock, Konig Pilsener, Schultheiss Berliner Weisse (Germany).

Admiralty Beverage Co.
2336 NW 21st Ave.
Portland, OR 97209
(503) 240-5522
Young's, Scottish & Newcastle (England); Paulaner, EKU, Chimay, Duvel, Hoegaarden, Sapten, Lucifer, Dentegems, more.

All Saints Brands
201 Main St. SE, #323
Minneapolis, MN 55414
Christoffel Bier Blond, La Trappe (Holland) many more.

Amazon
P.O. Box 1466
Brattleboro, VT 05302
(802) 254-3884
Contact: Anne Latchis
Xingu (Brazil). T-shirts available.

Anheuser-Busch
1 Busch Pl.
St Louis, MO 63118
(314) 577-2000
Carlsberg.

Asahi Breweries USA
(310) 541-8680
Asahi Beer Super Dry.

Associated Importers
P.O. Box 2902, Grand
   Central Station
New York, NY 10163
(212) 972-5111

Barton Beers
55 E Monroe St.
Chicago, IL 60603
(312) 346-9200
Fax (312) 346-2213
Double Diamond (UK); Tsingtao (China); Peroni (Italy); San Miguel (Philippines); St. Pauli Girl (Germany); Corona Extra, Corona Light, Coronita, Negra Modelo, Modelo Especial, Pacifico (Mexico).

Belukus Marketing
(609) 589-2414
Young's Beers (UK).

Bier Haus
Copiague, NY 11726
*Hue Beer (Vietnam), Old
Growler (UK).*

Brand Beer
600 Houze Way, #E6
Roswell, GA 30076
(404) 594-7774
Brand.

Brandevor USA
18211 NE 68th St., #E100
Redmond, WA 98052
(206) 881-5095
Simpatico.

**Bulunda Import-Export
Co.**
Jacksonville, FL
(904) 642-1077
Ngoma (Togo).

Century Importers
11911 Freedom Dr., #1100
Reston, VA 22090-5609
(703) 709-6600
Fax (703) 709-6999
*O'Keefe, Kronenbourg, Old
Vienna, Courage, Caribe,
Foster's, more. Taunton Cider
(UK).*

Cherry Company
4461 Malaai St., P.O. Box
1375
Honolulu, HI 96818
(808) 537-5245
Kirin.

Chrissa Imports
50 Cypress Ln.
P.O. Box 548
Brisbane, CA 94005
(415) 468-5770
*Spatenbrau, Konig Pils,
Goesser.*

Condal Imports
2300 Randall Ave.
Bronx, NY 10473
(718) 589-1100
Extracto de Malta.

Crown Jewel Importers
Fairfield, NJ
(201) 575-8886
Monrovia (Liberia).

DAB Importers
770 E Main St., #1A
Morristown, NJ 08057
(609) 234-9400
Fax (609) 234-9640
DAB (Germany).

Domaine Cellars
2040 N Loop W, #200
Houston, TX 77018
(713) 681-5461
Fax (713) 681-8521
Carib.

Dribeck Importers
57 Old Post Rd., #2, P.O.
Box 4000
Greenwich, CT 06830
(203) 622-1124
Beck's.

East Coast Importing
P.O. Box 2739
Acton, MA 01720
(508) 692-8466
*Bitburger, Maisel, Merrydown
Cider.*

Efco Importers
P.O. Box 741
Jenkintown, PA 19046
(215) 224-9022
Fax (215) 885-4584
*Brahma, Broyhan, EKU, St.
Bernard Brau, Tyrolian.*

Eidelweiss Imports
3765 Investment Ln.
West Palm Beach, FL 33404
Hofmark (Germany).

L. Fatato
318 Second St.
Brooklyn, NY 11215
(718) 965-7200
Canadian Ace, Malta El Sol.

**Fischer Beverages
International**
393 Totten Pond Rd.
Waltham, MA 02154
(617) 890-3534
Fischer.

Frank's Distributing
2 Adams St.
Denver, CO 80206
(303) 322-2728
*Algonquin, Gruner, Upper
Canada.*

Gambrinus Importing Co.
14800 San Pedro, #310
San Antonio, TX 78232
(210) 490-9128
*Corona, Modelo, Pacifico,
Cobra, Redback.*

Joseph Gies Import
3345 Southport Ave.
Chicago, IL 60657
(312) 472-4577
EKU, Kulmbacher.

Grolsch Importers
1985 N Park Pl.
Atlanta, GA 30339
(404) 955-8885
Fax (404) 955-7571
Dinkelacker (Germany).

Guinness Import Co.
Landmark Sq., 9th floor
Stamford, CT 06901
(203) 323-3311
*Bass, Guinness, Harp, Pilsner
Urquell, Moosehead, Dos
Equis.*

Frank M. Hartley
1630 Palisades Ave.
Ft. Lee, NJ 07024
(201) 461-4610
Hennenhauser, Horsy.

HDT Importers
6007 NE Stanton, P.O. Box
   13490
Portland, OR 97213-0490
(503) 249-1885
Fax (503) 264-4925
*Kulmbacher
Schweizerhofbrau.*

G. Heileman Brewing Co.
100 Harborview Plz.
La Crosse, WI 54601
(608) 785-1000
*Hacker-Pschorr, Swan,
Castlemaine.*

Highland Distributing Co.
Houston, TX
(713) 862-6364
Mamba (Ivory Coast).

**Hilton Commercial
   Group**
P.O. Box 2026
Toluca Lake, CA 91610
(818) 953-4160
*Vienna Lager, Giovane,
Burgbrau.*

Holsten Import Corp.
120 White Plains Rd.
Elmsford, NY 10523
(914) 345-8900
Fax (914) 332-7148
Holsten (Germany).

Hans Holterbosch
375 Park Ave.
New York, NY 10016
(212) 421-3800
Hofbrau Bavaria (Germany).

Hudepohl Schoenling
1625 Central Pkwy.
Cincinnati, OH 45214
(513) 241-4344
Fax (513) 241-2190
*Staatliches Hofbraeuhaus
(Germany).*

International Brands
441 N Kilbourn Ave.
Chicago, IL 60624
(312) 826-4001
*Guinness, Harp, Bass, St.
Pauli Girl, Kiwi, Nordik Woll,
Ringnes, Dinkelacker,
Mamba, OB, Bohemia, Carta
Blanca, Kirin, more.*

International Beverages
65 Shawmut Rd.
Canton, MA 02021-1461
(617) 821-2712
*Aass, Chimay, Holsten,
Mamba, Schloss Eggenberg,
Timmermans, Upper Canada,
Young's, Burghoff, August
Schell.*

Jacquin International
2633 Trenton Ave.
Philadelphia, PA 19125
(215) 425-9300
Birell.

Kelwil Importers
P.O. Box 1987
Bloomfield, NJ 07003
(201) 748-9010
*Silver Dragon, Yin Long,
Zhuhai.*

Kirin USA
600 Third Ave.
New York, NY 10016
(212) 687-1865
Kirin.

Leonard Kreusch
1 Caesar Pl.
Northvale, NJ 07647
(201) 784-2500
*Euler, Kloster, Maximilian
Bock.*

Labatt Importers
23 Old Kings Way S
Darien, CT 06820
(203) 656-1876
*Labatt's (Canada); Moretti
(Italy); Foster's (Australia);
Whitbread, Mackeson (UK);
Dos Equis (Mexico) and more.*

**Manneken-Brussel
   Imports**
1602 E Cesar Chavez St.
Austin, TX 78702
(512) 472-1012
Fax (512) 472-1544
Chimay (Belgium)

Markstein Enterprises
101 Park Pl.
San Ramon, CA 94583
(510) 838-1919
EKU.

Merchant du Vin Corp.
140 Lakeside Ave., #300
Seattle, WA 98122-6538
(206) 322-5022
Fax (206) 322-5185
Contact: Ian McAllister
Lindemans, Orval, St. Sixtus,
Watou (Belgium); Brasseurs
(France); Aying, Pinkus,
(Germany); Samuel Smith
(UK). And more.

Monarch Import Co.
845 Third Ave., 20th floor
New York, NY 10022
(312) 346-9200
Tsingtao (China).

Mosakin Corp.
Matawan, NJ 07747
(908) 566-9443
Guilder, Star (Nigeria).

Oriental Brewery Co.
619 E Palisade Ave.
Englewood Cliffs, NJ 07632-
1825
(201) 871-7300
Liefmans (Belgium); OB Beer
(Korea).

Pa's Bier
P.O. Box 3243
Long Beach, CA 90803
(310) 421-2818
Edelweiss (Switzerland).

Paterno Imports
2701 S Western Ave.
Chicago, IL 60608
(312) 247-7070
Fax (312) 247-0072
Berliner Kindl (Germany).

Phoenix Imports
2925 Montclair Dr.
Ellicott City, MD 21043
(800) 700-4ALE
Hexen Braeu, Rubens Red &

Gold, Thomas Hardy's Ale,
Royal Oak, Samuchlaus,
Liefmans, Corsendonk,
Gouden Carolus.

Rader Co.
RD 6, Box 12
Boyertown, PA 19512
(610) 367-6075
Brand, Krakus, Kulmbacher,
Paulaner, Gosser, Ringnes,
Holsten, Dinkelacker, Spaten,
Rischer, Tiger, Northern
Goose.

St. Killian Importing Co.
P.O. Box K
Kingston, MA 02364
(617) 585-5165
Wurzburger.

Sapporo USA
1290 Ave. of the Americas
New York, NY 10104
(212) 765-4430
Sapporo.

Scottish & Newcastle
Importers
444 De Haro, #125
San Francisco, CA 94107
(415) 255-4555
Newcastle Brown Ale,
McEwan's, Theakston's Old
Peculier.

Sieb Distributors
418 Seneca Ave.
Ridgewood, NY 11385
(718) 386-1480
Fax (718) 821-8120
Spaten, Franziskaner.

Spaten West
50 Cypress Ln.
Brisbane, CA 94005
(415) 468-7240
Spaten Munich (Germany).

Stawski Distributing Co.
1521 W Haddon Ave.
Chicago, IL 60622
(312) 278-4848
Fax (312) 278-5206
Gosser (Austria); Royal, Faxe
(Denmark); Taj Mahal,
Golden Eagle, Kingfisher
(India); Okocim, Krakus,
Zywiec (Poland); Golden
Pheasant (Slovak); Singha
(Thai).

Stroh Brewery Co.
100 River Pl.
Detroit, MI 48207
(313) 446-2000
Toronto.

Suntory International
1211 Ave. of the Americas
New York, NY 10036
(212) 921-9595
Fax (212) 398-0268
Suntory.

Thames America
Trading Co.
714 Penny Royal Ln.
San Rafael, CA 94903
(415) 492-2204
Fax (415) 492-2207
Maes Pils, Double & Triple
Grimbergen (Belgium);
Golden Promise (Scotland);
Taunton Cider (UK); Welsh
Ale, Welsh Bitter (Wales).

Vanberg & DeWulf
Importers
52 Pioneer St.
Cooperstown, NY 13326
(800) 656-1212
Affligem Abbey, Blanche de
Bruges, Boon Lambics,
Castelain, Duvel, Jenlain,
Mort Subite, Rodenbach,
Saison Dupont, Scaldis
(Belgium); Jade organic
country ale (France).

Van Munching & Co.
1270 Ave. of the Americas
New York, NY 10020
(212) 332-8500
Heineken, Amstel, Grizzly.

Victor Sales
4610 Booth Boyle Ave.
Los Angeles, CA 90058
(213) 583-1864
*Oranjeboom, Red Brewster,
Gosser.*

Warsteiner Importers
Market Tower 1, #500, 3033
  S Parker
Aurora, CO 80014
(303) 750-8862
Warsteiner (Germany).

**Western International
  Imports**
Los Angeles, CA
Snowflake (China).

Whyte & Whyte
Elk Grove Village, IL 60007
(708) 439-4355
Herout Cider (France).

Wines, Ltd.
Beltsville, MD 20705
(301) 210-4000
Xingu (Brazil).

Wisdom Import Sales Co.
17401 Eastman Ave.
Irvine, CA 92713
(714) 261-5533
*Tecate, Bohemia, Carta
Blanca, Chihuahua, Watney's
Red Barrel.*

Collectibles and Other Stuff: Organizations

**American Breweriana
  Association (ABA)**
P.O. Box 11157
Pueblo, CO 81001
(719) 544-9267
*Association of collectors and
historians interested in beer
industry, history, advertising,
collectibles. Library, exchange
service for collectors. Annual
trade show in June. Membership $20 including magazine,
6/year. Local chapters in CO,
MI, TX.*

ABA Bottlecap Exchange
11129 Barman Ave.
Culver City, CA 90230
Contact: David Friedman
Beer and soda bottle caps.

ABA Coaster Exchange
1623 N Lindwood Ave.
Appleton, WI 54914
Contact: Kenneth C.
  Kositzke
Beer coasters.

ABA Label Exchange
4330 W 152 St.
Cleveland, OH 44135
Contact: Pat Wheeler
Beer labels.

ABA Lending Library
5961 E Fountain Circle
Mesa, AZ 85205
Contact: Chris Pastor
*Books on beer, brewing, and
collectibles.*

**ABA Micro Coaster
  Exchange**
298 Charles Rd.
Southampton, PA 18966
Contact: Kevin Bracken
Craft brewery labels.

ABA Napkin Exchange
5132 Round Rock Dr.
El Paso, TX 79924
Contact: Jeffrey H. Coolaw
Beer napkins.

ABA Opener Exchange
448 Crandon Ave.
Calumet City, IL 60409
Contact: Lawrence Biehl
Bottle and can openers.

**ABA Sports Card
  Exchange**
P.O. Box 1492
Portsmouth, VA 23705
Contact: Hugh O. Griffin, Jr.
*Beer-sponsored sports
schedules.*

ABA Label Source
W 2569 Candlelite Way
Appleton, WI 54915
(414) 687-0752
Contact: Bob Meyer

**Beer Can Collectors of
  America**
747 Merus Ct.
Fenton, MO 63026-2092
(314) 343-6486
*News Report 6/year, member-
ship directory, national
Convention. Open to all
collectors of beer cans and
breweriana.*

"Did you ever taste beer? I had a sip of it once," said the small servant. "Here's a state
of things!" cried Mr. Swiveller . . . "She *never* tasted it — it can't be tasted in a sip!"

— Charles Dickens, *The Old Curiosity Shop*

Just for Openers (JFO)
701 E Audubon Lake Dr.
Durham, NC 27713
Contact: John Stanley
Collectors of bottle openers.

Micro Chapter, ECBA
P.O. Box 826
South Windsor, CT 06074-
0826
(203) 644-9582
Contact: Roger Levesque
*Collectors of microbreweriana,
from microbreweries.*

**National Association for
Breweriana Advertising**
2343 Met-to-Wee Ln.
Wauwatosa, WI 53226
(414) 257-0158
Contact: Robert Jaeger
*Encourages the collection,
preservation, and study of
American brewery advertising.
Local chapters. Newsletter 4/
year, membership directory,
annual convention.*

Stein Collectors International
3530 Mimosa Ct.
New Orleans, LA 70131-
8305
Magazine: *Prosit,* 4/year
*Association of collectors. Local
chapter activities, annual
international convention.*

Whiskey Pitcher Collectors Association
19341 W Tahoe Dr.
Mundelein, IL 60060
*Collectors of whiskey pitchers
and advertising, and
advertising water jugs.*

Collectibles: Sources

American Beer Classics
P.O. Box 9008
Solvang, CA 93463
T-shirts, caps.

Bavarian Alps
924 King St.
Alexandria, VA 22314
(703) 683-3994
Steins, glasses, mugs, more.

Beer Label Auctions
16 N Batavia Ave.
Batavia, IL 60510
Contact: Bob Kay
June and December.

Beer, The Catalog
Box 717
Hayward, CA 94543-0717
*Pins, magnets, T-shirts,
miscellaneous stuff.*

Brew Haus
112 High Hill Rd.,
Dept. GR
Wallingford, CT 06492
*Labels, coasters, trays, etc.
Free list.*

Brew-Tees
202 U.S. Rt. 1, #357
Falmouth, ME 04105
(800) 585-TEES
Catalog, T-shirt club.

CAT Collectibles
2734 Columbia Trail
Loveland, OH 45140
*Coasters, labels. SASE with
$1 postage for lists.*

Cheddar Beer Dip

12 oz cream cheese
1½ cup beer
16 oz Cheddar cheese, cubed

2 cloves garlic, peeled
24 small gherkins

Put cream cheese and 1¼ cups beer into a blender. Blend on high for 8 seconds. Add
remaining beer, Cheddar cheese, and garlic. Blend until smooth. Add gherkins and
blend 2 or 3 seconds, until chopped. Serve with crackers or crudites.

— *Pennsylvania recipe*

Chief Promotions
P.O. Box 1483
Oshkosh, WI 54902
Chief Oshkosh Red Lager Beer
t-shirts.

D & A Investments
2055 E Burnside Ctr.
Salt Lake City, UT 84109
(801) 283-6886
Mugs and steins. List
available.

Flash Collectibles
560 N Moorpark Rd.,
   Dept. GR
Thousand Oaks, CA 91360
(800) 266-BEER
American steins. Call for free
catalog.

Glasses, Mugs & Steins
P.O. Box 207
Sun Prairie, WI 53590
(608) 837-9423

Joe Kosmo's Label Line
5663 Lincoln Ave., #B
Cypress, CA 90630
(800) 541-8834
Budweiser collectibles and
more. Free catalog.

Bernie Kostic
30 Third St.
Falls Creek, PA 15840
(814) 375-9414
Beer labels.

Larwood Ltd.
2110 Grand Ave., #3
West Des Moines, IA 50265
(515) 224-5940
Contact: Ted Larsen
Vintage beer cans. Catalog.

Liberty Malt Co.,
   Merchant du Vin
140 Lakeside Ave.
Seattle, WA 98122
(206) 622-1880
Free magazine: *Alephenalia*
   Beer News.
In Pike Place Market. Beer
wear, books, homebrewing
supplies.

Micro Distributing
   Enterprises
2700 W College Ave., #293
Appleton, WI 54914
(310) 493-1682 or
(800) 942-9304 ext 21358
Fax (714) 773-1194
Free catalog: glassware,
steins, shirts, caps.

Rocky Mountain Brewery
   Collectibles
P.O. Box 242
370-A Forest Trail
Winter Park, CO 80482
(970) 726-5035
Fax (970) 726-9346
Contact: Dick Norman
Runs auctions with mailed
catalogs. Write for consign-
ment information.

St. Killian Importing Co.
P.O. Box K
Kingston, MA 02364
(617) 585-5165
J E Hefe-Weissbier glasses.

Sam's Steins &
   Collectibles
2207 Lincoln Hwy. E
Lancaster, PA 17602
(717) 394-6404
Open daily, June to Septem-
ber. Stein list available.

Sierra Nevada
   Brewing Co.
1075 E 20th St.
Chico, CA 95928
(916) 893-3520
Fax (916) 893-1275
Clothes, glassware, other
items. Free catalog. MC, Visa.

Thomas Stein Exchange
11111 Kingsley Rd., #154
Dallas, TX 75328
(800) 666-2684
In TX (214) 341-6133
Specialists in Budweiser
steins. List available.

Thomas Stein Exchange
Snooper's Paradise
U.S. 80
Forney, TX 75126
(214) 564-4214
Specialists in Budweiser
steins. Open daily. List
available.

Courses of Instruction

American Brewers'
   Guild
2110 Regis Dr., #B
Davis, CA 95616
(916) 753-0497
Fax (916) 753-0176
10-week Brewer's Apprentice-
ship course; weekend courses
across the country.

Brewing Courses,
   University Extension,
   UCD
Davis, CA 95616
(916) 757-8899
Fax (916) 757-8558
Intensive brewing courses, all
levels.

Hands-On Brewing School
23883 Madison St.
Torrance, CA 90505
(310) 375-BREW
Fax (310) 373-6097
Contact: Bohemian Brewery Importers
Courses run by brewery designers and equipment sellers.

Microbrewers Association of America Short Courses
4513 Vernon Blvd., #202
Madison, WI 53705
(414) 774-8558
Fax (414) 774-8556
In cooperation with University of Wisconsin. Brewing and malting in fall, packaging in spring.

Microbrewery Planning Course, URI Food Science
530 Liberty Ln.
North Kingston, RI 02852
(401) 792-2466

U.S. Brewers' Academy, Siebel Institute
4055 W Peterson Ave.
Chicago, IL 60646
(312) 463-3400
Fax (312) 463-4962
Diploma course for brewers, short courses in microbrewery operation, brewing, sensory evaluation of beer.

Bring us in Good Ale

Chorus:
Oh bring us in good ale, bring us in good ale,
For our blessed Lady's sake, bring us in good ale
Bring us in no brown bread, for that is made of bran
And bring us in no white bread, for therein is no gain
But bring us in good ale . . .

Bring us in no bacon, for that is passing fat,
But bring us in good ale, and give us enough of that
Bring us in no mutton, for that is passing lean
And bring us in no tripes, for they be seldom clean
But bring us in good ale . . .

Bring us in no eggs, for there are many shells
But bring us in good ale, and give us nothing else
Bring us in no butter, for there are many hairs
And bring us in no pig's flesh, for that will make us bears
But bring us in good ale . . .

Bring us in no puddings, for there is all God's good
And bring us in no venison, that is not for our blood
Bring us in no capon's flesh, for that is often dear
And bring us in no duck's flesh, they slobber in the mire
But bring us in good ale . . .

— *Traditional English drinking song.*

Magazines, Newsletters, Journals: Consumer

Alephenalia Beer News, Marchand du Vin, 140 Lakeside Ave., Seattle, WA 98122. Irregular, free. Beer lore, ads, information.

Ale Street News, P.O. Box 1125, Maywood, NJ 07607. (201) 368-9100, Fax (201) 368-9101. Contact: Tony Forder, Jack Babin. 6/year. Covers beer news in New York, DC, New England, and beyond.

All About Beer, 1627 Marion Ave., Durham, NC 27705. (800) 977-BEER. Contact: Daniel Bradford, Publisher. 6/year. Glossy magazine about beer. Reviews, articles, calendar; covers collectibles, beer cuisine, homebrewing, beer books, etc.

American Breweriana, P.O. Box 11157, Pueblo, CO 81001. (719) 544-9267. 6/year. Magazine of American Breweriana Association. Articles on collecting, history; ads; events calendar.

BarleyCorn, P.O. Box 2328, Falls Church, VA 22042. (703) 573-8970. Contact: George Rivers, Editor. 6/year. Newspaper covering the Mid-Atlantic states. News, reviews, articles, calendar, ads.

Beer and Tavern Chronicle, 277 Madison Ave., New York, NY 10016. Contact: Gregg Smith, Co-editor. 12/year.

Beer Drinkers International, P.O. Box 6402, Ocean Hills, CA 92056.

Beer, the magazine, P.O. Box 717, Hayward, CA 94543-0717. (510) 538-9500. Contact: Bill Owens, Publisher. 6/year.

Brew, 1120 Mulberry St., DesMoines, IO 50309. (515) 243-4929. Contact: Don Walsmith, Publisher. 6/year. Features 4–6 microbreweries in each issue. Featured on Real Beer Page of Internet.

Brew Hawaii, P.O. Box 852, Hauula, HI 96717. (808) 259-6884, Fax (808) 259-9566. Contact: A. S. Tynan, Editor. 6/year. Newspaper of the Hawaii Homebrewers Association. News, reviews, calendar, ads.

Celebrator Beer News, 564 W Sunset, P.O. Box 375, Hayward, CA 94543. (510) 670-0121, Fax (510) 670-0639. Contact: Thomas E. Dalldorf, Editor/Publisher. 6/year. News, articles, reviews, ads.

Dionysos, University of Wisconsin, Superior, WI 54880-2898. 4/year. Scholarly journal of literature and intoxication.

The Malt Advocate, 3416 Oak Hill Rd., Emmaus, PA 18049. (610) 967-1083. 4/year. Dedicated to the discerning consumption of beer and whiskey.

Matter World Times, P.O. Box 275, White Plains, NY 10602. (914) 633-2973. 4/year. No charge, just send two first-class stamps.

Midwest Beer Notes, 339 Sixth Ave., Clayton, WI 54004. (715) 948-2990. Contact: Mike Urseth, Editor/Publisher. 6/year. Covers midwestern states.

Moderation Reader, 4714 NE 50 St., Seattle, WA 98105-2908. (206) 525-0449. Contact: Gene Ford. 6/year. About drinking in moderation.

Northwest Beer Journal, 2677 Fircrest Dr. SE, Port Orchard, WA 98366-5771.

Northwest Brew News, 22833 Bothell-Everett Hwy., #1139, Bothell, WA 98021-9365. (206) 742-5327. Contact: Jim Jamison, Russ Ulrich, Pubishers. 6/year.

Pint Post, 12345 Lake City Way NE, #159, Seattle, WA 98125. (206) 527-7331. Contact: Larry Baush, Publisher. 4/year. Includes membership in Microbrew Appreciation Society.

The Sake Connection, P.O. Box 546, Portland, OR 97206-0546. (503) 289-7596. Contact: Fred Eckhardt, Editor. 4–5/year. Sake traditions, news, etc.

Southern Draft Brew News, 702 Sailfish Rd., Winter Springs, FL 32708-0425. (407) 327-9451 or (407) 677-6017. Contact: Jerry Gengler, Editor. 6/year. Covers the southeast. Articles, news, events, etc.

Suds 'n Stuff, P.O. Box 6402, 4764 Galicia Way, Ocean Hills, CA 92058. (800) 457-6543. Contact: Mike and Bunny Bosak. 6/year.

What's On Tap, P.O. Box 7779, Berkeley, CA 94707-7779. (800) 434-7779, Fax (510) 549-9952. Contact: William Brand. 8/year. Reviews imports and micros.

Yankee Brew News, P.O. Box 520250, Winthrop, MA 02152. (617) 461-5693. 4/year.

Zymurgy, American Homebrewers Association, P.O. Box 1679, Boulder, CO 80306-1679. (303) 447-0816, Fax (303) 447-2825. 5/year. Journal of the American Homebrewers Association.

Magazines and Newsletters: Trade

The American Brewer, P.O. Box 510, Hayward, CA 94541.

Bartender, P.O. Box 158, Liberty Corner, NJ 07938. (908) 766-6006, Fax (908) 766-6607. All about bartending.

Beer Marketer's Insights, 51 Virginia Ave., West Nyack, NY 10994. (914) 358-7751. Contact: Jerry Steinman, Publisher. 23/year, since 1970. Newsletter covering the competitive scene, legislation, court cases, sociological questions of abuse, etc. Also, *Alcohol Issues Insights,* 12/year; *Import Insights,* 1/year, covers import beer industry.

Beer Statistics News, 51 Virginia Ave., West Nyack, NY 10994. (914) 358-7751. Contact: Jerry Steinman, Publisher. 2/month, since 1974. Data on major brewers' shipments in 39 states. Also, *Beer Industry Update,* 1/year, all major developments in the U.S. beer industry.

Beverage World, 150 Great Neck Rd., Great Neck, NY 11021.

The Beverage Communicator, P.O. Box 43, Hartsdale, NY 10530.

Beverage Media, 161 Sixth Ave., New York, NY 10014. (212) 620-0100. 12/year. Trade magazine.

Brewers Digest, 4049 W Peterson Ave., Chicago, IL 60646. (312) 463-7484. 12/year. Covers all aspects of the brewing industry.

Brewers Bulletin, P.O. Box 677, Thiensville, WI 53092-0677.

The Brewing Industry News, P.O. Box 27037, Riverdale, IL 60627.

Brewingtechniques, P.O. Box 3222, Eugene, OR 97403. (800) 427-2993. Contact: Stephen A. Mallery, Publisher. 6/year. Technical information for home- and micro-brewers. Articles, reviews, calendar of events.

Modern Brewery Age, 50 Day St., P.O. Box 5550, Norwalk, CT 06856. (203) 853-6015, Fax (203) 852-8175. Glossy magazine, mainly for the big guys. Also publishers of "Brewing for Profit on a Small Scale," for microbreweries and brewpubs.

The New Brewer, P.O. Box 1679, Boulder, CO 80306-1679. (303) 447-0816, Fax (303) 447-2825. Contact: Virginia Thomas, Editor/Publisher. 6/year magazine of the Institute for Brewing Studies.

Books and Publishers

Beer Across America: A Regional Guide to Brewpubs and Microbreweries, by Marty Nachel. Published by Storey Publishing. To order, call Storey Communications, Inc. (800) 441-5700. A regional guide to American microbreweries.

Beer & Ale, A Video Guide (800) 546-5034. Guide to appreciating beer.

A Beer Drinker's Companion, by Alan Eames. Published by Ayers Rock Press, P.O. Box 1, Harvard, MA 01451. Five thousand years of quotes and anecdotes about beer.

Beer Drinking Games, Mustang Publishing. (901) 521-1406. Fifty beer games, some quite silly.

The Beer Enthusiast, Association of Brewers, P.O. Box 1679, Boulder, CO 80306-1679. (303) 447-0816 (office), (303) 546-6514 (orders), Fax (303) 447-2825. (Phone and fax are for orders.) Catalog of books and paraphernalia for the beer lover, brewer, and homebrewer. Accepts Visa and MasterCard.

The Beer Enthusiast's Guide, by Gregg Smith. Published by Storey Publishing. To order, call Storey Communications, Inc. (800) 441-5700. A comprehensive guide to tasting and judging beers, with notes on hosting a beer-tasting.

Beer Flavor Wheel, P.O. Box 1817, Healdsburg, CA 95448. (707) 431-0947, Fax (707) 431-0358. Contact: Howe Noble Lee. A four-tier laminated wheel to help identify and remember beer flavors.

Beer: Legends, Lore, and Little-Known Facts, by Alan Eames. Published by Storey Publishing. To order, call Storey Communications, Inc. (800) 441-5700. Engaging and amusing facts about beer through the ages.

The Beer Log, by James Robertson. Bosak Publishing, 4754 Galicia Way, Oceanside, CA 92056. (800) 457-6543. Looseleaf book describing over 3,500 beers from over 500 U.S. and world breweries. Annual updates.

Better Beer & How to Brew It, by M.R. Reese. Published by Garden Way Publishing. To order, call Storey Communications, Inc. (800) 441-5700. Includes clear, can't-fail instructions for nineteen ales and beers.

Beverage Marketing Corp., 840 Third Ave., New York, NY 10022. (212) 688-7640. Annual studies on domestic and imported beers. Expensive; for the trade.

Bluewood Books, Box 460313, San Francisco, CA 94146. (415) 285-3354. Contact: Richard Michaels. *Beers of North America, Beer Labels of the World.*

Bosak Publications, (800) 457-6543. Books include *The Beer Drinker's Guide to South Germany*, by James Robertson.

Brewers Publications, P.O. Box 1679, Boulder, CO 80306-1679. (303) 447-0816, Fax (303) 447-2825. Various books and practical manuals on beer and brewing, including *Brewers Resource Directory*, listing all the breweries in the U.S. and Canada, plus ingredient and equipment suppliers, consultants, etc.

Brewing the World's Great Beers: A Step-by-Step Guide, by Dave Miller. Published by Storey Publishing. To order, call Storey Communications, Inc. (800) 441-5700. Includes 85 easy-to-follow recipes — some for beginners, some for veterans.

The Complete Handbook of Home Brewing, by Dave Miller. Published by Garden Way Publishing. To order, call Storey Communications, Inc. (800) 441-5700. Learn to brew fine lagers and ales.

A Concise Guide to Beer Snobbery, by Gary Fish. 1044 NW Bond St., Bend, OR 97701. Free for SASE (2 stamps).

Guide to America's Micro Brewed Beer, by Colin T. Flynn and Randy DelFranco. Published by Rosehill Ents, P.O. Box 1015, Washington, DC 20013-1015. Tasting notes on 230 bottled beers.

Homebrew Favorites: A Coast-to-Coast Collection of More Than 240 Beer and Ale Recipes, by Karl F. Lutzen and Mark Stevens. Published by Storey Publishing. To order, call Storey Communications, Inc. (800) 441-5700. Recipes from all over the U.S. and information on how to create your own recipe.

G. W. Kent, Ann Arbor, MI. Publishers of books about beer and beer making. Available from your bookstore.

Lone Mountain Designs, P.O. Box 113, Silver City, NV 89428. Publishes *Road-Map Guides to the Microbreweries,* by Brian Cooperrider: guide and map to micros in CA, Rocky Mountain States, and Pacific Northwest. Addresses, phone numbers and hours.

New World Guide to Beer, by Michael Jackson. Published by Running Press, 125 S. 22nd St., Philadelphia, PA 19103. Beers and breweries from around the world. Illustrated coffee table book.

On Tap Publications, P.O. Box 71, Clemson, SC 29633. (803) 654-3360. Contact: Steve Johnson, Publisher/Editor. Publisher of brewery guide books. Also, newsletter called *On Tap.* 6/year. For the discriminating beer lover. Beer reviews, brewpub and micro news, ads, and more.

Passport to Adventure Press, P.O. Box 516, Niwot, CO 80544. (303) 652-8179, Fax (303) 652-2268. Publishes *Beer Explorer's Logbook.* Write your own beer diary.

Pocket Guide to Beer, by Michael Jackson. Published by Simon & Schuster.

Redbrick Press, P.O. Box 2184, Reston, VA 22090. Publishers of *California Brewin',* by Jack Erickson. A history and directory of microbrewing in California. Erickson is also the author of other books.

A Short, but Foamy, History of Beer, by William Paul Haiber and Robert Haiber. Published by Info Devels Press, Reilly Rd., La Grangeville, NY, 12540. Fascinating volume on the history of beer, beer around the world, and beer styles.

Storey Communications, Inc., Schoolhouse Rd., Pownal, VT 02561. (802) 823-5200, Fax (802) 823-5810, orders (800) 441-5700. Publishers of books on beer and brewing.

Sweet & Hard Cider: Making It, Using It, & Enjoying It, by Annie Proulx and Lew Nichols. Published by Storey Publishing. To order, call Storey Communications, Inc. (800) 441-5700.

A Taste for Beer, by Stephen Beaumont. Published by Storey Publishing. To order, call Storey Communications, Inc. (800) 441-5700. A general book on the fine art of appreciating beer as a beverage and cooking ingredient.

Beer People

North American Guild of Beer Writers, Reilly Road, La Grangeville, NY 12540. Fax (914) 227-5520. Contact: Rob Haiber. Professional organization. Contact them if you need writers.

Robert Bennet, P.O. Box 1631, Nashville, AR 71852. Author of *Cooking Hot and Spicy Food with Beer.*

James A. Dorsch, 1600 Prince St., #415, Alexandria, VA 22314. E-mail: 74277.2452@CompuServe.com. Beer writer and columnist.

Alan Eames, 75 Pine St., Brattleboro, VT 05301. (802) 254-6100, Fax (802) 254-3884. Dubbed "The Indiana Jones of Beer" and "The Beer King," Eames is a beer writer, historian, and anthropologist, as well as the founding director of the American Museum of Brewing History (KY) and associate editor of *All About Beer.* He appears frequently on television and radio.

Gene Ford, 4714 NE Fiftieth St., Seattle, WA 98105-2908. Author of *The Benefits of Moderate Drinking, The French Paradox and Drinking for Health,* and other books. Publisher of *The Moderation Reader* magazine.

Steve Hindy, c/o Brooklyn Brewery, 118 N Eleventh St., Brooklyn, NY 11211. (718) 486-7422. Writer, lecturer, speaker. Much experience in arranging beer tastings and dinners.

Michael Jackson, 23 Nasmyth St., London W6 OHA, England. Fax 081-741 5267. Writer, lecturer, broadcaster, and TV personality. Probably the best known beer authority in the world. Writes frequently in the U.S. and UK.

Garrett T. Oliver, c/o Brooklyn Brewery, 118 N Eleventh St., Brooklyn, NY 11211. (718) 486-7422. Writer, lecturer, professional brewer, and beer judge.

Bill Owens, Box 717, Hayward, CA 94543-0717. Fax (510) 538-7644. Writer, brewer, and all-round good person.

Roger Protz, c/o CAMRA, 34 Alma Rd., St. Albans, Herts, AL1 3BW, England. Editor of *What's Brewing,* writer, columnist, speaker. Appears regularly on radio and TV.

Gregg Smith, 1900 Parkwood, #E101, Idaho Falls, ID 83401. Writer, journalist, and beer judge.

Peter Terhune, 23 Banks St., Somerville, MA 02144. (617) 776-9506. Beer columnist and writer. New England editor of *Ale St. News;* manager of The Modern Brewer, a homebrew supply store.

Bill Yenne, P.O. Box 460313, San Francisco, CA 94146. (415) 285-8799. Author of many articles and books, including *Beers of North America, Beer Labels of the World, The Ultimate Book of Beer Trivia.*

Responsible Drinking Programs

Anheuser-Busch Consumer Awareness, 1 Busch Place, St. Louis, MO 63118. Education branch that works for responsible drinking. Programs include Know When to Say When; Alert Cab; BACCHUS, on college campuses; I'm Driving, the designated driver concept; and more. Write for information.

Beer Institute, 1225 Eye St. NW, #825, Washington, DC 20005. Works to promote responsible consumption of beer.

The Century Council, 550 S Hope St., #1950, Los Angeles, CA 90071-2604. (213) 624-9898. Nonprofit organization dedicated to reducing alcohol abuse and misuse.

Adolf Coors & Co., 13 & Ford, Golden, CO 80402. (800) 642-6116. Sponsors of the Alcohol, Drugs, Driving and You (ADDY) program. Helps teenagers understand drinking issues.

MADD: Mothers Against Drunk Driving. (800) GET-MADD.

Miller Brewing Co., 3939 W Highland Blvd., Milwaukee, WI 53201. Publishes *Legislative Digest,* news bulletin on state proposals that impact drinking.

Travel Services

State and national tourist offices can be helpful when it comes to traveling, but are mostly woefully ignorant about micros and brewpubs in their areas. Wisconsin is an exception. Local chambers of commerce can be more useful.

Travel Guidebooks. These have become noticeably more beer-aware in the last couple of years. Particularly recommended are the *Lonely Planet Guides* and the *Rough Guides.*

Actually Quite Nice, 5703 Yarrow St., Arvada, CO 80002. (800) 951-PUBS. Contact: Don or Geoff. Guided pub tours of the UK that include bed and breakfast, ground transportation, and beer. Regularly 10 days; custom tours available.

Bavarian Beer Tasting Tours, 228 Commercial St., #120, Nevada City, CA 95959. (916) 274-7955. Contact: Jerry Greif. Intimate tour of Munich with Greif, homebrewer and former Munich resident. Brewery tours, little-known pubs, etc.

Backroads, Brewpub Bicycle Tours, 1516 Fifth St., Berkeley, CA 94710-1740. (800) 462-2848. Six-day tours, July–November, visiting northern California breweries.

Brew Tours International, San Francisco, CA. Fax (415) 851-4181. Travel agency offering tours of Mendocino and San Francisco pubs.

Hermit hoar, in solemn cell,
Wearing out life's evening grey;
Smite thy bosom, sage, and tell
What is bliss, and which the way?
Thus I spoke, and speaking sigh'd
— Scarce repressed the starting tear —
When the smiling sage reply'd —
— Come, my lad, and drink some beer.

— Samuel Johnson (1709-1784)

Gemuetlichkeit, 2892 Chronicle Ave., Hayward, CA 94542-9981. 6/year. Travel newsletter for Germany, Austria, Switzerland.

Great British Pub Crawl, P.O. Box 725, Georgetown, CT 06829. Mid-March, nine days.

Historic Inns of England (800) 227-5550. Visit British pubs, ale tastings, history of brewing, plus darts and skittles.

New Zealand Beer Tasting Pub Tour (800) 951-PUBS. Tour in 1994 includes cruise, plenty pub and brewery visits.

Pub Crawl Cruises, 1120 N Walnut, Bloomington, IN 47404. (800) 457-5717. Narrowboat cruises along UK Midlands canals with experienced pub-crawlers.

Ship 'n' Shore Cruises, 6040 Commerce Blvd., #104, Rohnert Park, CA 94928. (707) 585-0881. Beer cruises with Royal Caribbean.

To Your Health

Ale is a singular remedy against all melancholic diseases, tremor cordis, and maladies of the spleen; it is purgative and of great operation against iliaca passic, and all grippings of the small guts; it cures the stone in the bladder and kidneys and provokes urine wonderfully; it mollifies tumors and swellings in the body; and is very predominant in opening obstructions of the liver. Ale is most effectual for clearing the sight, being applied outwardly it asswageth the insufferable pain of gout, the yeast being laid not to the part pained. It is easeful to pain in the hip called sciatica; indeed, for all defluxions and epidemic diseases whatsoever, and equal good against all contagious diseases, feavers, agues, rhumes, choughes, and all cattarres — of all sicknesses — ale doth heal.

— John Taylor (1580–1653), *The Bard of Beer*

. . . hot beer is excellent good for the keeping of the stomach in good order for concoction, and consequently good health; so it is most excellent for the quenching of thirst. For I have not known thirst since I have used hot beer; let the weather be never so hot, and my work great, yet have I not felt thirst as formerly . . . Cold beer is very pleasant when extreme thirst is in the stomach; but what more dangerous to the health. Many by drinking a cup of cold beer in extreme thirst, have taken a surfeit and killed themselves. Therefore we must not drink cold beer . . .

— Henry Overton (1641)

From *Secret Life of Beer: Legends, Lore, and Little-Known Facts*
by Alan Eames
(©1995, Storey Publishing, Pownal, Vermont)

Homebrew Supplies— U.S. Retail Catalogs

Alfred's Brewing Supply
Carroll Rd.
P.O. Box 5070
Slidell, LA 70469-5070
(504) 641-2545
Fax (504) 641-1883

Ashdown House
612 East Pheasant Way
Bountiful, UT 84010
(801) 295-1005

Beer and Wine Hobby
P.O. Box 3104
Wakefield, MA 01880-3104
(617) 933-8818
Fax (617) 662-0872

Best Brew
5236 Beach Blvd.
Jacksonville, FL 32207
(904) 396-7666

Bierhaus International, Inc.
3723 West 12th St.
Erie, PA 16505
(814) 833-7747

Brew and Wine Hobby
68 Woodbridge Ave.
East Hartford, CT 06108
(203) 528-0592

Brewhaus
4955 Ball Camp Pike
Knoxville, TN 37921
(615) 523-4615

Cellar Homebrew
14411 Greenwood Ave. N.
P.O. Box 33525
Seattle, WA 98133
(206) 365-7660
Fax (206) 365-7677

DeFalco's Home Wine & Beer Supplies
5611 Morningside Dr.
Houston, TX 77005
(713) 523-8154
Fax (713) 523-5284

E.C. Kraus
733 S. Northern
P.O. Box 7850
Independence, MO 64054-7850
(816) 254-7448

Great Fermentations of Marin
87 Larkspur
San Rafael, CA 94901
(415) 459-2520

Home Brew Headquarters
P.O. Box 835166
Richardson, TX 75083-5166
(214) 234-4411
Fax (800) 966-4144

Home Brewery, Inc.
South Old Highway 65
P.O. Box 730
Ozark, MO 65721-0730
(417) 581-0963
Fax (417) 485-0965

International Wine Accessories, Inc.
11020 Audelia Rd., Suite B113
Dallas, TX 75243
(214) 349-6097
Fax (214) 349-8712

James Page Brewery
1300 Quincy St. NE
Minneapolis, MN 55413-1541
(612) 781-8247
Fax (612) 781-5829

O'Briens Cellar Supplies
P.O. Box 284
Wayne, IL 60184-0284
(708) 289-7169

Semplex of USA
4159 Thomas Ave. N.
Minneapolis, MN 55412
(612) 522-0500

Specialty Products International
820 North 14th St.
P.O. Box 784
Erwin, NC 28339-0784
(919) 929-4277

Williams Brewing Company
2594 Nicholson St.
P.O. Box 2195
San Leandro, CA 94577-2195
(510) 895-2739
Fax (510) 895-2745

Wine & Brew By You, Inc.
5760 Bird Rd.
Miami, FL 33155
(305) 667-5757
Fax (305) 667-4266
(winenbrew) — on line

State by State Listings

Entries are alphabetical by city.

Alabama

Alabama Bureau of Tourism and Travel
401 Adams Ave.
P.O. Box 4309
Montgomery, AL 36103-4309
(800) ALA-BAMA
Tourist information.

Breweries, Regional and Micro

Birmingham Brewing Co.
3118 Third Ave. S
Birmingham, AL 35233
(205) 326-6677
Tours Saturday, 10AM–noon.
Call to book. Red Mountain
beers.

Brewpubs

Mill Restaurant
1035 20th St. S
Birmingham, AL 35205
(205) 939-3001
Open daily from 6:30AM.

Port City Brewery
225 Dauphin St.
Mobile, AL 36602
(205) 438-2739

Places to Enjoy Beer

Cosmo's
2012 Magnolia Ave.. #R3
Birmingham, AL 35217
(205) 930-9971

The Diplomat
1413 Montgomery Ave.
Birmingham, AL 35216
(205) 979-1515

Joe Bar
2833 Seventh Ave. S
Birmingham, AL 35233
(205) 252-3237

Finnegan's
3310 Memorial Pkwy. SW
Huntsville, AL 35801
Irish pub. Draft Guinness,
local brews, food, darts,
piano.

Retail Stores

Dee's Alabama Beverage Co.
2398 Greenspring Hwy.
Birmingham, AL 35209
(205) 322-3333

Class Six
Bldg 2906
Ft. Rucker, AL 36362
(205) 598-0283

Festivals and Events

Oktoberfest, Jefferson Civic Center
Birmingham, AL 35288
(205) 923-6564
Contact: C. H. Keasler
512 Grant St.
Mid-October, 3 days. German
food, music, dancing,
beverages, imported gifts from
Alpine countries.

Red Mountain Birthday Party
Southside
Birmingham, AL
(205) 326-6677
Contact: Birmingham
Brewing Co.
Mid-July. Street fair with
entertainment, food, beer,
and fun.

Oktoberfest, Downtown
Cullman, AL 35055
(205) 739-1258
Contact: County Museum,
221 Second Ave. NE
Early October, 3 days.
Celebration of German
heritage with music, food,
dancing, tours of historic
houses, arts and crafts. Call
for schedule of events. Free.

C19 Beer & Winemaking

Constitution Village
404 Madison
Huntsville, AL 35801
In AL (205) 535-6565
Mid-Aug, 3 days. Living
history village gives costumed
demonstrations of traditional
beer and wine-making.

Oktoberfest
VFW Post 49
2222 Dauphin Island Pkwy.
Mobile, AL 36605
(334) 471-5178
Mid-September. Food, drink,
music, and more.

Of Historic Interest

Looney's Tavern
U.S. Hwy. 78E
Dora, AL 35062
(205) 489-5000
Amphitheater and theme park.
Civil War musical detailing
the meeting at Looney's Tavern.
(Dry county.)

Pope's Tavern Museum
203 Hermitage Dr.
Florence, AL 35630
(205) 760-6439
Built in 1811 as a stagecoach
stop and inn, later a Confed-
erate hospital. Exhibits
include decorative glass
bottles.

Lucas Tavern
Old Alabama Town
310 N Hull St.
Montgomery, AL, 36104
(334) 240-4500
*In three blocks of restored
houses and shops.*

Old Tavern Museum
2800 University Blvd.
Tuscaloosa, AL 35401
Fax (205) 758-8163
*1827 inn and stagecoach stop,
now a museum.*

Alaska

**Alaska Division of
Tourism**
P.O. Box 110801
Juneau, AK 99811-0801
(907) 465-2010
Tourist information.

Breweries, Regional and Micro

Bird Creek Brewery
310 E 76nd St., #B
Anchorage, AK 99518
(907) 344-BIRD
Fax (907) 344-5416
Contact: Ike Kelly
*Visitors welcome, tours by
appointment. Old 55 Pale Ale.*

**Raven Ridge
Brewing Co.**
Fairbanks, AK

**Alaskan Brewing &
Bottling Co.**
5429 Shaune Dr.
Juneau, AK 99801-9540
(907) 780-5866
Mail: P.O. Box 241051
Douglas AK 99824
*Free tours: May to September,
Tuesday to Saturday; October*

*to April, Thursday to
Saturday. Alaskan Amber
Beer, Pale Ale, and seasonals.
Gift store, great T-shirts.*

Places to Enjoy Beer

Anchor River Inn
P.O. Box 154
Anchor Point, AK 99556
(907) 235-8531
Fax (907) 235-2296
*Restaurant, lounge, liquor
store.*

**Rumrunners Olde
Town Bar**
Anchorage Hotel
330 E St.
Anchorage, AK 99501
(907) 272-4553
Fax (907) 277-4483

Overlook Bar & Grill
P.O. Box 70
Denali National Park, AK
99755
(907) 683-2641
Fax (907) 683-2323
Restaurant with 47 beers.

Ft. Seward Saloon
P.O. Box 307
Haines, AK 99827
(907) 766-2009
Lodge, saloon, and restaurant.

Alaskan Hotel & Bar
167 S Franklin St.
Juneau, AK 99801
(907) 586-1000

Red Dog Saloon
278 S Franklin St.
Juneau, AK 99801

Anchor Tavern
Front St.
Nome, AK 99762

Arizona

**Arizona Office of
Tourism**
1100 W Washington
Phoenix, AZ 85007
(602) 542-8687
Fax (602) 542-4068
*Tourist information, calendar
of events.*

Breweries, Regional and Micro

Black Mountain Brewery
6245 E Cave Creek Rd.
P.O. Box 1940
Cave Creek, AZ 85331
(602) 254-8594 or 488-6597
Contact: Ed Chilleen
*Ed's Original Cave Creek Beer
and Chili Beer.*

Brewpubs

Beaver St. Brewery
11 S Beaver St.
Flagstaff, AZ 86001
(520) 779-0079
And Whistle Stop Cafe.

O Beer! O Hodgson,
Guinness, Allsopp, Bass!
Names that should be on
every infant's tongue!

— C.S. Calverley
(1831-1884)

Flagstaff Brewing Co.
16 E Rt. 66
Flagstaff, AZ 86001
(520) 773-1442

**Coyote Spring Brewing
Co. & Cafe**
4883 N 20th St.
Phoenix, AZ 85016
(602) 468-0403
Fax (602) 468-0821
Contact: Bill Garrard
*Full service bar and restau-
rant featuring beer-based
recipes. Live blues weekend
nights, outdoor patio. Regular
beers and seasonal specials.
Coyote Gold, Three Blind
Monks, Old Quaker Oatmeal
Stout, Forever Amber, Nutz,
Koyote Koelsch, Trick Pale
Ale.*

Prescott Brewing Co.
130 W Gurley St.
Prescott, AZ 86301
(520) 771-2795

Hops! Bistro & Brewery
7000 E Camelback Rd.
Scottsdale, AZ 85251
(602) 945-4677
*Upscale brewpub serving
award-winning beer and
American bistro cuisine.
Pilsner, Amber Ale, Peter's
Porter, Barley Wine, more.*

Bandersnatch Brewpub
125 E Fifth Ave.
Tempe, AZ 85281
(602) 966-4438
*In the heart of Old Town,
featuring handcrafted ales,*

*pale, bitter, stout, and
seasonals. Real German
breads and bratwurst,
authentic Italian cooking,
specials. Lunch and dinner
daily. Tours any time.*

**Gentle Ben's
Brewing Co.**
841 N Tyndall Ave.
Tucson, AZ 85719
(520) 624-4177
*Bear Down Brown, Taylor's
Raspberry Wheat, Copperhead
Ale.*

Places to Enjoy Beer

**Charley's Restaurant &
Pub**
23 N Leroux St.
Flagstaff, AZ 86001

Main Street Bar & Grill
4 S San Francisco St.
Flagstaff, AZ 86001

The Big Palace Bar
Monteczuma St.
Prescott, AZ 86302
(520) 778-4227

Crow's Nest
4321 N Scottsdale Rd.
Scottsdale, AZ 85251
(602) 941-0602
*Huge selection of micros and
imports.*

**Casey Moore's Oyster
House**
850 S Ash
Tempe, AZ 85281
(602) 968-9935

**Old Chicago Pub &
Pizza**
530 W Broadway
Tempe, AZ 85282
(602) 921-9431

**San Francisco Bar &
Grille**
3922 N Oracle
Tucson, AZ 85705
(520) 292-2233

The Shanty
401 E Ninth St.
Tucson, AZ 85281
(520) 623-2664

Z's Pizza
Sixth St.
Tucson, AZ 85281
*Good selection of draft and
bottles, excellent pizza.*

Retail Stores

Fresco Beer Shop
101 E Butler Ave.
Flagstaff, AZ 86001
(520) 774-8073
*Micros, imports, homebrew
supplies.*

Western Post
10 S San Francisco
Flagstaff, AZ 86001
(602) 774-6521

Sun Devil Liquors
235 N Country Club
Mesa, AZ 85201
(602) 834-5050
*Liquor store, homebrew
supplies. Open daily, accepts
Visa, Mastercard.*

Tops Liquors
909 S Mill Ave.
Tempe, AZ 85281
(602) 967-5643

"I'm only a beer teetotaller, not a champagne
teetotaller."
— George Bernard Shaw, *Candida*

Festivals and Events

Oktoberfest
Mount Lemmon, AZ 85619
(602) 576-1321
Early October, 2 weekends.
German bands, dancers, food.

Oktoberfest
Community Center
Prescott Valley, AZ 86312
(520) 775-4023
Mid-October. German food,
drink, and music.

Beer and Water Tasting
  Festival
Scottsdale Galleria
Scottsdale, AZ 85251
(602) 231-0500
Late October. 100+ imported
and domestic beers and
waters. Live music, silent
auction.

Way Out West
  Oktoberfest
Hayden Square
Tempe, AZ 85281
(602) 350-8181
Early October, 3 days. Polka
and western bands, barbecue.

Arkansas

Arkansas Department of
  Parks and Tourism
1 Capitol Mall
Little Rock, AR 77201
(800) NATURAL
Tourist information, calendar
of events.

Brewpubs

Ozark Brewing Co.
430 W Dickson St.
Fayetteville, AR 72701
(501) 521-2739
Contact: John Gilliam
Restaurant and pub.

Traditionally brewed ales and
lagers. IPA, Alumni Ale,
Koelsch, Weizen.

Weidman's Old Fort
  Brewpub
422 N Third St.
Ft. Smith, AR 72901
(501) 782-9898
1840s German brewery with
underground cellar, now a
restaurant and display of
vintage beer-making
memorabilia.

Vino's Brewpub
923 W Seventh
Little Rock, AR 72201
(501) 375-8468
Contact: Henry E. Lee
Pizzas, brews, live entertain-
ment.

Places to Enjoy Beer

Trolley Car Lounge
Eureka Inn
1 Van Buren
Eureka Springs, AR 72632
(501) 253-9551

Mr. Dunderbak's
McCain Mall
North Little Rock, AR
  72118
(501) 753-8705

Spectator's Grill
3124 Pike Ave.
North Little Rock, AR
  72114
(501) 791-0990

Festivals and Events

Mid-South Beer Festival
Weidman's
422 N Third St.
Ft. Smith, AR 72901
(501) 782-9898
Mid-March.

Oktoberfest
Hot Springs National Park
Hot Springs, AR 71902
(501) 321-1700
Contact: Chamber of
  Commerce, P.O. Box 6090
Late October, 5 days. German-
themed celebration. Parade,
sausage-eating contest, music,
more.

Of Historic Interest

O'Malley's Dinner
  Theatre
600 Main St.
Ft. Smith, AR 72902
Built in 1892, old Anheuser-
Busch brewery.

Potts Tavern
Pottsville, AR 72868
Now houses a hat museum.

Tavern Inn
Old Washington Historic
  Park
Washington, AR 71862
(501) 983-2684
Restored inn, C19 frontier
town.

California

California Office of
  Tourism
801 K St., #1500
Sacramento, CA 95814
(800) 862-2543
Tourist information.

Breweries, Large

Anheuser-Busch
  Brewery
3101 Busch Dr.
Fairfield, CA 94533
(707) 429-2000
Free tours by appointment
only, Monday to Friday
September to April, Monday to

*Saturday May to August, gift
shop. Budweiser, Busch,
Michelob.*

Anheuser-Busch Brewery

16054 Roscoe Blvd.
Van Nuys, CA
(818) 989-5300
*Gift shop. Budweiser, Busch,
Michelob.*

Breweries, Regional and Micro

Humboldt Brewery

856 Tenth St.
Arcata, CA 95521
(707) 826-BREW
*Open daily. Complete pub
menu. Tours available on
request. Gold Rush Pale Ale,
Red Nectar, Stormcellar
Porter, Oatmeal Stout.*

American River Brewing Co.

100 Borland Ave.
Auburn, CA 95603

Old River Brewing Co.

Bakersfield, CA
(805) 398-0454

Bay Brewing Co./Devil Mountain Brewery

2283 Camel Rd.
Benicia, CA 94510
(707) 747-6961
*Railroad Ale, Devil's Brew
Porter.*

Mad River Brewing Co.

Box 767948
Blue Lake, CA 95525
(707) 668-4151

Anderson Valley Brewing Co.

P.O. Box 505
14081 Hwy. 128
Boonville, CA 95415
(707) 895-BEER
Contact: Kenneth Allen,
owner
*Built on site of 1873
Buckhorn Saloon. Open
Thursday to Tuesday for lunch
and dinner. Tours Thursday to
Monday, 3 to 4PM. High
Rollers wheat beer, Poleeko
Gold Light, Belk's Bitter, and
Boont Amber ales, Barney
Flats oatmeal stout,
Deependers Dark porter.*

Beverly Hills Beerhouse Co.

Brisbane, CA 94005
Contract brewed.

Angeles Brewing Co.

10009 Canoga Ave.
Chatsworth, CA 91311
(818) 407-0340

Sierra Nevada Brewing Co.

1075 E 20th St.
Chico, CA 95928
(916) 893-3520
*Sierra Nevada Pale Ale,
Stout, Porter, Pale Bock,
Summerfest; Bigfoot
Barleywine Style Ale.*

Brewski's

Culver City, CA 90230
(310) 202-9400

William & Scott Co.

8460 Higuera St.
Culver City, CA 90232
(310) 815-9950
Contact: Scott Griffiths,
President
*Rhino Chasers Amber Ale and
Lager. Line of T-shirts, etc.
Part of all profits goes to
African Wildlife Foundation.
Contract brewed.*

Golden Pacific Brewing Co.

5515 Doyle St.
Emeryville, CA 94608
(510) 655-3322

Etna Brewing Co.

131 Callahan St.
P.O. Box 757
Etna, CA 96027
(916) 467-5277
*California's northernmost
brewery, built on site of pre-
prohibition Etna Brewery.
Tasting room with old brewery
memorabilia; open house every
Saturday, 1PM. Etna Weizen,
Ale, Dark and Export lagers.*

North Coast Brewing Co.

444 N Main St.
Ft. Bragg, CA 95437
(707) 964-2739
*Brewery and brewpub. Open
for lunch and dinner. Tours by
appointment. Red Seal Ale,
Scrimshaw Pilsner, Old #38
Stout.*

Moonlight Brewing Co.

Fulton, CA 95439
(707) 528-2537

Covany Brewing Co.
Fourth and Grand Sts.
Grover Beach, CA 93433
(805) 489-4042

San Andreas Brewing Co.
737 San Benito St.
Hollister, CA 95023
(408) 637-7074
*Microbrewery with pub
restaurant. Earthquake Pale,
Porter; Seismic, Apricot,
Woodruff, and Cranberry ales;
Survivor Stout; Kit Fox
Amber; Oktoberquake.*

Mendocino Brewing Co.
13351 S Hwy. 101
P.O. Box 400
Hopland, CA 95449
(707) 744-1015
*Hopland Brewery, tours by
appointment. See also
Hopland Brewpub. Peregrine
and Blue Heron Pale Ales,
Red Tail Ale, Black Hawk
Stout.*

Heritage Brewing Co.
Lake Elsinore, CA 92330
(909) 245-1752
Contact: John Stoner, Mark
  Merickle
*Tours, tastings, gift shop. Red
Fox Pale Ale, Mulligan
Premium Lager.*

**St. Stan's Brewery &
  Pub**
821 L St.
Modesto, CA 95354
(209) 524-4782
*And restaurant. Tours on
request. St. Stan's Alt Bier.*

El Toro Brewing Co.
Morgan Hill, CA 95037
(408) 778-BREW

**Murphy's Creek
  Brewing Co.**
French Gulch and Murphys
  Grade Rds.
Murphys, CA 95247
(209) 736-2739

Napa Valley Ale Works
Napa, CA 94559

Nevada City Brewing Co.
75 Bost Ave.
Nevada City, CA 95959
(916) 265-2446
*Tours and complimentary
tastings Friday year-round,
Saturday May to December.
California Gold, Dark, and
Stout lagers.*

Pacific Hop Exchange
156 Hamilton Dr.
Novato, CA 94947
(415) 884-2820

Preservation Ale
Orinda, CA 94563
Contract brewed.

Pete's Brewing Co.
514 High St.
Palo Alto, CA 94301
(415) 328-7383
Fax (415) 327-3675
*Pete's Wicked Ale, Pete's
Wicked Lager. Distributed in
37 states. Contract brewed.*

Hangtown Brewery
Placerville, CA 95667
(916) 621-3999

Tuscan Brewing Co.
Red Bluff, CA 96080

Rubicon Brewing Co.
2004 Capitol Ave.
Sacramento, CA 95814
(916) 448-7032
*Restaurant and brewery. Tours
available. Open daily.
Rubicon Wheat, IPA, Stout,
Hefe Weizen, Amber Ale.*

Anchor Brewing Co.
1705 Mariposa St.
San Francisco, CA 94107
(415) 863-8350
Contact: Fritz Maytag,
  Brewmaster
*Anchor Steam Beer, Anchor
Porter, Liberty Ale, Old
Foghorn Barley Wine.*

McKenzie River Corp.
617 Front St.
San Francisco, CA 94111
*Black Star Premium Lager
Beer. Contract brewed.*

Sankt Gallen Brewery
333 Bush St.
San Francisco, CA 94104
(415) 296-8203
Fax (415) 296-9348
And Cafe Pacifica.

T. Roy Brewing Co.
San Jose, CA 95113
Contract brewed.

Lind Brewing Co.
1933 Davis St., #177
San Leandro, CA 94577
(510) 562-0866
*One of the smallest breweries
in the world, producing only
draft beers. Tours Friday 4–
5:30PM. Produces Drake's Ale
line of beers.*

SLO Brewing Co.
1119 Garden St.
San Luis Obispo, CA 93401
(805) 543-1843

J & L Brewing Co.
P.O. Box 2067
San Rafael, CA 94912
San Rafael Amber and Golden ales.

Yen Sum
3097 Wood Valley Rd.
Sonoma, CA 94476
Yen Sum beer contains ginseng. Contract brewed.

Heckler Brau
Tahoe City, CA 96145
(916) 583-2728

Lake Tahoe Brewing Co.
Tahoe City, CA
Contract brewed.

Southern California Brewing Co.
Torrance, CA
(310) 329-8881

Brewpubs

Tied House Cafe & Brewery #3
8 Pacific Marina
P.O. Box 190
Alameda, CA 94501
(510) 521-4321

Bootleggers Brew Co.
Bakersfield, CA

Bison Brewing Co.
2598 Telegraph Ave.
Berkeley, CA 94704
(510) 841-7734
Open daily for lunch and dinner. Tours by appointment. Monthly art shows.

Triple Rock Brewing Co.
1920 Shattuck Ave.
Berkeley, CA 94704
(510) 843-2739
Home-cooked food; 85 varieties of chili. Pinnacle Pale and Red Rock Ales, Black Rock Porter, plus specialty brews. T-shirts and pins available.

Boulder Creek Brewing Co.
13040 Hwy. 9
Boulder Creek, CA 95006
(408) 338-7882, Office
(408) 338-7175
Open daily, noon to 11PM Monday to Friday, to midnight weekends. Food, live entertainment Wednesday to Saturday, darts, pool. St. Severins Koelsch, O'meal Stout, Pilsner Vaclar, Old Maclunk's Scottish Ale.

Napa Valley Brewing Co.
1250 Lincoln Ave.
Calistoga, CA 94515
(707) 942-4101
Calistoga Inn. Open daily for lunch and dinner. Tours by appointment. House brews are English style ales, plus other

micros and over 100 bottles. Calistoga Red and Wheat ales, Golden Lager.

Heritage Brewing Co.
24921 Dana Point
  Harbor Dr.
Dana Point, CA 92629
(714) 240-2060
Open daily for lunch and dinner. Live entertainment Thursday to Sunday. Tours on request. Sail Ale, Lantern Bay Blonde, High Seas Oatmeal Stout.

Sudwerk, Privatbrauerei Huebsch
2001 Second St.
Davis, CA 95616
(916) 756-BREW
Contact: Karl Eden,
  brewmaster
Year round brews include lager, pilsner, maerzen, plus seasonal offerings. Restaurant open 7 days for lunch and dinner, German and American food. Beer garden.

Lost Coast Brewery & Cafe
617 Fourth St.
Eureka, CA 95501
(707) 445-4480
Fax (707) 445-4483
Brewpub and cafe. Downtown Brown, Summerset Wheat, Lost Coast Amber and Stout.

Fremont Brewing Co.
3350 Stevenson Blvd.
Fremont, CA 99538
(510) 651-5510
Contact: Tom and Dave
  Lawler
Restaurant and sports pub. Mission Wheat, California Amber, Black Cow Stout, Mission Peak Porter, ESB.

They who drink beer will think beer.

— Washington Irving, "Stratford-on-Avon"

Butterfield Brewing Co.
777 E Olive Ave.
Fresno, CA 93728
(209) 264-5521
*Bar and grill featuring San
Joaquin Golden, Bridal Veil
Ale, Tower Dark. Open daily
for lunch and dinner. Tours on
request.*

Fullerton Hofbrau
323 State College Blvd.
Fullerton, CA 92631
(714) 870-7400

Buffalo Bill's Brewery
1082 B St.
Hayward, CA 94541
(510) 886-9823
Contact: Geoff Harries
*Serves lunch. Beer on tap, "in
the box" to go, and limited
bottled beers. Tours available:
Monday is best day.*

Hopland Brewpub
13351 S Hwy. 101
P.O. Box 400
Hopland, CA 95449
(707) 744-1361
*Homestyle cooking. Dart
room, live music on weekends.
Beer garden with trellised
hops and sandbox for kids.
Merchandise store with
display of antique breweriana.
Open daily. See also
Mendocino Brewing Co.*

**Huntington Beach
Brewery**
201 Main St., #E
Huntington Beach, CA
92648
(714) 960-5343

Hops Bistro & Brewery
La Jolla Village Dr.
La Jolla, CA 92037
(619) 587-6677

La Jolla Brewing Co.
7536 Fay Ave.
La Jolla, CA 92037
(619) 551-9253

Marin Brewing Co.
1809 Larkspur Landing
Circle
Larkspur, CA 94939
(415) 461-4677
Contact: Brendan Moylan,
Craig Tasley
*Award-winning brews, good
food. Open for lunch and
dinner, tours on request. Mt.
Tam Pale Ale, Albion Amber
Ale, Pt. Reyes Porter, Marin
Weiss, many more.*

Belmont Brewing Co.
25 39th Place
Long Beach, CA 90803
(310) 433-3891
*Top Sail Ale Long Beach
Crude.*

Los Gatos Brewing Co.
Los Gatos, CA 95030

**Manhattan Beach
Brewing Co.**
124 Manhattan Beach Blvd.
Manhattan Beach, CA
90266
(310) 798-2744

**Tied House Cafe &
Brewery #1**
954 Villa St.
Mountain View, CA 94041
(415) 965-BREW
*Redwood Coast Brewing Co.
Open for lunch and dinner.
Tours Saturday or by
appointment. Alpine Pearl
Pale, Cascade Amber, Wheat-
Bock, Passion Pale.*

Downtown Joe's
902 Main St.
Napa, CA 94559
(707) 258-BEER

TJ's Bar & Grill
7110 Redwood
Novato, CA 94947
(415) 892-3474
J & L Brewing Co.

**Pacific Coast
Brewing Co.**
906 Washington St.
Oakland, CA 94607
(510) 836-2739
*Twenty beers on tap, four
brewed here. Pub is beauti-
fully restored. Award-winning
Gray and Blue Whale Ales,
Killer Whale Stout, Christmas
Ale. Outdoor beer garden.*

**Pacific Beach
Brewhouse**
4475 Mission Blvd.
Pacific Beach, CA 92109
(619) 274-2537
Smokefree.

Brewmeisters
369 N Palm Canyon
Palm Springs, CA 92262

**Gordon Biersch
Brewing Co.**
625 Emerson St.
Palo Alto, CA 94301
(415) 323-7723
*Eclectic lunch and dinner
menu, brewing process visible
from restaurant. German style
beers: Export, Maerzen,
Dunkels. Changing exhibits
of works by local artists.*

Crown City Brewery
300 S Raymond Ave.
Pasadena, CA 91105
(818) 577-5548
Open for lunch and dinner,
tours available (call ahead).

Gordon Biersch Brewery
Restaurant
41 Hugus Alley
Pasadena, CA 91103
(818) 449-0052
Brewers' Lunch every fourth
Saturday.

Sonoma Brewing Co.
50 E Washington St.
Petaluma, CA 94952
(707) 765-9694
Contact: Peter and
Bernadette Bunell
And Dempsey's Pub, on the
river in historic downtown.
Three regular beers: Golden
Eagle and Red Rooster Ales,
Ugly Dog Stout, plus seasonal
specials.

Red, White & Brew
2181 Hilltop Dr.
Redding, CA 96002
(916) 222-5891

Redondo Beach
Brewing Co.
1814 Catalina Ave.
Redondo Beach, CA 90277
(310) 316-8477
Contact: Mike and Dave
Zislis

Riverside Brewing Co.
3397 Seventh St.
Riverside, CA 92501
(909) 784-2739

Hogshead Brewpub
114 J St.
Sacramento, CA 95814
(916) 443-BREW
Open daily. Tours available.

River City Brewing
Sacramento, CA
(916) 447-BREW

Rubicon Brewpub
2004 Capitol Ave.
Sacramento, CA 95814
(916) 448-7032

Brewski's Gaslamp Pub
310 Fifth Ave.
San Diego, CA 92101
(619) 231-7700
Fax (619) 231-0787
Contact: Brin Thompson
Brewery and bistro. Casual
atmosphere, fun and upbeat.
Open 11:30AM to 2AM
Monday to Saturday;
11:30AM to midnight Sunday.
Over 14 different beers
including Red Sails and Aztec
Amber ales, Pioneer Porter.

Callahan's Pub &
Brewery
8280A Mira Mesa Blvd.
San Diego, CA 92126
(619) 578-7892
Callahan Red on tap, plus
Mesa Pale Ale, Bernado
Bitter, Black Mountain Porter,
Lights Out Stout, Nameless
Nut Brown.

Hops Bistro &
Brewery #2
San Diego, CA 92126

Karl Strauss' Old
Columbia Brewery
1157 Columbia St.
San Diego, CA 92101
(619) 234-BREW
Open for lunch and dinner,
American menu. Beer taster
series available. Free tours on
weekends. Thirty different
beers, with 10 or 12 always on
tap. Karl Strauss Amber
Lager, Pt. Loma Lighthouse
Light, Karl's Cream Ale,
Gaslamp Gold Ale, Horton's
Hootch.

Karl Strauss' Brewery
Garden
805 Mira Mesa Blvd.
San Diego, CA 92120

San Diego Brewing Co.
10450 Friars Rd.
San Diego, CA 92120
(619) 284-BREW
Fifty taps.

Cafe Pacifica Brewpub
333 Bush St.
San Francisco, CA 94104
(415) 296-8203
At Sankt Gallen Brewery.

Gordon Biersch
Brewing Co.
2 Harrison St.
San Francisco, CA 94105
(415) 243-8246
Eclectic lunch and dinner
menu, brewing process visible
from restaurant. German style
beers: Export, Maerzen,
Dunkles. Changing exhibits of
works by local artists.

**San Francisco
Brewing Co.**
155 Columbus Ave.
San Francisco, CA 94133
(415) 434-3344
Contact: Allan G. Paul,
Brewmaster
*Open for lunch and dinner.
Tours by appointment.
Albatross Lager, Emperor
Norton, Gripman's Porter,
Serpent Stout, specialty brews.*

20 Tank Brewpub
316 Eleventh St.
San Francisco, CA 94133
(415) 255-9455

**Gordon Biersch
Brewing Co.**
33 E San Fernando St.
San Jose, CA 95113
(408) 294-6785
*Eclectic lunch and dinner
menu, brewing process visible
from restaurant. German style
beers: Export, Maerzen,
Dunkles. Changing exhibits of
works by local artists. Outdoor
beer garden with live jazz in
spring and summer.*

**Tied House Cafe &
Brewery #2**
San Jose, CA 95113
(408) 295-2739

SLO Brewing Co.
1119 Garden St.
San Luis Obispo, CA 93401
(805) 543-1843
*Tours available (call 24 hours
ahead).*

**San Marcos Brewery &
Grill**
1080 W San Marcos Blvd.
San Marcos, CA 92069
(619) 471-0050

Pacific Tap & Grill
812 Fourth St.
San Rafael, CA 94901
(415) 457-9711

Santa Clara Brewing Co.
Santa Clara, CA

**Santa Clarita
Brewing Co.**
20655 Soledad Canyon
Santa Clarita, CA 91351
(805) 298-5676

**Live Soup Brewery &
Cafe**
1602 Ocean St.
Santa Cruz, CA 95060
(408) 458-3461

Los Gatos Brewing Co.
130 G St. N
Santa Cruz, CA 95060
(408) 395-9929

Santa Cruz Brewing Co.
516 Front St.
Santa Cruz, CA 95060
(408) 429-8838
*And Front St. Pub. Open 7
days, tours by appointment.*

**Seabright Brewery, Pub
& Restaurant**
519 Seabright Ave.
Santa Cruz, CA 95062
(408) 426-2739
*Open daily, tours by appoint-
ment. Seabright Amber and
India Pale ales, ESB, Weizen;
Pleasure Point Porter; Ace's
Strong Ale.*

Santa Rosa Brewing Co.
458 B St.
Santa Rosa, CA 95401
(707) 544-4677

Pizza Port
135 N Hwy. 101
Solana Beach, CA 92075
(619) 481-7332
*Solana Beach Brewing Co.
Fine brews, inc a great porter,
and "the best pizza known to
mankind."*

Brewery at Lake Tahoe
3542 S Lake Tahoe Blvd.
South Lake Tahoe, CA

El Dorado Brewing Co.
157 W Adams St.
Stockton, CA 95204
(209) 948-ALES
Stockton Brewery & Cafe.

**Stoddard's Brewhouse &
Eatery**
111 S Murphy Ave.
Sunnyvale, CA 94086
(408) 733-7824

Blue Water Brewing Co.
850 N Lake Blvd.
Tahoe City, CA 96145
(916) 581-BLUE
Contact: Phil Millbrand,
Chris Loughlin

Blind Pig Brewing
Temecula, CA 92390

Pizza Junction
11404 Donner Pass Rd.
Truckee, CA 95734
(916) 587-7411
*Truckee Brewing Co.
Restaurant open daily.
Brewing operation visible
from restaurant.*

Old Baldy Brewing Co.
271 N Second Ave.
Upland, CA 91786
(909) 946-1750
Micro-brewery and restaurant.

Shields Brewing Co.
24 E Santa Clara St.
Ventura, CA 93001
(805) 643-1807
*Self-guided tours. Lunch and
dinner. Open Tuesday to
Sunday. Channel Islands Ale,
Gold Coast Beer, Shields
Stout.*

U-Brew Stores
*A Canadian idea that is
spreading. Brew your own
beer on their premises.*

**Hamilton Gregg
Brewworks**
Hermosa Beach, CA 90254

Places to Enjoy Beer
Jupiter Brewpub
2181 Shattuck Ave.
Berkeley, CA 94704
(510) 843-8277

Bit of England
1448 Burlingame Ave.
Burlingame, CA 94010
(415) 344-1540

Lord Derby Arms
1923 Lake St.
Calistoga, CA 94515

Depot Pub & Billiards
1839 Colfax St.
Concord, CA 94518
(510) 825-POOL
*Twenty-eight micros on tap,
special events.*

**Henry & Harry's Goat
Hill Tavern**
1830 Newport Blvd.
Costa Mesa, CA 92697
(714) 548-8428
*Large tap selection, micros,
imports. Pub games, pub food.*

Mansion Cellars
132 E St.
Davis, CA 95616

Lyon's Brewery
7294 San Ramon Rd.
Dublin, CA 94568
(510) 829-9071
*Forty beers on draft, pub grub,
pool, darts, entertainment.*

Daily's Grill & Bar
5035 Mowry Ave.
Fremont, CA 94536
(510) 791-0545
*Serves custom-brewed Daily's
Gator Bait Ale, many micros
and imports on draft.*

**The Original Barney's
Beanery**
8447 Santa Monica Blvd.
Hollywood, CA
(213) 654-2287
*Vast selection of beers. Open
daily, 10AM to 2AM.*

**Belgium Bistro, de
Kavalier Pub**
Center Livermore and
Pacific Aves.
Livermore, CA 94550
(510) 449-3444
*Large selection of Belgian
beer and Flanders ales, food.*

Mrs. Coffee & Bistro
3004 Pacific Ave.
Livermore, CA 94550
(510) 449-1988

Fogg's
303 Bryant St.
Mountain View, CA 94040
(415) 390-9696
*Around 80 imports, several
drafts.*

Brown Street Grill
1300 Brown St.
Napa, CA 94559
(707) 255-6395
*Restaurant with good range of
micros.*

Harry O'Shortals
304 Lincoln
Napa, CA 94559

Mad Dogs & Englishmen
211 Spring St.
Nevada City, CA 95959

Northridge Inn
19773 Nevada St.
Nevada City, CA 95959

**Barclay's Restaurant &
Pub**
5940 College Ave.
Oakland, CA 94618
(510) 654-1650
*Twenty-six draft beers. Lunch
and dinner 7 days. Beer
garden.*

Hunters Saloon
Doubletree Hotel
100 The City Dr.
Orange, CA 92668
(714) 634-4500
Forty bottled micros.

Fox & Goose
1001 R St.
Sacramento, CA 95814

The Pig's Ear
1987 Diner's Ct.
San Bernardino, CA 92408
(909) 889-1142
Fifteen taps.

Newport Bar & Grill
4935 Newport Ave.
San Diego, CA 92107
(619) 222-0168
Micros on draft.

O'Brien's
4646 Convoy St.
San Diego, CA 92111
(619) 278-9908
Contact: Jim O'Brien
Twenty draft micros plus
Guinness.

CW Saloon
917 Folsom St.
San Francisco, CA 94107
(415) 974-1585
Twenty taps, live bands
Tuesday–Thursday, DJ
dancing weekends.

Edinburgh Castle
950 Geary
San Francisco, CA 94109
British beers on tap. Home of
the Caledonian Society and
the Castle Folk Club.

Jack's Bar
1601 Fillmore
San Francisco, CA 94115
(415) 567-3227
Over 20 taps.

Jack's Elixir
4200 16th St.
San Francisco, CA
(415) 552-1633
Well over 50 taps.

Jack's Taps
1300 Church
San Francisco, CA 94114
(415) 824-3080
Over 30 taps.

Penny Farthing Pub
670 Sutter St.
San Francisco, CA 94102
English style pub, good beer
selection, food, real cider.

Pig & Whistle
2801 Geary Blvd.
San Francisco, CA 94118
(415) 885-4779
Twenty-two taps, lunch and ·
dinner daily, pool, darts.

The Toronado
547 Haight St.
San Francisco, CA 94117
(415) 863-2276
Open daily for lunch and
dinner. Wide range of micros
on tap and bottled, imports.

Father's Office
1018 Montana Ave.
Santa Monica, CA 90403
(310) 451-9330
Around 30 taps.

Ye Olde King's Head
116 Santa Monica Blvd.
Santa Monica, CA 90401
(310) 451-1402
British style pub with Brit
food (gulp!) darts, several
taps.

Old Vic
731 Fourth St.
Santa Rosa, CA 95404

Old Vienna Restaurant
3845 Telegraph Rd.
Ventura, CA 93003
(805) 654-1214
German restaurant, German
food, German beer on draft
and bottled.

Retail Stores

Valley Wine Co.
416 G St.
Davis, CA 95616

Beverage Warehouse
4935 McConnell
Mar Vista, CA 90064
(310) 306-2822
Good selection of micros and
imports.

Thom's Liquors
3354 Grand
Oakland, CA 94610

Chip's Liquor
1926 Garnet Ave.
Pacific Beach, CA 92109

Eddie's Market
217 S Michigan Ave.
Pasadena, CA 91105
(818) 795-2447

McCormick Beverage Co.
4325 Dominguez, #B
Rocklin, CA 95677
(916) 652-8085

Mesa Liquor
4919 Convoy St.
San Diego, CA 92111
(619) 279-5292

Jug Shop
1567 Pacific
San Francisco, CA 94109

99 Bottles of Beer
104 Walnut, #99
Santa Cruz, CA 95060

Village Bottle Shop
222 Mt. Herman
Scotts Valley, CA 95066

Wine Exchange
452 First St. E
Sonoma, CA 95476
(707) 938-1794
Wide selection of micros and
imports. Beer tasting bar.
Open daily.

Festivals and Events

California Midstate Varietal Beerfest
Lake Park, Hwy. 41 W
Atascadero, CA 93423
(805) 466-6680
Contact: Elks, P.O. Box
   1085, Atascadero
*Mid-September. Beer tasting
by variety rather than by
brewery. Food, live music.*

Berkeley BeerFest
Berkeley, CA
Late May.

Beer & Sausage Festival
Calistoga Chamber of
   Commerce
Calistoga, CA 94515
(707) 942-6333
Early October.

Octoberfest at Lyon's Brewery
7284 San Ramon Rd.
Dublin, CA 94568
(510) 829-9071
*Mid-October. Brews from local
micros, food, live German
music. Non-smoking.*

Microbrewers & Antiques Faire
Downtown
Gilroy, CA 95020
*Late Aug, 2 days. Microbrews,
antiques, fine arts, and
breweriana.*

Brew-Ha-Ha Beer Tasting Festival
Ides Hall
735 Main St.
Half Moon Bay, CA 94019
(415) 726-2729
*Early June. Over 50 Califor-
nia micros, live music.*

College Beer Fest
St. Mary's College
Moraga, CA 94556
(510) 631-4200
Contact: Susan Stabler
*Mid-June. Brews from 19
micros, food, live music.*

Small Brewers Festival
Tied House Brewery
Mountain View, CA 94040
Mid-July, 2 days.

Octoberfest
Alpine Meadows
North Lake Tahoe, CA
(916) 581-6900
*Mid-October. Dining,
dancing, and libations with a
Bavarian flair.*

Summer HopFest
Pleasanton, CA 94566
(510) 462-3570
Mid-August.

California Beer Festival
San Diego Sports Arena
San Diego, CA
(619) 225-9813
Fax (619) 224-3010
Contact: Box 1387,
   Temecula CA 92593
*Late April. Brewers, vendors,
speakers, demonstrations, live
music, food, and more.*

KQED International Beer & Food Fest
Concourse Exhibition
   Center
San Francisco, CA
(415) 864-1500
Mid-July.

Brew-Ha-Ha
San Pedro Square
San Jose, CA
(408) 279-1775
Contact: Beth Trask
*Early October, two days.
Micros, non-stop comedy.*

Pacific Coast Beerfest
Earl Warren Showgrounds
Santa Barbara, CA
(805) 687-0766
*Mid-October, two days. Local
and national micros, food,
live music.*

Beer Festival
Northstar Resort
California Hwy. 267
Truckee, CA 96160
(916) 562-2288
Mail: P.O. Box 129
*Mid-June. Over a dozen
microbreweries, beer tasting.
Charity event for Arts for the
Schools.*

Of Historic Interest

Mattei's Tavern
Hwy. 154
Los Olivos, CA 93441
(805) 688-4820
*Historic landmark stagecoach
and railroad inn, now a
restaurant.*

Colorado

Colorado Tourism Board
1625 Broadway, #1700
Denver, CO 80202
(303) 592-1939
*Vacation Guide listing
museums, pioneer villages,
mining towns, ranches, and
much more.*

American Breweriana
16510 E Eleventh Ave.
Aurora, CO 80011
Contact: Nick Clous
Columbine Chapter. For
collectors of breweriana.

Breweries, Large
Anheuser-Busch Brewery
2531 Busch Dr.
Ft. Collins, CO 80524
(303) 490-4500
Free tours daily, concluding
with a visit to the Clydesdale
Hamlet. Budweiser, Busch,
Michelob.

Adolf Coors Co.
12th and Ford
Golden, CO 80402
(303) 277-BEER
Free tours daily except
Sunday and holidays.

Breweries, Regional and Micro

Avery Brewing Co
5763 Arapahoe
Boulder, CO 80301
(303) 440-4324

Beartooth Brewing Co.
Boulder, CO
(303) 444-6993
Contract brewed.

Rockies Brewing Co.
2880 Wilderness Place
Boulder, CO 80301
(303) 444-8448
Oldest microbrewery in
America. Tours daily. Also
pub with lunch and dinner
Monday to Saturday. Boulder
Amber, Porter, and Extra Pale
Ale, Wrigley Red, Fall
Festival, Rockies.

Breckenridge Brewery & Pub
600 S Main St.
Breckenridge, CO 80424
(970) 453-1550
Fax (970) 453-2150
Colorado's first mountain
brewpub, with award-winning
brews. Avalanche Ale,
Mountain Wheat, Oatmeal
Stout, India Pale Ale, Blue
River Bock, Maerzen/
Oktoberfest.

Lone Wolf Brewing Co.
Carbondale, CO
(970) 963-8777

Bristol Brewing Co.
4740 Forge Rd., Suite 108
Colorado Springs, CO 80907
(719) 535-2824
Microbrewery with half
gallons to go. Laughing Lab
Scottish Ale, Red Rocket Pale
Ale, Beehive Honey Wheat,
Winter Warlock Oatmeal
Stout.

Breckenridge Brewery
2220 Blake St.
Denver, CO 80205
(303) 297-3644
Fax (303) 297-2341
The second and larger
Breckenridge. Brewing,
bottling, and kegging. Tours
available, call for times.
Restaurant and bar on
premises. Watch the bottling
line as you dine. Just across
from the new Coors Field
stadium.

Broadway Brewing Co.
2441 Broadway
Denver, CO 80205
(303) 292-5027
Contact: C. S. Derrick, Paul
Starnick

Great Divide Brewing Co.
Denver, CO
(303) 296-9460

Lonetree Brewing Ltd.
375 E 55th Ave.
Denver, CO 80216
(303) 297-3832
Contact: Jim Dallarosa, Ken
Piel

Durango Brewing Co.
3000 Main Ave.
Durango, CO 81301
(970) 247-3396
Durango Dark, Colorfest.

H C Berger Brewing Co.
1900 E Lincoln Ave.
Ft. Collins, CO 80524
(970) 493-9044
Tours by appointment. Kegs,
bottles, and brewery jugs
available. Indigo Pale and
Red Banshee ales, Whistlepin
Wheat Beer.

Odell Brewing Co.
119 Lincoln Ave.
Ft. Collins, CO 80524
(970) 498-9070
Odell's Special Bitter,
Heartland Wheat, 90 Shilling
Ale, Golden Ale.

Life ain't all beer and skittles, and more's the
pity, but what's the odds, so long as you're
happy?

— George du Maurier, *Trilby*

Golden City Brewing Co.
920 12th St.
Golden, CO 80401
(303) 279-8092

Irons Brewing Co.
12354 W Alameda Pkwy.,
Unit E
Lakewood, CO 80228
(303) 985-2337
*Irons Ale, Pilsner, Amber
Lager.*

Silver Plume Brewing Co.
458 Main St.
Silver Plume, CO 80476
(303) 569-3040

Brewpubs

Flying Dog Brewpub
413 E Cooper
Aspen, CO 81611
(970) 925-7464
*Rin Tin Tan, Bullmastiff,
Airedale Pale Ale, Doggie
Style, English Setter Bitter,
Scottie, Ol' Yeller, Hair of the
Dog . . . you get the idea.*

**The Beer Store — You
Brew It**
Boulder, CO
(303) 494-7000
Contact: Doug O'Classen,
Manager
*A Canadian idea that is
spreading. Brew your own
beer on their premises.*

**Mountain Sun Pub &
Brewery**
1535 Pearl St.
Boulder, CO 80302
(303) 345-6360

**Oasis Brewery &
Restaurant**
1095 Canyon Blvd.
Boulder, CO 80302
(303) 449-0363
*Lunch, dinner, late-night
dining, brunch. Five full-time
ales: Oasis Pale, Scarab Red,
Capstone ESB, Tut Brown,
and award-winning Zoser
Stout. Patio, pool tables.*

Walnut Brewery
1123 Walnut St.
Boulder, CO 80302
(303) 447-1345
*Buffalo Gold, Blue Note Ale,
Big Horn Bitter, Devil's Thumb
Stout.*

**Judge Baldwin's
Brewing Co.**
Palmer Center
4 S Cascade Ave.
Colorado Springs, CO 80903
(719) 473-5600
Fax (719) 389-0259
*Beers brewed right behind the
bar, as fresh as they come.
Amber, Porter, Wheat, Pale.*

**Phantom Canyon
Brewpub**
2 E Pikes Peak Ave.
Colorado Springs, CO 80903
(719) 635-2800

Pike's Peak Brewery
2547 Weston Rd.
Colorado Springs, CO 80910
(719) 391-8866

Crested Butte Brewery
214 Elk Ave.
P.O. Box 906
Crested Butte, CO 81224
(970) 349-5026
*And Idle Spur Restaurant.
Red Lady Ale, Bucks Wheat,
3-Pin Porter, Raspberry-
Oatmeal Stout.*

**Wild West Gambling Hall
& Brewery**
443 Bennett Ave.
Cripple Creek, CO 80813
(719) 689-3736

Champion Brewing Co.
1442 Larimer St.
Denver, CO 80202
(303) 534-5444

**Old Louisville
Brewing Co.**
1600 Wynkoop, #4D
Denver, CO 80202
(303) 666-9982

Rock Bottom Brewery
1001 16th St.
Denver, CO 80265
(303) 534-7616
Fax (303) 534-2129
*Also offers fine food and live
jazz. Falcon Pale Ale, Molly's
Titanic Brown, Red Rocks,
Black Diamond Stout,
Jazzberry, Lagerhead, Schwarz
Hacker, Rockies Premium.*

Lo! the poor toper whose untutor'd sense,
Sees bliss in ale, and can with wine dispense;
Whose head proud fancy never taught to steer,
Beyond the muddy ecstasies of beer.

— George Crabbe, *Inebriety*

Tabernash Brewing Co.
205 Denargo Market
Denver, CO 80216
(303) 293-2337

Wynkoop Brewing Co.
1634 18th St.
Denver, CO 80202
(303) 297-2700
Contact: John Hickenlooper
*Colorado's first brewpub. Six
fresh ales on tap, plus daily
specials. Lunch, dinner, and
Sunday brunch.*

Carver Brewing Co.
1022 Main Ave.
Durango, CO 81301
(970) 259-2545
*Raspberry Wheat Ale, Carvers
IPA.*

High Country Brewery
1800 Commerce St.
Estes Park, CO 80517
(970) 586-5421
Estes Park Brewery.

Casa de Colorado
320 Link Ln.
Ft. Collins, CO 80524
(970) 493-2739

**CooperSmith's Pub &
Brewing**
5 Old Town Square
Ft. Collins, CO 80524
(970) 498-0203
*Not Brown, Punjabi Pale, and
Dunraven Ale; Sigda's Green
Chili Beer, CooperSmith's
DunkenWeizen.*

Dimmers Brewpub
The Depot
Ft. Collins, CO
(970) 490-2477

**New Belgium
Brewing Co.**
350 Linden St.
Ft. Collins, CO 80524
(970) 221-0524

Left Hand Brewing Co.
1265 Boston Ave.
Longmont, CO 80501
(303) 772-0258

Namaqua Brewpub
Fourth St.
Loveland, CO
(970) 635-9288

Il Vicino
136 E 2nd St.
Salida, CO 81201
(719) 539-5219

Heavenly Daze Brewery
1860 Ski Times Square
Steamboat Springs, CO
80477
(970) 879-8080

**Steamboat Brewery &
Tavern**
435 Lincoln Ave.
Steamboat Springs, CO
80477
(970) 879-2233

**Brewed & Baked in
Telluride**
127 S Fir, Box 575
Telluride, CO 81435
(970) 728-6324
*Brewery plus bakery, deli,
pizza and pasta. Snow Wheat,
Runner's High, Pandora
Porter.*

San Juan Brewing Co.
00 S Townsend
P.O. Box 1989
Telluride, CO 81435
(970) 728-0100
*Black Bear Porter, Boomer-
ang Brown, Tomboy Bitter,
Galloping Goose Golden Ale.*

**Hubcap Brewery &
Kitchen**
143 E Meadow Dr.
P.O. Box 3333
Vail, CO 81658
(970) 476-5757
*Hi-tech decor. Rainbow Trout
Stout, Solstice Ale, Bock n'
Roll, Vail Fest, White River
Wheat, Camp Hale Golden,
Ace, and Beaver Tail Brown
ales.*

Places to Enjoy Beer

Woody Creek Tavern
0002 Woody Creek Plaza
Aspen, CO 81611
(970) 923-4585

**Old Chicago Bar &
Restaurant**
1102 Pearl St.
Boulder, CO 80302
(303) 443-5031
*Fourteen taps, 114 bottles,
great pizza.*

**Beckett's Brewhouse &
Restaurant**
128 S Tejon St.
Colorado Springs, CO 80903
(719) 633-3230

**Old Chicago Beer, Pasta
& Pizza**
7115 Commerce Center Dr.
Colorado Springs, CO 80919
(719) 593-7678
*Fresh pasta, deep dish pizza,
world beer tour of 114 brews.*

Old Chicago Beer, Pasta & Pizza
118 N Tejon St.
Colorado Springs, CO 80903
(719) 634-8812
Fresh pasta, deep dish pizza, world beer tour of 114 brews.

Duffy's Shamrock
1635 Court Place
Denver, CO 80202
(303) 534-4935

B&B's Pickle Barrel
122 W Laurel
Ft. Collins, CO 80524
(970) 484-0235

Chesterfield, Bottomsley & Potts
1415 W Elizabeth
Ft. Collins, CO 80521
(970) 221-1139

County Cork
313 W Drake Rd.
Ft. Collins, CO 80526
(970) 498-7550
Sixteen beers on tap.

Mulligan's
2439 S College
Ft. Collins, CO 80525
(970) 482-3554

Old Town Ale House
25 Old Town Square
Ft. Collins, CO 80524
(970) 493-2213

Washington's
132 La Porte Ave.
Ft. Collins, CO 80524
(970) 493-1603

Smiling Moose
2501 Eleventh Ave.
Greeley, CO 80631
(303) 356-7010

Matty Silk's Restaurant
Ski Time Square
Steamboat Springs, CO 80477
(970) 879-2441

Retail Stores

Grog Shop
710 E Durant
Aspen, CO 81611
(970) 925-3000

A-OK Liquors
2690 28th St.
Boulder, CO 80301
(303) 444-4711

Cheers Liquor Mart
1105 N Circle Dr.
Colorado Springs, CO 80909
(719) 574-2244

Argonaut
700 E Colfax Ave.
Denver, CO 80203
(303) 831-7788

Bonnie Brae Wine & Liquor Mart
785 S University Blvd.
Denver, CO 80209
(303) 733-7261
Over 30 boutique beers, over 100 imports.

Aggie Liquors
429 Canyon Ave.
Ft. Collins, CO 80521
(970) 482-1968

Pringle Bros. Liquors
2100 W Drake Rd.
Ft. Collins, CO 80526
(970) 221-1717

Cottonwood Liquors
2513 U.S. Hwy. 6 and 50
Grand Junction, CO 81501
(970) 243-1062

Brewer's Pot Roast

4–5 lb. beef pot roast
2 tblsp English mustard (made with water and mustard powder)
2 tblsp cooking oil

1 large onion, sliced
1¼ cups beer
1¼ cups sour cream
Salt and pepper to taste

Spread mustard over meat, sprinkle with salt and pepper. Heat oil in flameproof casserole and brown meat quickly on all sides. Add onion and ¼ cup beer. Simmer for 3–4 hours, adding beer at intervals. Meat should be barely covered with liquid. When meat is tender, skim fat from the top. Just before serving, stir sour cream into the liquid.

— English recipe

Climax Liquors
Taft Rd. and SW 14
Loveland, CO 80537
(970) 663-1766

Dry Creek Liquors
109 E 37th
Loveland, CO 80537
(970) 669-1363

Applejack Liquors
3320 Youngfield
Wheatridge, CO 80033
(303) 233-3331

Festivals and Events

**Boulder Brewer's
Festival**
Boulder, CO
(303) 444-8448
Contact: Carla Khabbaz
*Late August Microbrews, food,
KBCO radio.*

Oktoberfest
Penrose Stadium
1045 W Rio Grande
Colorado Springs, CO 80906
(719) 520-6711
*Late August, 11 days.
Beergarden, German food,
music, entertainment,
dancing.*

**The Great American
Beer Festival**
Downtown
Denver, CO
(303) 447-0816
Fax (303) 447-2825
Contact: P.O. Box 1679,
Boulder, CO 80306
*Early October, 2 days. Over
800 beers from 200 U.S.
breweries. Medals awarded.*

**Colorado Brewers'
Festival**
Old Town
Ft. Collins, CO 80524
*Late June, two days. Local
brews, food, live music.*

Of Historic Interest

Diamond Belle Saloon
Historic District
Durango, CO 81302
(303) 247-0312
(800) 247-4431
*Lavishly restored frontier and
mining town saloon.*

Connecticut

**Connecticut Tourism
Division**
865 Brook St.
Rocky Hill, CT 06067-3405
(800) CT-BOUND
Tourist info, events calendar.

Breweries, Regional and Micro

Charter Oak Brewing Co.
Bristol, CT 06010

New Haven Brewing Co.
458 Grand Ave.
New Haven, CT 06513
(203) 772-2739
*Tours year round; reservations
requested.*

**New England
Brewing Co.**
25 Commerce St.
Norwalk, CT 06850
(203) 866-3814
Fax (203) 838-7168
Contact: Phil Markowski,

Ron Page, brewers
*Free tours third Saturday.
Reservations requested.
Atlantic Amber, Gold Stock
and Holiday ales, Light
Lager, Oatmeal stout.*

Brewpubs

The Hartford Brewery
35 Pearl St.
Hartford, CT 06103
(203) 246-BEER
*Brewpub and restaurant.
Brews over 25 beers, with five
on tap at a time. Good food
too.*

Places to Enjoy Beer

Greenwood's
Greenwood Ave.
Bethel, CT 06801
*Pub restaurant. Five draft
beers.*

Retail Stores

Francos Wine Merchants
130 Elm St.
New Canaan, CT 06840
(203) 966-9571

Stop & Save Liquors
Sand Hill Plaza, Rt. 25
Newtown, CT 06470
(203) 270-0429
*Excellent selection of micros
and imports; homebrewing
supplies.*

Festivals and Events

**Micro Brew & Blues
Festival**
Fairfield, CT 06430
(707) 422-0103
Contact: Gary Howell
*Mid-September. Micros,
homebrews, food, music,
demos.*

Norwalk Oyster Festival
Veterans Memorial Park
Seaview Ave.
Norwalk, CT 06851
(203) 838-9444
Contact: Norwalk Seaport
　Association
Mid-September, 3 days.
Oysters, music, crafts, food,
tall ships, and beer by New
England Brewing Co.

Of Historic Interest

Leffingwell Inn
348 Washington St.
Norwich, CT 06360
(203) 889-9440
Built in 1675. Open summer
Tuesday to Sunday, winter by
appointment.

Keeler Tavern Museum
132 Main St.
Ridgefield, CT 06877
(203) 438-5485
Historic 1720 tavern still has
British cannonball embedded
in wall (from 1777 battle).
Costumed guides. Open
February to December,
Wednesday, Saturday and
Sunday.

Delaware

Delaware Tourism
99 Kings Hwy.
P.O. Box 1401
Dover, DE 19903
(800) 441-8846
Tourist information. Toll-free
in-state: (800) 282-8667.

Breweries, Regional and Micro

Blue Hen Beer Co.
Newark, DE
(302) 737-8375
Contract brewed.

Places to Enjoy Beer

Buckley's Tavern
Rt. 52
Centreville, DE 19807
(302) 656-9776
Restaurant with good beer
selection. Lunch & dinner
daily; Sunday brunch.

Peddlers Pub
Christiana, DE 19711
(302) 731-1769

The Rose & Crown
108 Second St.
Lewes, DE 19958
English style pub.

Festivals and Events

Oktoberfest
49 Salem Church Rd.
Newark, DE 19711
(302) 366-8868
Mid-September, 3 days.

District of Columbia

See also nearby areas of Maryland,
Delaware, and Virginia.

Breweries, Regional and Micro

**Olde Heurich
　Brewing Co.**
1111 34th St. NW
Washington, DC 20007
(202) 333-2313
Olde Heurich Maerzen beer.
Contract brewed.

Brewpubs

Capitol City Brewing Co.
1100 New York Ave. NW
Washington, DC 20005
(202) 628-2222
Brewery and full-service
restaurant with American

cuisine and reasonable prices.
Open daily, tours available at
any time.

Places to Enjoy Beer

The Big Hunt
1345 Connecticut Ave. NW
Washington, DC 20036
(202) 785-2333

Brickskeller
1523 22nd St. NW
Washington, DC 20037
(202) 293-1885
Over 500 brands, domestic
and imports. Steaks, burgers,
seafood, pizza.

Cafe Berlin
322 Massachusetts Ave. NE
Washington, DC 20002
(202) 543-7656

Chadwick's
3205 K St. NW
Washington, DC 20007
(202) 333-2565

Colonel Brooks Tavern
901 Monroe St. NE
Washington, DC 20017
(202) 529-4002

The Crowbar
1006 20th St. NW
Washington, DC 20036
(202) 223-2972

The Dubliner
520 N Capitol St. NW
Washington, DC 20001
(202) 737-3773

Kelly's Irish Times
14 F St. NW
Washington, DC 20001
(202) 543-5433

Murphy's
2609 24th St. NW
Washington, DC 20008
(202) 462-7171
Features Murphy's Stout from Cork, Ireland, Mooney's Stout, VA, and Guinness. National and local sports via satellite.

9:30 Night Club
930 F St. NW
Washington, DC 20004
(202) 638-2008

The Saloon
3239 M St. NW
Washington, DC 20007
(202) 547-7564

Tiber Creek Pub
15 E St. NW
Washington, DC 20001
(202) 638-0900

Retail Stores

Barrel House
1341 14th St. NW
Washington, DC 20005
(202) 332-5999

Berose
1711 17th St. NW
Washington, DC 20009
(202) 667-5010
Good selection of micros and imports.

Cairo Wine & Liquor
1618 17th St. NW
Washington, DC 20009
(202) 387-1500
Fax (202) 387-2337
If they don't have it, they'll get it for you.

Chevy Chase Wine & Spirits
5544 Connecticut Ave. NW
Washington, DC 20015
(202) 363-4000
Fax (202) 537-6067
Eight hundred beers in stock.

Dixie Liquors
3429 M St. NW
Washington, DC 20007
(202) 337-4412

The Wine Specialist
2115 M St. NW
Washington, DC 20037
(202) 833-0707
Fax (202) 833-9507
Open Monday–Saturday. Over 300 beers and ciders in stock.

Festivals and Events

International Wine & Beer Festival
Washington, DC
(703) 764-2399
Late September, two days.

Mid-Atlantic Beer Fest
H and 12th Sts.
Washington, DC
(703) 527-1441
Contact: Bud Hensgen
Mid-September, 2 days. Outside Cap City Brewco. Brews, food, live bands.

Florida

Florida Division of Tourism
126 W Van Buren St.
Tallahassee, FL 32399-2000
(904) 488-5607
Tourist information, calendar of events.

Breweries, Large

Anheuser-Busch Brewery
111 Busch Dr.
Jacksonville, FL 32218
(904) 751-8116
Free brewery tours Monday to Saturday. Gift shop. Budweiser, Busch, Michelob.

Anheuser-Busch Brewery
3000 Busch Blvd.
Tampa, FL 33618
(813) 988-4111
Free tours, gift shop. Budweiser, Busch, Michelob.

The Stroh Brewery Co.
Tampa Brewery
11111 N 30th St.
Tampa, FL 33612
(813) 972-8500

Breweries, Regional and Micro

Florida Brewery
Auburndale, FL 33823
(813) 965-1825

"I do now remember the poor creature, small beer."

— William Shakespeare, *Henry IV, Part 2*

Beach Brewing Co.
5905 S Kirkman Rd.
Orlando, FL 32819
(407) 345-8802
Florida's first microbrewery.
Showcase beers: Red Rock,
Magic Brew. Tours available.

Florida Beer Brands
645 W Michigan St.
Orlando, FL 32805
Gator Lager, Flying Aces,
Famous Old West, Warrior
Brand Beer. Contract brewed.

Brewpubs

Ragtime Tavern &
  Seafood Grill
207 Atlantic Blvd.
Atlantic Beach, FL 32233
(904) 241-7877

Hops Grill & Bar #5
Bradenton, FL 33505
(813) 756-1069

Hops Grill & Bar #1
Clearwater, FL
(813) 531-5300

Thai Orchid Restaurant
Coral Gables, FL 33134
(305) 443-6364

River Walk Brewery
Ft. Lauderdale, FL
(305) 764-8448
Boca Beer Works.

Mill Bakery, Eatery &
  Brewery
11491 Cleveland Ave.
Ft. Myers, FL 33907
(813) 939-2739

Santa Rosa Bay
  Brewing Co.
54 Miracle Strip Pkwy.
Ft. Walton Beach, FL 32548
(904) 664-2739

Market Street Pub
120 SW First Ave.
Gainesville, FL 32601
(904) 377-2927

Hops Grill & Bar #7
Jacksonville, FL
(904) 645-9355

River City Brewing Co.
835 Gulf Life Dr.
Jacksonville, FL 32207
(904) 398-2299

Kelley's Caribbean Bar
  & Grill
301 Whitehead St.
Key West, FL 33040
(305) 293-8484

Hops Grill & Bar #6
Lakeland, FL
(813) 471-6200

Irish Times Pub &
  Brewery
9920 Alternate A1A
Palm Beach Gardens, FL
  33410
(407) 624-1504

Hops Grill & Bar #3
33086 U.S. Hwy. 19 N
Palm Harbor, FL 33563
(813) 789-5678

McGuire's Irish Pub &
  Brewery
600 E Gregory St.
Pensacola, FL 32501
(904) 433-6789
Lite, Irish Red, Porter, and
Stout. Contract brewed.

Sarasota Brewing Co.
6607 Gateway Ave.
Sarasota, FL 34231
(813) 925-BEER
Contact: Andy Rathman,
  brewmaster
Florida cuisine, classic and
seasonal brews.

Highlands Brewery
Sebring, FL 33870

Hops Grill & Bar #2
14303 N Dale Mabry
Tampa, FL 33618
(813) 264-0522

Hops Grill & Bar #4
Tampa, FL
(813) 871-3600

Mill Baker, Eatery &
  Brewery
430 W Fairbanks Rd.
Winter Park, FL 32789
(407) 644-1544

Places to Enjoy Beer

Hubb's
265 W Hwy. 436
Altamonte Springs, FL
  32714
Twenty-eight beers on draft,
total 99. Food.

Pat's Place
5275 W Hwy. 436, #1017
Altamonte Springs, FL
  32701
(407) 568-6152

Crown & Thistle
2519 Gulf Dr. N
Bradenton Beach, FL 34217
(813) 778-5173

**Mr. Dunderbak's Deli &
  Restaurant**
Regency Square Mall
9501 Arlington Exp.
Jacksonville, FL 32225
*Seventy-five international
brews.*

Buena Vista Palace
Walt Disney World Village
Lake Buena Vista, FL
  32830
(407) 827-2727
*Ninety-nine beers, changing
twice yearly.*

Cricketers Arms
8445 International Dr.
Orlando, FL 32819
(407) 354-0686

London Tavern
15 N Orange St.
Orlando, FL 32819
(407) 423-0124

Billabong Pub
3000 Country Club Ln.
Pembroke Park, FL 33009
(305) 985-1050

Rendezvous
206 St. George St.
St. Augustine, FL 32084
(904) 824-1090

B Merrel's
1433 E Lafayette St.
Tallahassee, FL 32301
(904) 656-0330

Irish Pub
1721 Seventh Ave. E
Ybor City, FL 33605
(941) 248-2099

Retail Stores

Pat's Discount Beverage
337 NE Second Ave.
Delray Beach, FL 33440
(407) 276-2356

The Liquor Store
8101 Phillips Hwy.
Jacksonville, FL 32256
(904) 731-9463

The Beer Store
4469 Morrison Ave.
Lake Worth, FL 33460
(407) 968-9586

Big Daddy's
2721 Bird Ave.
Miami, FL 33133
(305) 445-2132

Plaza Liquors
8739 International Dr.
Orlando, FL 32819
(407) 352-7665

Festivals and Events

Octoberfest
German American Social
  Club
Cape Coral, FL 33904
(813) 283-1400
Mid-October, ten days.

Oktoberfest
Cape Coral, FL 33904
(941) 283-1400
*October. Munich in Cape
Coral, with bands from
Germany, German food, beer,
and more.*

Emerald Coast Beerfest
Santa Rosa Bay Brewery
Ft. Walton Beach, FL 32548
*Late September, three days.
Beer tastings, food, live music.*

Oktoberfest
5 Ave. Business District
Naples, FL 33940
(813) 262-4177
Mid-October.

Oktoberfest
Fox Lake Park
Titusville, FL 32780
(407) 267-3036
Late October, three days.

Georgia

Georgia Tourism
P.O, Box 1776
Atlanta, GA 30301
(404) 656-3590
Tourist information.

**Georgia Association of
  Craft Brewers**
P.O. Box 15437
Atlanta, GA 30333
(404) 998-7898
Contact: Joe Maifeld
*Associationn of brewpub and
micro supporters lobbying for
legalization.*

Breweries, Large

Miller Brewery
405 Cordele Ave.
Albany, GA 31705-2109
(912) 888-3000
Miller, Lowenbrau.

G. Heileman Brewing Co.
1850 Parkway Pl., Suite 420
Marietta, GA 30067
(404) 429-9441

Atlanta Brewing Co.
1219 Williams St. NW
Atlanta, GA 30344
(404) 892-4436
Contact: Greg Kelly, Harry
  Wallace
*Red Brick Ale, Red Brick
Golden Lager.*

Friends Brewing Co.
Atlanta, GA
(404) 986-8505
Contract brewed.

Georgia Brewing Co.
P.O. Box 8329
Atlanta, GA 30306
(404) 633-0924
Fax (404) 633-1029
*Gold Medal-winning Wild
Boar Special Amber. Contract
brewed.*

Helenboch Brewery
P.O. Box 29464
Atlanta, GA 30359
*Friends Brewing Co.
Helenboch Beer.*

Marthasville Brewing Co.
3960 Shirley St. SW
Atlanta, GA 30336
(404) 699-9936
Contact: Doug Hubbard
Martha's Pale Ale.

Places to Enjoy Beer

County Cork
5600 Roswell Rd., #19
Atlanta, GA 30350
(404) 303-1976

Reggie's British Pub
317S CNN Center
Atlanta, GA 30303
(404) 525-1437
British pub foods and ales.

The Tavern at Phipps
3500 Peachtree Rd. NE
Atlanta, GA 30326
(404) 814-9640

B. Merrel's
2603 Manchester Expwy.
Columbus, GA 31904
(706) 324-5464

Winston's Pub
2100 Upper Roswell Rd.,
#100a
Marietta, GA 30062
(404) 971-8877

Crystal Beer Parlor
301 W Jones
Savannah, GA 31401
(912) 232-1153

**Mill Bakery, Eatery, &
Brewery**
7806 Abercorn St.
Savannah, GA 31406
(912) 355-1625

**Archibald's Restaurant &
Tavern**
470 S Main St.
Statesboro, GA 30458
(912) 764-6597

Retail Stores

Boo's
5524 Whitesville Rd.
Columbus, GA, 31904
(706) 327-6035

Barrett Package
1200 Barrett Pkwy. NW
Kennesaw, GA 30144
(404) 499-0276

Depot Package Store
738 Pio Nono Ave.
Macon, GA 31204
(912) 741-1717

Mink's
2555 Delk Rd.
Marietta, GA 30057
(404) 952-2337

**Sherlock's Beer
Warehouse**
135 Barrett Pkwy. NE
Marietta, GA 30062
(404) 426-6744

**Sherlock's Beer
Warehouse**
2156 Roswell Rd. NE
Marietta, GA 30062
(404) 971-6333

Beverage Warehouse
11005 Alpharetta Hwy.
Roswell, GA 30076
(404) 992-0007

**Chatham Beverage
Center**
5921 Ogeechee Rd.
Savannah, GA 31419
(912) 925-1662

Festivals and Events

Oktoberfest
Welcome Center
P.O. Box 730
Helen, GA 30545
(706) 878-2181
*Mid-September to October.
Live Bavarian music, plus
food and beer.*

Of Historic Interest

Bedingfield Inn Museum
Town Square
Lumpkin, GA 31815
(912) 838-6419
*1836 stagecoach inn and
family residence with period
furnishings.*

**Eagle Tavern Welcome
Center/Museum**
U.S. 441, Downtown
Watkinsville, GA 30677
(706) 769-5197
*Early stagecoach inn and
store. Furnishings late 1700s.*

Hawaii

Hawaii Visitors Bureau
2270 Kalakaua Ave., #801
Honolulu, Oahu, HI 96815
(808) 924-0266
Fax (808) 922-8991
*Tourist information calendar
of events.*

Ali'i Brewing Co.
Kalihi, HI

Maui Beer Co.
Lahaina
Maui, HI 96761
Contact: Paula Thompson
*Whale Ale, Aloha Lager.
Contract brewed.*

Brewpubs

Gordon Biersch Brewery Restaurant
101 Ala Moana Blvd., #1123
Honolulu, HI
(808) 599-4877

Charging Bull Pub & Grill
Kailua, HI

Old Lahaina Brewing Co.
Front St.
Lahaina
Maui, HI 96761

Coconut Willie's
International Marketplace
Waikiki, HI

Places to Enjoy Beer

Le Guignol
1614 Kalakaua Ave.
Honolulu, HI 96826
*Restaurant with good beer
and occasional special tasting
events.*

Murphy's
2 Merchant St.
Honolulu, HI 96813
(808) 531-0422

West Maui Rhum Co.
Lahaina
Maui, HI 96761
Eleven beers, 4 seasonals.

Old English Pub
Kemo'o Farm
Wahiawa, HI 96857
(808) 621-1835
*Twelve taps, large selection of
bottles.*

Down Under Club
International Marketplace
Waikiki, HI

Retail Stores

The Liquor Collection, Ward Warehouse
1050 Ala Moana Blvd.
Honolulu, HI 96813
(808) 524-8808
Fax (808) 597-1588
*Import, micro, and specialty
brews, plus homebrew supplies.*

Kamuela Liquor Store
Mamalohoa Hwy.
Kamuela, HI 96743
(808) 885-4674
Fax (808) 885-7385
*Large selection of specialty
beers.*

Festivals and Events

Big Island Bounty Festival
Ritz-Carlton Mauna Lani
Honolulu, HI
*Early May. Local produce,
microbrews.*

Hawaiian Brewer's Festival
Honolulu, HI
(808) 259-6884
Contact: Hawaii Home-
brewer's Association
Summer.

Idaho

Idaho Travel Council
700 W State St.
Boise, ID 83702
(800) 635-7820
Tourist information.

Breweries, Regional and Micro

Beier Brewing Co.
202 E 37th St., #13
Boise, ID 83714
(208) 338-5133.

Coeur d'Alene Brewing Co.
204 N Second St.
Coeur d'Alene, ID 83814
(208) 664-2739
*Tours daily at 1:30 and 5:30.
T W Fisher's beers (see
brewpub).*

Sun Valley Brewing Co.
Hailey, ID 83333
(208) 788-5777

Thunder Mountain Brewery
Ketchum, ID 83340
(208) 726-1832

Brewpubs

Harrison Hollow Brewhouse
2455 Harrison Hollow
Boise, ID 83702
(208) 343-6820

Table Rock Brewpub & Grill
705 Fulton
Boise, ID 83704
(208) 342-0944

T W Fisher's Brewpub
204 N Second St.
Coeur d'Alene, ID 83814
(208) 664-BREW
*Lunch and dinner. Six beers
on tap: set of samples $2.50.
Beers on draft, three styles in
bottles: Festival Dark and
Centennial Pale Ales, Light
Wheat Beer. Souvenirs.*

McCall Brewing Co.
807 N Third St.
McCall, ID 83638
(208) 634-2333

Treaty Grounds Brewpub
W 2124 Pullman Rd.
Moscow, ID 83843
(208) 882-3807

Places to Enjoy Beer

Kootenai River Inn
Hwy. 95
Bonner's Ferry, ID 83805
(208) 267-8511

Catcher in the Rye
414 Mullen
Coeur d'Alene, ID 83702
(208) 667-7966

Godfather's
2615 N Fourth
Coeur d'Alene, ID 83702
(208) 765-3767

Iron Horse
407 Sherman
Coeur d'Alene, ID 83702
(208) 667-7314

Litre House
Cleveland Blvd.
Nampa, ID 83651
(208) 466-8089

Bugatti's Pub
105 S First Ave.
Sandpoint, ID 83864
(208) 263-4796

Retail Stores

Albertson's
218 W Ironwood
Coeur d'Alene, ID 83702
(208) 664-9101

Super One Foods
305 W Kathleen
Coeur d'Alene, ID 83702
(208) 765-2285

Tidyman's Warehouse Foods
1600 Seltice Way
Post Falls, ID 83854
(208) 773-3383

Festivals and Events

Septemberfest
Kellogg, ID 83837
(208) 784-0821
*September, weekend after
Labor Day. Bavarian festival.*

Oktoberfest
Twin Falls, ID 83301
(208) 733-3974
Early October, 2 days.

Of Historic Interest

Wood River Restaurant & Saloon
Fort Hall
Pocatello, ID 83201
*Restored Oregon Trail days
saloon.*

Illinois

Illinois Bureau of Tourism
100 W Randolph St.
Chicago, IL 60601
(800) 223-0121
Tourist information.

Breweries, Regional and Micro

Chicago Brewing Co.
1830 N Besly Ct.
Chicago, IL 60622
(312) 252-8196
Contact: Steve, Jennifer,
Craig Dinehart
*Housed in a renovated 1920s
pickle factory. Legacy Lager,
Legacy Red Ale, Heartland
Weiss, Big Shoulders Porter.*

Golden Prairie Brewing Co.
Chicago, IL
(312) 862-0106

RJ's Ginseng Co.
14828 McKinley Ave.
Posen, IL 60469
(708) 389-4274
*RJ's Ginseng Beer. Contract
brewed.*

Pavichevich Brewing Co.
383 Romans Rd.
Elmhurst, IL 60162
(708) 617-5252
*Free tours by appointment.
Naughty Boy Lager, Bone Ale.*

Star Union Brewing Co.
Hennepin, IL 61327
(815) 925-7400

Woodstock Brewing & Bottling
202 E Calhoun
Woodstock, IL 60098
(815) 337-1970
Herman's Golden Pilsner, Arnold's Amber Lager, named after the founders of the original brewery, 1858–1902.

Brewpubs

Weinkeller Brewery
6417 W Roosevelt Rd.
Berwyn, IL 60402
(708) 749-2276
Brewpub, restaurant, liquor store with over 500 different beers. Duesseldorfer Doppelbock, Doublin Stout, Bavarian Weiss, Oktoberfest.

Joe's Brewing Co.
706 S Fifth St.
Champaign, IL 61820
(217) 384-1790

Goose Island Brewing Co.
1800 N Clybourn
Chicago, IL 60614
(312) 915-0071
Fax (312) 337-0172
Contact: John Hall, President
Five year old brewpub. In 1992, brewed over 2000 bottles and 30 styles of beer. Beer available to go in ½ gallon growlers filled at the bar for $8. Golden Goose Pilsner, Oktoberfest, Tanzen Gans Koelsch, Oatmeal Stout, more.

Box Office Brewery
De Kalb, IL 60115
(815) 748-2739

Galena Main Street Brewpub
300 N Main St.
Galena, IL 61036
(815) 777-0451
Contact: Jeff Tendick
English style pub. Pub lunches, tapas.

Brewbakers Ale House & Deli
425 15th St.
Moline, IL 61265
(309) 762-3464
Contact: John Vroman, Mark Wille, Ken Gelski
Golden Harvest, Red, Cream, Dark Cream, and Light Cream ales. Root beer for the kids.

Taylor Brewing Co.
Naperville, IL 60540
(708) 717-8000 or
(708) 241-0002

J D Nicks Brewery & Restaurant
1711 W Hwy. 50
O'Fallon, IL 62269
(618) 624-2100

Blue Cat Brewing Co.
113 18th St.
Rock Island, IL 61201
(309) 788-8247
Contact: Martha Cleaveland
Glassed-in brewhouse, full menu, games room. Railyard Ale, Orange beer, IPA, Audrey Brown Ale, Big Bad Dog.

Mill Rose Brewing Co.
I-90 and Barrington Rd. N
South Barrington, IL 60010
(708) 382-7673

Capitol City Brewing Co.
Springfield, IL
(217) 753-5720

Weinkeller Brewpub #2
Westmont, IL 60559
(708) 789-2236

Places to Enjoy Beer

Susie's Cafe
602 N Main St.
Bloomington, IL 61701
(309) 827-7577
Selection of imports and micros.

Great Beer Palace
4128 N Lincoln
Chicago, IL 60618
(312) 525-4906
Twenty-four taps.

Quencher's Saloon
2401 N Western Ave.
Chicago, IL 60647
(312) 276-9730

Rannali's Pizzeria & Pub
1925 N Lincoln
Chicago, IL 60614

Rannali's Pizzeria & Pub
24 W Elm St.
Chicago, IL 60610

Mulgrew's Tavern & Liquor Store
230 Sinsinawa Ave.
East Dubuque, IL 61025
(815) 747-8861

Die Bierstube
42 Kansas St.
Frankfort, IL 60423
German restaurant.

Kingston Inn Restaurant
300 N Main St.
Galena, IL 61036
(815) 777-0451
American/Continental menu,
over 90 beers. Dinner nightly,
lunch hours vary. Live music.

The Cafe
8 West Side Square
Macomb, IL 61455
(309) 837-4272
Good beer selection.

Jimmy's Pub
2801 W Farmington Rd.
West Peoria, IL 61604
(309) 676-4021

Peoria Hofbrau House
2210 NE Jefferson
Peoria, IL 61603
(309) 686-9739
Imports, micros. Complete
their beer tour card and win
prizes and undying fame.

Sully's
121 SW Adams
Peoria, IL 61602
(309) 674-0238
Irish pub with beer tour card.

Filling Station Pub &
  Grill
300 W Main St.
St. Charles, IL 60174
(708) 584-4414

Retail Stores

Famous Liquors
1404 E Empire
Bloomington, IL 61701
(309) 663-8303

University Liquors
706 W Beaufort
Bloomington, IL 61761
(309) 452-4912

Gill & Co.
1238 E 47
Chicago, IL 60653
(312) 786-4747

I & N Liquors
2428 N Lincoln
Chicago, IL 60614
(312) 477-3526

Miskas Wine, Beer &
  Liquor
2353 N Clark
Chicago, IL 60614
(312) 472-4242

Park West Liquors
2427 N Lincoln
Chicago, IL 60614
(312) 477-7030

Park West Liquors
2581 N Lincoln
Chicago, IL 60614
(312) 935-8197

Q & A Liquors
8704 S Loomis
Chicago, IL 60620
(312) 445-2113

Sam's Wine & Liquors
1000 W North Ave.
Chicago, IL 60622

Treasure Island
2121 N Clybourn
Chicago, IL 60614
(312) 880-8880
Supermarket with good
selection of imports and
micros.

Galena River Wine &
  Cheese
420 S Main St.
Galena, IL 61036
(815) 777-9430
Extensive selection of imported
beers.

Treasure Island
Rt. 176 and Waukegan Rd.
Lake Bluff, IL 60044
(708) 615-0900
Supermarket with good
selection of imports and
micros.

Country Food & Liquor
19454 S Mannheim Rd.
Mokena, IL 60448
(708) 479-2900
350 beers.

Stan's Wine & Spirits
  Shop
1108 W Glen Ave.
Peoria, IL 61614
(309) 693-9463

Wine Country
4604 N Prospect
Peoria Heights, IL 61604
(309) 686-0234
Around 70 different beers.

Armanette Liquors
4000 Algonquin
Rolling Meadows, IL 60008
(708) 397-7373

Midway Liquors
724 S Grand Ave.
Springfield, IL 62704
(217) 528-4377

Festivals and Events

Oktoberfest
College and Rt. 17
Aledo, IL 61231
(309) 582-7241
Late September, 3 days.
Carnival midway, food booths,
beer garden, live entertain-
ment, flea market.

Oktoberfest
Carthage Square
308 Walnut St.
Carthage, IL 62321
(217) 357-3024
*Mid-September. German food,
drink, music on historic
courthouse lawn.*

Microbrewery
   ## Oktoberfest
Chicago, IL
(312) 563-1212
Contact: Ralph Roberts
*Late September, 4 days.
Micros, German food, WXRT
radio.*

Midwest Brewers'
   ## Oktoberfest
Goose Island Pub
1800 N Clybourn
Chicago, IL 60614
(312) 915-0071
Fax (312) 337-0172
*Mid-September, 2 days. Over
20 breweries from Colorado to
Ohio.*

Oktoberfest
Lewiston Square
Lewiston, IL 61542
(309) 547-4300
*Mid-September, 2 days. Polka
and country dancing, beer,
wine, arts and crafts.*

World Beer Festival
Maywood Park
8600 W North Ave.
Maywood, IL 60153
Contact: Steve Fiske
5252 N Broadway
Chicago, IL 60640
(312) 880-1308
*Late October, three days. Over
100 beers from around the
world plus books, etc.
Seminars, gourmet dinner,
judged event, tastings.*

Of Historic Interest

City Brewery Museum
318 Spring St., Hwy. 20
Galena, IL 61036
(815) 777-0354
Contact: Charles Fach
*History of City Brewery, which
operated until 1881, displays
of brewing, visit to lagering
cellars. Tours 1 to 5PM daily.*

Indiana

Indiana Tourism
1 N Capitol
Indianapolis, IN 46204
(800) 289-6646
Tourist information.

*Breweries, Regional and
Micro*

Evansville Brewing Co.
1301 W Lloyd Expressway
Evansville, IN 47710-1051
(812) 425-7101

Indianapolis Brewing Co.
3250 N Post Rd., #285
Indianapolis, IN 46226
(317) 898-1235
Tours available, call for times.

Lafayette Brewing Co.
Lafayette, IN
(317) 742-2591

Brewpubs

Broad Ripple
   ### Brewing Co.
842 E 65 St.
Indianapolis, IN 46220
(317) ALE-BREW
*Brewery and brewpub. Porter,
Koelsch, ESB, IPA.*

Mishawaka Brewing Co.
3703 N Main
Mishawaka, IN 46544
(219) 256-9994
*American food and pub fare.
Mishawaka Gold Lager, South
Shore Amber Ale, Lake Effect
Pale Ale.*

Places to Enjoy Beer

Crazy Horse
214 W Kirkwood
Bloomington, IN 47401

Union Jack Pub
924 Broadripple Ave.
Indianapolis, IN 46220
(317) 257-4343

Shello's Pub
County Line Mall
Indianapolis, IN

Rich O's Public House &
   ### BBQ
3312 Plaza Dr.
New Albany, IN 47150
(812) 949-2804

Sonka Irish Pub & Cafe
1366 Wabash
Terre Haute, IN 47807

Retail Stores

Hamilton Beverage
2290 E 116 St.
Carmel, IN 46032

Festivals and Events

Oktoberfest
P.O. Box 343
Crown Point, IN 46307
(219) 663-1800
Contact: Elaine Mills
*Early October. At Lake County
Fairgrounds. German food
and beer, live music, games,
dancing.*

Oktoberfest
8600 S Meridian St.
Indianapolis, IN 46217
(317) 888-6940
Contact: Joe Lehman
September, 2 weekends. Held in German Park. German and American food, dancing, entertainment, crafts.

Oktoberfest
P.O. Box 659
Michigan City, IN 46360
(219) 874-8927
Contact: Gail Bos
Early September, 4 days. Lakefront, Washington Park. Traditional food, drink, entertainment. Free.

Of Historic Interest

Stagecoach Inn Museum
127 Main St.
Hebron, IN 46341
Open Sunday, noon to 4PM. Free.

Stone's Tavern Museum
4946 N SR 5
Ligonier, IN 46767
(219) 856-2871
Built in 1839, used by travelers on the Goshen to Ft. Wayne Trail. Open Sunday, June to August. Free.

Iowa

Iowa Tourism
200 E Grand Ave.
Des Moines, IA 50309
(515) 242-4705 or
(800) 345-4692
Tourist information, calendar of events.

Breweries, Regional and Micro

Millstream Brewing Co.
P.O. Box 283
Amana, IA 52203
(319) 622-3672
Hospitality room with samples, views of brewing and bottling areas and lagering cellars. Open daily, special events. Millstream Lager, Schild Brau, Millstream Wheat Beer.

Dubuque Brewing & Bottling Co.
500 E Fourth St. Extension
Dubuque, IA 52001
(319) 583-2042
Fax (319) 583-0009
Built in 1898 on the banks of the Mississippi. Simpatico Golden Lager, Amber.

Frontier Brewing Co.
Norway, IA 52318
Contract brewed.

Brewpubs

Dallas County Brewing Co.
301 S Tenth St.
Adel, IA 50003
(515) 993-5064
Contact: Kevin Rice, President
Old Depot Pub, built in old Milwaukee Railroad depot. Game served in restaurant. Bottled beer, gift shop. Old Depot Lager, Light Beer, Ale, and Porter.

Front Street Brewery
208 E River Dr.
Davenport, IA 52801
(319) 322-1569
Contact: Steve Zuidema, Randy Junis
Usually five brews available. Raging River Ale, named after the flood of 1993, Old Davenport Gold, Charvat's Legacy (named for Otto Charvat) Bucktown Stout.

Babe's
417 Sixth Ave.
Des Moines, IA 50309
(515) 244-9319

Fitzpatrick's Brewing Co.
525 S Gilbert
Iowa City, IA 52240
(319) 356-6900

Places to Enjoy Beer

Fat Tuesday's
1121 University Ave.
Dubuque, IA 50314

Retail Stores

Cyclone Country Liquor
626 Lincoln Way
Ames, IA 50010

Drake Liquor Store
2106 Forest Ave.
Des Moines, IA 50311

Ingersoll Wine & Spirits
3503 Ingersoll Ave.
Des Moines, IA 50312

Last Stop Beverage Store
2839 E University Ave.
Des Moines, IA 50317

What two ideas are more inseparable than Beer and Britannia?
— Rev. Sydney Smith (1771-1845)

The Liquor Locker
520 Army Post Rd.
Des Moines, IA 50315

Rodger's Spirits & Ale
828 N First St.
Winterset, IA 50273

Festivals and Events

Oktoberfest
Middle Amana, IA
(319) 622-3828
German festival, food, drink, entertainment, crafts.

Of Historic Interest

Stagecoach Inn
Moorehead Park
Ida Grove, IA 51445
(712) 364-3816
Early 1860 inn, county's first stagecoach stop. Open 2–4PM Sunday from Memorial Day to Labor Day and by appointment.

Kansas

Kansas Travel & Tourism
700 SW Harrison, Suite 1300
Topeka, KS 66603-3712
(800) 2-KANSAS
Tourist information, calendar of events.

Breweries, Regional and Micro

Miracle Brewing Co.
311 S Emporia
Wichita, KS 67202
(316) 265-7256
Tours available, call to schedule.

Brewpubs

Free State Brewing Co.
636 Massachusetts St.
Lawrence, KS 66044
(913) 843-4555
First micro in Kansas since Prohibition. Historic downtown district. Tours Saturday, 2PM. Ad Astra Ale, Oatmeal Stout, Wheat State Golden, Copperhead Pale Ale.

Little Apple Brewing Co.
1110 Westloop Center
Manhattan, KS 66502
(913) 539-5500

River City Brewing Co.
150 N Mosley
Wichita, KS 67202
(316) 263-2739

Festivals and Events

Oktoberfest
Citywide
Atchison, KS 66002
(800) 234-1854
Early October, 2 days. German food, entertainment, arts and crafts.

Oktoberfest
Boot Hill Museum
Dodge City, KS 67802
(316) 225-8186
Early October German food and music.

Oktoberfest
Frontier Park
S Main
Hays, KS 67601
(913) 735-2230
Mid-October. Reflecting city's Volga-German heritage.

German Fest
319 N 19th St.
Marysville, KS 66508
(913) 562-2659
Early June, 2 days. Celebration of German heritage. Dance, music, foods, crafts.

Oktoberfest
Main St.
Stafford, KS 67578
(316) 234-5266
Early October, 2 days. Decorated streets, parade, crafts, food and drink.

Kentucky

Kentucky Department of Travel
Capital Plaza Tower
Frankfort, KY 40601
(800) 225-TRIP
Tourist information.

Breweries, Regional and Micro

Oldenberg Brewery
2477 Royal Dr.
Ft. Mitchell, KY 41017
(606) 341-2804
Fax (606) 341-5644
Contact: David Heidrich, Vice President
Brewery and entertainment complex, I-75 and Buttermilk Pike. J D Brew's brewpub serving lunch and dinner, beer garden, Great Hall (private parties) museum, gift shop. Tours, tastings daily. Oldenberg Premium Verum, Weiss, Blonde; Celebration and Vail ales.

Oertel Brewing Co.
Louisville, KY
(502) 585-1800
Contract brewed.

Brewpubs

Bluegrass Brewing Co.
3929 Shelbyville Rd.
Louisville, KY 40207
(502) 899-7070

**Silo Brewpub &
Restaurant**
630 Barret Ave.
Louisville, KY 40204
(502) 589-BREW
Contact: David Pierce,
brewer
*Contemporary American
cuisine. Tours available. Open
daily. Silo Premium Light,
Red Rock Ale, River City
Raspberry, seasonal brews.*

Retail Stores

End-o-Bin Wine Shop
1654 Lucia Ave.
Louisville, KY 40204
(502) 451-7446

Liquor Outlet
1800 S Hurstbourne Pkwy.
Louisville, KY 40220
(502) 491-0753

Old Town Liquors
1529 Bardstown Rd.
Louisville, KY 40205
(502) 451-8591

Festivals and Events

Beer Camp
Oldenberg Brewery
Ft. Mitchell, KY 41017
(800) 426-3841
*March and September, 3-day
camp on beer appreciation,*

*making, and history. Includes
tour of museum and brewery,
home brew course, much more.*

Of Historic Interest

Old Talbott Tavern
107 W Stephen Foster Ave.
Bardstown, KY 40004
(502) 348-3494
*Oldest western stagecoach stop
in America. Enjoy a meal in
the same rooms where
Abraham Lincoln, Andrew
Jackson, and Jesse James
once sat.*

Cooperage Museum
American Outpost
I-65 Exit 112 on KY-245
Clermont, KY 40110
(502) 543-9877
*From the 1800s. Actually,
they're whiskey barrels, but a
barrel is a barrel.*

American Beer Museum
Oldenberg Complex
I-75 Exit 186
Ft. Mitchell, KY 41017
(606) 341-2802
*World's largest collection of
beer and brewing memora-
bilia. Open daily.*

Duncan Tavern
323 High St.
Paris, KY 40361
(606) 987-1788
*Tavern built in 1788 is now
Kentucky DAR headquarters,
with 1820s furnishings,
history and genealogical
library. Open Tuesday to
Saturday.*

Shaker Tavern
Shakertown
South Union, KY 42283
(502) 542-6801
*Restaurant housed in original
1869 Shaker Hotel. Festival
in June.*

Louisiana

**Louisiana Office of
Tourism**
P.O. Box 94291
Baton Rouge, LA 70804-
9291
(800) 33-GUMBO or
(504) 342-8119
Tourist information.

**150 Great Neighborhood
Bars, New Orleans**
By Janis Tilton-Stipelcovich
and Carolyn Pinero
10801 Jefferson Hwy.
River Ridge, LA 70120

Breweries, Regional and
Micro

Abita Brewing Co.
P.O. Box 762
100 Levenson St.
Abita Springs, LA 70420
(504) 893-3143

Rikenjaks Brewing
9916 Hwy. 421
Jackson, LA 70748
(504) 634-2785

Dixie Brewing Co.
2401 Tulane Ave.
New Orleans, LA 70119
(504) 822-8711

Brewpubs

Crescent City Brewhouse
527 Decatur St.
New Orleans, LA 70130
(504) 522-0571
Contact: Wolfram Koehler
Good food, good beer, and hot jazz.

Places to Enjoy Beer

Chimes Restaurant & Bar
3357 Highland Rd.
Baton Rouge, LA 70802
(504) 383-1754

River Shack Tavern
3449 River Rd.
Jefferson, LA 70121
(504) 835-6933

Red Barn Pub
501 Lafitte St.
Mandeville, LA 70448
(504) 626-3002
English style pub.

The Bulldog
3236 Magazine St.
New Orleans, LA 70115
(504) 891-1516

Carrollton Station
8140 Willow St.
New Orleans, LA 70118
(504) 865-9190
Sixteen taps, live music.

Cooter Brown's
509 S Carrollton Ave.
New Orleans, LA 70118
(504) 866-9104
Tavern and oyster bar. Sixty-four taps, 150 bottles.

Sidney's
1674 Barataria
New Orleans, LA
(504) 341-0103

Triangle West Bar
10801 Jefferson Hwy.
River Ridge, LA 70123
(504) 737-9083

Pickle Barrel
1827 Ave. of America
Shreveport, LA
(318) 869-0931

Retail Stores

The Beersmith
1818 Wooddale Blvd., #18
Baton Rouge, LA 70806
(504) 926-2337
Contact: James Waits
Imported and domestic beers, homebrew supplies.

Marcello's Wine Market
3601 Johnston St.
Lafayette, LA 70503
(318) 984-8289

College Town Liquors
405 Sterlington Rd.
Monroe, LA 71203
(318) 322-8661

Cuban Liquor
920 Pierremont Rd.
Shreveport, LA 71106
(318) 869-1236

Festivals and Events

Bavarian Oktoberfest
Downtown
Ponchatoula, LA 70454
(504) 386-6414 or 386-2533
Contact: P.O. Box 217,
  Ponchatoula LA 70545
October.

Of Historic Interest

Jackson Brewery
Jackson Square
New Orleans, LA
(504) 566-7245
Renovated 1891 brewhouse, now a shopping complex.

Maine

Maine Publicity Bureau
P.O. Box 2300
Hallowell, ME 04347-2300
(207) 623-0363
Tourist information.

Breweries, Regional and Micro

Atlantic Brewing Co.
30 Rodick St.
Bar Harbor, ME 04609
(207) 288-9513
Free tours daily in summer. Lompoc Cafe & Brewpub. Bar Harbor and Acadia Pale Ales, Coal Porter.

Bar Harbor Brewing Co.
Rt. 3, Otter Creek Rd.
HC 30, Box 61
Bar Harbor, ME 04609
(207) 288-4592
Free tours and tastings by appointment and from 3:30 to 5PM Monday to Friday in July and August. All ales bottle conditioned in 22 oz. longneck bottles. Thunder Hole Ale, Cadillac Mountain Stout, Harbor Lighthouse and Brewer's Choice Ales.

Seadog Brewing Co.
43 Mechanic St.
Camden, ME 04843
(207) 236-6863

**Lake St. George
  Brewing Co.**
Liberty, ME 04949
(207) 589-4180

Andrew's Brewing Co.
RFD 1, Box 4975
Lincolnville, ME 04849
(207) 763-3305
Contact: Andy Hazen
*Tours available; call for
directions. Andrew's Old
English Ale, Brown Ale, Old
St. Nick Porter, Ruby's Golden
Ale.*

Casco Bay Brewing Co.
57 Industrial Way
Portland, ME 04103
(207) 797-2020
Contact: Michael LaCharite
*Tours available; call for
schedule. Katahdin Golden,
Katahdin Red Ale.*

D L Geary Brewing Co.
38 Evergreen Dr.
Portland, ME 04103
(207) 878-2337
Contact: David Geary,
  founder

Brewpubs

Great Falls Brewing Co.
Auburn, ME 04210
(207) 784-3919
No Tomatoes Restaurant.

**Lompoc Cafe &
  Brewpub**
36 Rodick St.
Bar Harbor, ME 04609
(207) 288-9392

**Sunday River
  Brewing Co.**
1 Sunday River Rd.
Bethel, ME 04217
(207) 824-4253

Sea Dog Brewing Co.
Camden, ME
(207) 236-6863

Sugarloaf Brewing Co.
Carrabassett Valley, ME
(207) 237-2211

**Kennebunkport
  Brewing Co.**
Unit 6, 8 Western Ave.
Kennebunkport, ME 04043
(207) 967-4311 or
(800) BREW-ALE
Fax (207) 967-4903
Contact: Alan Pugsley
*Federal Jack's Restaurant &
Brewpub. Features Shipyard
Export Ale, Goat Island Light,
Shipyard Taint Town Pale Ale,
Moose Brown Ale, Blue Fin
Sout, Old Thumper Extra
Special Ale.*

Gritty McDuff's
396 Fore St.
Portland, ME 04101
(207) 772-2739
Fax (207) 874-9776
*Traditional English style pub
with six real ales at all times.
English pub fare: fish and
chips, steak and kidney pie,
plus burgers, etc. Blues on
Sunday and Tuesday nights.*

Places to Enjoy Beer

Whig & Courier Pub
Haymarket Square
Bangor, ME 04401

Castine Inn
Main St.
Castine, ME 04421
(207) 326-4365
Restaurant and bar.

Great Lost Bear
540 Forest Ave.
Portland, ME 04101
(207) 772-0300
Thirty-six taps.

3-Dollar Deweys
446 Fore St.
Portland, ME 04101

Nickerson Tavern
Rt. 1
Searsport, ME 04974
(207) 548-2220
*Restaurant. Open Tuesday to
Sunday.*

Festivals and Events

Maine Brewers' Festival
239 Park Ave.
Portland, ME 04102
(207) 780-8229
*Early November. Brews and
food.*

Of Historic Interest

Bradbury Barrel Co.
100 Main St.
Bridgewater, ME 04735
(207) 429-8141
Plant tour available.

Burnham Tavern
Main and Free Sts.
Machias, ME 04654
(207) 255-4432
Built in 1770. Open summers.

Jefferd's Tavern
Lindsay Rd.
York, ME 03909
(207) 363-4703
Contact: Old York Historical
  Society
Built in 1750.

Maryland

See also District of Columbia

Office of Tourism Development

217 E Redwood St.
Baltimore, MD 21202
(800) 543-1036
Tourist information.

Breweries, Regional and Micro

Wild Goose Brewery

20 Washington St.
Cambridge, MD 21613
(410) 221-1121
Fax (410) 221-1121
Contact: Jim Lutz
Wild Goose Amber Beer,
Thomas Point Golden Ale,
Samuel Middleton's Pale Ale.

Frederick Brewing Co.

103 S Carroll St.
Frederick, MD 21701
(301) 694-7899

Oxford Brewing Co.

611G Hammonds Ferry Rd.
Linthicum, MD 21090
(410) 789-0003

Brewpubs

Baltimore Brewing Co.

104 Albemarle St.
Baltimore, MD 21202
(410) 837-5000
Brewpub and restaurant,
decorated with Baltimore
breweriana.

Sissons Restaurant & Brewery

36 E Cross St.
Baltimore, MD 21230
(410) 539-2093
Contact: Hugh Sisson
Brewpub and Cajun restau-

rant. Many styles of beer.
Stone Cutter Stout, Marble
Golden Ale, Stockade Amber,
seasonals.

South Baltimore Brewing Co.

Baltimore, MD
(410) 539-2093

Wharf Rat

206 W Pratt St.
Baltimore, MD 21201
(410) 244-8900
Open daily, lunch and dinner.
Specializes in Olivers hand-
pulled, cask conditioned ales.
Golden Best Ale, Best Bitter,
Blackfriar Stout.

Olde Town Tavern & Brewing Co.

227 E Diamond Ave.
Olde Towne
Gaithersburg, MD 20877
(301) 948-4200
Bar, grille, and brewery.
Brewery tours. Open daily,
11AM–1AM. Live entertain-
ment.

Places to Enjoy Beer

McGarvey's

8 Market Space
Annapolis, MD 21401
(410) 263-5700

Middleton's Tavern

2 Market Space
Annapolis, MD 21401
(410) 263-3323

Ram's Head Tavern

33 West St.
Annapolis, MD 21401
(410) 268-4545
Good food, 32 taps, 170
different beers.

Black Forest Cafe

7 Olney-Sandy Spring Rd.
Ashton, MD 20861
(301) 774-1708
Open daily. Over 175 beers
and ales, homebrew supplies,
German foods.

Alonzo's

415 W Cold Spring Ln.
Baltimore, MD 21210
(410) 235-3433

Bohager's

515 S Eden St.
Baltimore, MD 21231
(410) 563-7220
Hosts annual Brew Review
festival in mid-October.

Cafe Tatoo

4825 Bel Air Rd.
Baltimore, MD 21206
(410) 325-7427

Beer Money

From 1800 to 1823, each soldier and NCO in the British army was paid one penny a day, in lieu of an issue of beer.

Ale-Silver

The money that was paid to the Lord Mayor of London for the privilege of selling ale within the city.

Racers Cafe
7732 Harford Rd.
Hanfield, MD 21234
(410) 882-5212

Wharf Rat
801 S Ann St.
Baltimore, MD 21231
(410) 244-8900
Serves Olivers ale, 29 taps.

Rips Country Village
3809 N Crain Hwy.
Bowie, MD 20715
(301) 805-5902
*Inn and restaurant with
selection of imported and
domestic beers.*

Margellina Restaurant
9009 Stuart Ave.
Clinton, MD 20735
(301) 868-0400
Over 80 beers.

Last Chance Saloon
5888A Robert Oliver Pl.
Columbia, MD 21045
(410) 730-5656
*Fifty taps, large variety of
seasonals.*

**Gentleman Jim's Back
  Door Pub**
2005 Veirs Mill Rd.
Rockville, MD 20851
(301) 762-3440

**Elsie's Gourmet German
  Deli**
8141 Telegraph Rd.
Severn, MD 21144
(410) 551-8000
*Open daily. Food, beers,
Octoberfest beer tastings.*

Quarry House Tavern
Georgia Ave. and Bonifant St.
Silver Spring, MD 20910
(301) 587-9406
*Open Monday–Saturday.
Forty-five taps.*

Schooner "Woodwind"
Annapolis Marriott
Waterfront
Annapolis, MD 21403
(800) 336-0072
*Seventy-four foot schooner.
Two-hour cruises with large
selection of micros.*

Retail Stores

Mills Wine & Spirit Shop
87 Main St.
Annapolis, MD 21401
(410) 263-2889

Well's Discount Liquors
6310 York Rd.
Baltimore, MD 21212
(410) 435-2700

Village Pump Liquors
4901 Greenbelt Rd.
College Park, MD 20740
(301) 474-8922
Imports and micros.

**Bun Penny Food & Wine
  Shop**
1364 Columbia Mall
Columbia, MD 21044
(410) 730-4100
*Close to 400 beers, homebrew
supplies, deli, biergarten. And
50+ single-malt Scotches.*

State Line Liquors
1610 Elkton Rd.
Elkton, MD 21921
(800) 446-WINE
*Open daily. Five hundred
beers. Monthly tastings,
weekly specials.*

All View Liquor
9495 Old Annapolis Rd.
Ellicott City, MD 21043
(410) 730-6670

Silesia Liquors
10909 Livingston Rd.
Ft. Washington, MD 20744
(301) 292-1542

Goldberg's Liquors
5106 Ritchie Hwy.
Glen Burnie, MD 21061
(410) 789-1234

Festivals and Events

Bohager's Brew Review
515 S Eden St.
Baltimore, MD 21231
(410) 563-7220
*Mid-October. Beer and food
tasting, to benefit Maryland
Lupus Foundation.*

Oktoberfest
Schifferstadt Museum
Frederick, MD 21701
(301) 663-3885
*Mid-October, two days.
German food, music,
biergarten, juried craft show,
museum open house.*

Germantown Octoberfest
Rt. 118 and Aircraft Dr.
Germantown, MD 20874
(301) 217-3380
Early October.

Bavarian Festival
Convention Center
Ocean City, MD 21842
(800) 626-2326
Contact: Mike Wicklein,
  (410) 213-1599
Late October, two days.

Oktoberfest
Town Center
Rockville, MD
(301) 309-3340
Mid-September, 2 days.
Traditional German celebra-
tion, food, biergarten, kids'
activities.

Mid-Atlantic Brewers
    Festival
Howard County Fairgrounds
West Friendship, MD 21794
(410) 821-6656
Early October, 2 days. Food,
music, and beer from micros
in the region.

Of Historic Interest

Clarysville Inn
U.S. 40A
Clarysville, MD 21532
(301) 689-9912
Historic inn used as a
military hospital during the
Civil War.

Mary Surratt House &
    Tavern
9118 Brandywine Rd.
Clinton, MD 20772
(301) 868-1121
Tavern and post office, home
of Mary Surratt, conspirator
in the Lincoln assassination,
first woman hanged in the
U.S.

Rodgers Tavern
Rt. 7, Old Post Rd.
Perryville, MD 21903
(410) 642-6281
Restored C18 tavern on Old
Post Road, favorite Washing-
ton to Philadelphia stopping
place for Jefferson, Washing-
ton, and others. Open May to
October, second Sunday, or by
appointment.

Salisbury Pewter
Rt. 13 N, Salisbury Blvd.
Salisbury, MD 21801
(410) 546-1188
Modern pewter factory using
traditional handcrafting
methods. Showroom, gift shop,
tours by appointment.

Massachusetts

Massachusetts Travel &
    Tourism
100 Cambridge St., 13th
    floor
Boston, MA 02202
(800) 447-MASS
Tourist information. Calendar
of Events, Attractions Guide.

The Brewer's Gourmet
Holliston, MA 01746
(800) 591-BREW
Beer club with monthly
selections by mail. For MA
residents only.

Breweries, Regional and Micro

Boston Beer Co.
30 Germania St.
Boston, MA 02130
(617) 482-1332
Tours and tastings, gift shop.
Samuel Adams Boston Lager,
Double Bock, Wheat,
Cranberry Lambic, Cream
Stout, and more.

Mass Bay Brewing Co.
306 Northern Ave.
Boston, MA 02210
(617) 574-9551
Free tours Friday and
Saturday, 1PM, with samples.
Brand name Harpoon.
Contract brewing company.

Atlantic Coast
    Brewing Co.
50 Terminal St.
Boston, MA 02129
(617) 2426464
Contact: Jeff Biegart, brewer
Tremont Ale.

Old Marlborough
    Brewing Co.
P.O. Box 1157
59 Fountain St.
Framingham, MA 01701
(508) 875-0990
Post Road Real Ale, contract
brewed by Catamount.

Ipswich Brewing Co.
25 Hayward St.
Ipswich, MA 01938
(508) 356-3329
Old Harbor Brewing Co. Tours
Saturday, 1 and 3PM.

Lowell Brewing Co.
Lowell, MA
(508) 937-1200

Ould Newbury
    Brewing Co.
Newbury, MA 01950
(508) 462-1980

The Brewery on
    Martha's Vineyard
Oak Bluffs Ave.
Oak Bluffs, MA 02557
(508) 696-8400
In historic building overlook-
ing the harbor, across from the
oldest carousel in America.
Menemsha Golden Ale, Oak
Bluffs Amber Ale.

Berkshire Brewing Co.
12 Railroad St.
South Deerfield, MA 01373
(413) 665-6600
Extra pale ale, pale ale, porter.
Tours Saturday 1 and 3PM.

Brewpubs

Boston Beer Works
61 Brookline Ave.
Boston, MA 02215
(617) 536-2337
Brewery tours, restaurant/pub.

Brew Moon
Stuart St.
Boston, MA 02116

**The Brewery at 34
   Depot St.**
34 Depot St.
Pittsfield, MA 01201
(413) 442-2072
*Restaurant serves lunch and
dinner. Gimlich's Golden Ale,
Red Room Pale Ale, Ironworks
India Pale Ale, Raven's Rock
Stout. Tours by request.*

**Commonwealth
   Brewing Co.**
138 Portland St.
Boston, MA 02114
(617) 523-8383
Fax (617) 523-1037
*Old English style brewpub
and restaurant. Boston's
original microbrewery. Tours,
live music. Golden, Special
Old, India Pale, and Burton
Ales; Famous Porter.*

Jacob Wirth's
3337 Stuart St.
Boston, MA
(617) 338-8586
*Boston's second oldest
restaurant (established 1868),
featuring 15 beers on tap
including 2 housebrews and
numerous German Specialty
beers. Restaurant features
German-style food. Live piano
music Friday nights with
songbooks for singalongs.*

Cambridge Brewing Co.
1 Kendall Square, #1
Cambridge, MA 02139
(617) 494-1994
*Brewery, restaurant, pub, live
music. Cambridge Amber,
Charles River Porter, Tripel
Threat.*

**John Harvard's Brew
   House**
33 Dunster St.
Cambridge, MA 02138
(617) 868-3585
*Brewery, restaurant, pub, live
music.*

**Old Salem Village
   Brewing**
Danvers, MA 01923
(508) 772-2260
Contact: G. Bridget Stone

Cape Cod Brewing
Hyannis, MA 02601
(508) 775-4110

Northampton Brewery
11 Brewster Ct.
Northampton, MA 01030
(413) 584-9903
*Brewster Court Bar & Grill.
Tours Saturday 2PM, live entertainment Sunday 10PM on.*

Places to Enjoy Beer

Sunset Grill & Tap
130 Brighton Ave.
P.O. Box 659
Allston, MA 02134
(617) 254-1331
*Over 75 taps, 300 bottled
beers. Good food. Sunset Beer
Club.*

**Boodles, Back Bay
   Hilton**
40 Dalton St.
Boston, MA 02115
(617) 266-3537
*Around 70 microbrews, food,
monthly Brewer's Dinner.*

Christopher's
1920 Massachusetts Ave.
Cambridge, MA 02138
(617) 876-9180
Nearly 50 beers, food.

Cornwalls
510 Commonwealth Ave.
Boston, MA 02115
(617) 262-3749

Plough & Stars
912 Massachusetts Ave.
Cambridge, MA 02139
(617) 441-3455
Good Irish pub. Live music.

Say, for what were hopyards meant,
Or why was Burton built on Trent?
Oh many a peer of England brews
Livelier liquor than the Muse,
And Malt does more than Milton can
To justify God's ways to man.
Ale, man, ale's the stuff to drink
For fellows whom it hurts to think.

— A.E. Housman (1859-1936)

The Wursthaus
Harvard Square, 4 JFK St.
Cambridge, MA 02129
(617) 491-7110
One hundred forty different beers.

Doyle's
3484 Washington St.
Jamaica Plain, MA 02130
(617) 524-2345
Around 25 beers, pub grub.

Blackthorne Tavern
402 Turnpike St.
South Easton, MA 02375
(508) 238-9017

Publick House
On the Common, Rt. 131
Sturbridge, MA 01566
(800) PUB-LICK

Retail Stores

Spirit Haus
338 College St.
Rt. 9 E
Amherst, MA 01004
(413) 253-5384
Over 450 beers from around the world.

Blanchards
103 Harvard Ave.
Allston, MA 02135
(617) 782-5588

Cardullo's
Harvard Square
Cambridge, MA 02129

Aubut's Liquor
1768 Main St.
Tewksbury, MA 01876
(508) 851-2031

Festivals and Events

Harpoon Octoberfest
Northern Ave.
Boston, MA 02210
(617) 455-1935
Contact: Mass Bay
  Brewing Co.
Early October, Authentic German celebration with oompah bands, German food, prizes, contests, and plenty of good beer under the traditional beer tent.

Valentine's Days
Sunset Grill
130 Brighton Ave.
Boston, MA 02134
(617) 254-1331
Mid-February, two days. Tasting of beer and chocolate. Reservations suggested.

WBUR Brewers Offering
808 Commonwealth Ave.
Boston, MA 02159
(617) 353-3800
Late August. Over 50 brewers and gourmet food purveyors.

Michigan

Michigan Travel & Tourism Association
222 N Washington, #340
Lansing, MI 48933
(800) 543-2937
Tourist information, calendar of events.

American Breweriana
23951 15-Mi Rd., Lot 11
Bellevue, MI 49021
Contact: Robert J. Smith
Patrick Henry Chapter. For collectors of breweriana. Monthly meetings, newsletter. Annual buy-sell-trade show late May.

The Stroh Brewery Co.
100 River Pl.
Detroit, MI 48207-4291
(313) 446-2000

Breweries, Regional and Micro

Detroit & Mackinac Beer
15408 Mack Ave.
Detroit, MI 48224
(313) 881-2337
Fax (313) 881-7466
Contact: Chad McDaniels
West Canfield Golden Ale, D&M Irish Red Ale, Mackinac Black.

Frankenmuth Brewery
425 S Main St.
Frankenmuth, MI 48734
(517) 652-6183
Frankenmuth German Style Pilsener, Dark, Bock, Weisse; Old Detroit Amber Ale, Cherry Weiss Beer, Extra Light.

Kalamazoo Brewing Co.
355 E. Kalamazoo Ave.
Kalamazoo, MI
(616) 382-2338
Tours available; call to schedule.

Duster's Microbrewery
Lawton, MI 49065
(616) 624-3771

Brewpubs

Grizzly Peak Brewing Co.
Ann Arbor, MI
(313) 741-7325

Traffic Jam & Snug
4268 Second Ave.
Detroit, MI 48201
(313) 831-9470

**Grand Rapids
Brewing Co.**
Grand Rapids, MI
(616) 285-5970

Festivals and Events

**St. Stanislaus Polish
Festival**
Bay City, MI 48708
(517) 892-5054
*June, last weekend. Plenty of
beer and sausages.*

Oktoberfest
Downtown
East Tawas, MI 48730
(800) 55-TAWAS
Late October, three days.

Oktoberfest
Heritage Park
Frankenmuth, MI 48734
(517) 652-6106
*Early October, 3 days.
German music, dancing, food,
and Frankenmuth beer.*

Taste of the Great Lakes
Bavarian Inn
1 Covered Bridge Ln.
Frankenmuth, MI 48734
Mail: 940 Flint St,
Frankenmuth MI 48734
Early November.

German Oktoberfest
Eidelweiss Club
Monroe Amphitheater
Grand Rapids, MI
(616) 361-5448
Late September, two days.

Collectibles

**Handles Stein & Gift
Shop**
7523 S Westnedge
Kalamazoo, MI 49002
Contact: Ron and Sally
Derhammer
*Gift shop for collectors of
breweriana.*

Minnesota

**Minnesota Office of
Tourism**
100 Metro Square
121 Seventh Pl. E
St Paul, MN 55101-2112
(800) 657-3700
*Tourist information, calendar
of events.*

Breweries, Large

The Stroh Brewery Co.
St. Paul Brewery
707 E Minnehaha
St. Paul, MN 55164
(612) 778-3100

Breweries, Regional and Micro

Cold Spring Brewing Co.
219 Red River Ave.
Cold Spring, MN 56320
(612) 685-8686

James Page Brewing Co.
1300 Quincy St.
Minneapolis, MN 55413
(612) 331-2833

**August Schell
Brewing Co.**
P.O. Box 128
New Ulm, MN 56073
(507) 354-5528
*Tours available of brewery,
mansion, and gardens. Gift
shop, museum open daily
Memorial day to Labor Day,
other times by appointment.
Call for free gift catalog.*

Minnesota Brewing Co.
882 W Seventh St.
St. Paul, MN 55102
(612) 228-9173
*Tours Monday, Wednesday,
Friday. Gift shop. Landmark
Oktoberfest, Pigs Eye Pilsner,
Landmark, Grain Belt
Premium Light.*

Pete's Brewing Co.
St. Paul, MN
(612) 290-2492

Summit Brewing Co.
2264 University Ave.
St. Paul, MN 55114
(612) 645-5029
*Summit Extra Pale Ale, Great
Northern Porter.*

Brewpubs

Rock Bottom Brewery #2
Minneapolis, MN
(612) 332-BREW

**Sherlock's Home
Brewery**
11000 Red Circle Dr.
Minnetonka, MN 55343
(612) 931-0203
*Good food, also over 75 single
malt Scotches. Stag's Head
Stout, Bishop's Bitter, Piper's
Pride.*

> Dost thou think, because thou art virtuous, there shall
> be no more cakes and ale?
>
> — William Shakespeare, *Twelfth Night*

Places to Enjoy Beer

Compañeros
The Boardwalk
Dorset, MN 56470
(218) 732-7624
Mexican food and beer.

Brit's Pub and Eating Establishment
1110 Nicollet Mall
Minneapolis, MN 55403
(612) 332-3908
A British pub with beers, cider, pub food, darts.

Pracna
117 SE Main St.
Minneapolis, MN 55414
(612) 379-3200
Built in 1890. Twenty taps. Selected samplings free on Thursday. Homebrew classes.

Cat Boulou's
112 N Main St.
Stillwater, MN 55082

Gasthaus Bavarian Hunter Restaurant
County Rd. 15 at 64
Stillwater, MN 55082
(612) 439-7128
Authentic German cuisine, beers. Bavarian buffet Sunday noon to 4PM, Sommerfest late June, Oktoberfest mid-September, 2 weekends.

Madcappers Saloon
224 S Main St.
Stillwater, MN 55082

Trumps Deluxe Grill & Bar
317 S Main St.
Stillwater, MN 55082
(612) 439-0024

Retail Stores

Byerly's
401 W 98 St.
Bloomington, MN 55420

Blue Max Liquors
14640 Tenth Ave.
Burnsville, MN 55337

Lake Aire Bottle Shoppe
2530 London Rd.
Duluth, MN 55812
(218) 724-8818
Domestic and imports.

Greenway Liquor
105 W Grant St.
Minneapolis, MN 55403

Byerly's
13801 Ridgedale Rd.
Minnetonka, MN 55305

Festivals and Events

Germanfest
Downtown
Benson, MN 56215
(612) 843-3618
September 30. Celebration of German culture, food.

Summerfest
Deerwood, MN 56444
(218) 534-3123
Mid-August, 2 days. Crafts, live music, food, beer garden, kids' events.

Historic Oktoberfest
Lanesboro, MN 55949
(507) 467-2902
Early October.

Oktoberfest
Madison, MN 56256
(612) 598-7373
Early October, 3 days. German music, bratwurst supper, dance.

Dosinzky
Main St.
New Prague, MN 56071
(612) 758-4360
Contact: Chamber of Commerce
Mid-September. Czech harvest festival celebrates Czech heritage with food, beer garden, entertainment.

Heritagefest
Brown County Fairgrounds
New Ulm, MN 56073
(507) 354-8850
Contact: P.O. Box 461
Mid-July, 4 days. German festival with music, crafts, food, costumes, and local Scheel's beer.

Oktoberfest
Turner Hall and Holiday Inn
New Ulm, MN 56073
(507) 354-4217
Contact: Chamber of Commerce, Box 384SD
Mid-October, second and third weekends. German music, dance, food, scarecrow contest.

Schell's Bock Festival
Schell Brewing Co.
New Ulm, MN 56073
(507) 354-5528
Late February.

Of Historic Interest

Fitger's Brewery Complex
600 E Superior St.
Duluth, MN 55802
(218) 722-8826
Shopping, dining, and lodging complex.

Museum of Brewing and Brewery

Schell Brewing Co.
New Ulm, MN 56073
(507) 354-5528
Open 3 and 4PM weekdays, 1, 2 and 3PM Saturday and Sunday. Free.

Wolf Brewery Caves

402 S Main St.
Stillwater, MN 55082
(612) 439-3588
1870s brewery.

Mississippi

Mississippi Division of Tourism

P.O. Box 22825
Jackson, MS 39205
(800) 927-6378
Tourist information.

Kershenstine Diamond

Eupora, MS 39744
Contract brewed.

Retail Stores

Village Party Shop

1805 Lelia St.
Jackson, MS 39216
(601) 981-2511

Festivals and Events

Oktoberfest

Keppner's Gasthaus
1798 Beach Blvd.
Biloxi, MS 39531
(601) 436-4878
Late September, 2 days. German food, drink, music, contests, arts and crafts.

Of Historic Interest

Magnolia Hotel

119 rue Magnolia
Biloxi, MS 39530
(601) 432-8806
Pre-Civil War hotel, now a Mardi Gras museum.

Mount Locust Inn

RR1, NT 143
Natchez Trace Pkwy.
Tupelo, MS 38801
(601) 680-4025
1780s inn on the old trace, restored to 1810 appearance. Headquarters of Natchez Trace Parkway.

Missouri

Missouri Division of Tourism

P.O. Box 1055
Jefferson City, MO 65102
(800) 877-1234
Tourist information, calendar of events.

Breweries, Large

Anheuser-Busch Brewery

1127 Pestalozzi
1 Busch Pl.
St. Louis, MO 63118
(314) 577-2626
Tours include Clydesdale stable, Brewing Video Gallery, packaging plant, hospitality room, gift shop. Year round, free, but tickets for specific tour times necessary. Budweiser, Busch, Michelob.

Breweries, Regional and Micro

Boulevard Brewing Co.

2501 SW Blvd.
Kansas City, MO 64108
(816) 474-7095

Gilbert Robinson Brewing

Kansas City, MO
(816) 756-2200
Contract brewed.

Signature Beer Co.

2737 Hereford St.
St. Louis, MO 63139
(314) 772-5911
Contact: Tony and Fran Caradonna
Distributor of microbrews, plus own beers, Spirit of St. Louis Ale, by Oldenberg Brewing Co., Kentucky and Goat's Breath Bock, by Cold Spring Brewing, MN.

Brewpubs

Flat Branch Brewing Co.

Columbia, MO 65201
(314) 499-0400

75th St. Brewery

520 W 75th St.
Kansas City, MO 64114

St. Louis Brewery/The Taproom

2100 Locust
St. Louis, MO 63114
(314) 241-2337
British and German-style food. Schlafly.

The Weathervane

Springfield, MO
(417) 831-6676

Places to Enjoy Beer

Bier Haus
602 Washington St.
Hermann, MO 65041
(314) 486-5343
Home of Hermann Lager, a beer made specially for the town. Outdoor beer garden, daily lunch specials, barbecue Friday and Saturday.

Caleco's Bar & Grill
420 Olive St.
St. Louis, MO 63102
(314) 421-0708

Hooter's
301 St. Louis Union Station
St. Louis, MO 63103
(314) 436-8888

John D. McGurk's
1200 Russell Blvd.
St. Louis, MO 63104
(314) 776-8309
Traditional Irish food, music, and beer.

Maggie O'Brien's
2000 Market St.
St. Louis, MO 63103
(314) 421-1388
Restaurant and Irish pub.

O'Connell's Pub
4652 Shaw Ave.
St. Louis, MO 63110
(314) 773-6600
Imported beers.

Riddle's Cafe & Wine Bar
6307 Delmar
University City, MO 63130
(314) 725-6985

Retail Stores

International Wines
3702 W Truman
Jefferson City, MO 65101

West End Wines
307 Belt St.
St. Louis, MO 63112

Western Liquor
4338 Telegraph St.
St. Louis, MO 63129
Festivals and Events

Black Forest Oktoberfest
County Rd. 638
Cape Girardeau, MO 63702
(314) 335-0899
Early October, 3 days. 1870s village celebrates German heritage.

Maifest
Townwide
Hermann, MO 65041
(314) 486-2744
Mid-May, 2 days. Celebration of German heritage. Parade, crafts, tours, German food and drink.

October Weekend Activities
Hermann, MO 65041
(314) 486-2744
Contact: Visitor Center, 306 Market St.
October, all weekends. German music, dance, food, and drink.

Oktoberfest
Frontier Park
St. Charles, MO 63302
(314) 946-7776
Early October, 2 days. Parade, German bands, food, music, dance.

Of Historic Interest

Wayside Inn Museum
119 W Spring St.
El Dorado Springs, MO 64744
(417) 876-5118
Local history in 1884 inn.

Montana

Travel Montana, Department of Commerce
Helena, MT 59620
(800) 541-1447
Tourist information, calendar of events.

Breweries, Regional and Micro

Bridger Brewing Co.
Belgrade, MT 59714
(406) 388-1833

Rock'n M Brewing
Belgrade, MT 59714
(406) 388-2007

Spanish Peaks Brewing Co.
120 N 19th Ave.
Bozeman, MT 59715
(406) 585-2296
And Italian Cafe. Spanish Peaks Porter, Yellowstone Pale Ale, Black Dog Bitter, Eye of the Rockies Wheat, Autumn Fest Ale.

Kessler Brewing Co.
1439 Harris St.
Helena, MT 59601
(406) 449-6214

Lang Creek Brewery
Marion, MT 59925
(406) 858-2200

Milestown Brewing Co.
The Golden Spur
1014 S Haynes Ave.
Miles City, MT 59301
(406) 232-3544
Tours available. Brewery,
casino, visitor information
center, liquor store.

Bayern Brewing/Iron
  Horse Brewpub
100 Railroad St.
P.O. Box 8043
Missoula, MT 59802
(406) 728-8866

Whitefish Brewing Co.
P.O. Box 1949
Whitefish, MT 59937
(406) 862-2684
Contact: Minott Wessinger
Black Star.

Places to Enjoy Beer

Heiser's Bar
Baker, MT 59313

Montana Bar & Cafe
Broadus, MT 59317
(406) 436-2454

Izaak Walton Inn
Essex, MT 59916
(406) 888-5700
Historic railroad inn.

Brunswick Bar
Hysham, MT 59038

Curt's Saloon
220 First Ave S
Laurel, MT 59044
(406) 628-8241

Montana Bar
612 Main
Miles City, MT 59301

Mogul's Bar & Grille
Big Mountain
Whitefish, MT 59937
(406) 862-3511

Festivals and Events

Oktoberfest
Anaconda, MT 59711
(406) 563-2422
Contact: Arts Center
Early October, two days.

Oktoberfest
Helena, MT 59601
(406) 442-4120
Contact: Chamber of
  Commerce, 210 E Lyndale
Early October, three days.

The Barley Mow

A traditional cumulative drinking and forfeit song from England. Whoever makes
a mistake in the chorus has to buy a round.

> Here's good luck to the pint pot, good luck to the barley mow.
> Jolly good luck to the pint pot, good luck to the barley mow,
> To the pint pot, half-pint, gill pot, half-gill, quarter-gill, nipperkin,
>   and the brown bowl,
> Here's good luck, good luck, good luck to the barley mow.
>
> Here's good luck to the quart pot, good luck to the barley mow.
> Jolly good luck to the quart pot, good luck to the barley mow,
> To the quart pot, pint pot, half-pint, gill pot, half-gill, quarter-gill,
> nipperkin, and the brown bowl,
> Here's good luck, good luck, good luck to the barley mow.
>
> Here's good luck to the half-gallon, etc.

And so on, through the gallon, the half-barrel, the barrel, the landlord, the land-
lady, their daughter, the slavey, the drayer, the brewer, and finally the company.
The last verse should be sung in double-time.

Homesteader Days
Homesteader Park
Old Hwy. 10
Huntley Project, MT 59037
(406) 967-3395
July, third weekend. Parade,
crafts, food, beer garden.

Herbstfest
Laurel, MT 59044
(406) 628-8105
Contact: Chamber of
  Commerce, 415 E Main
September, fourth weekend.
Authentic German festival.

Big Mountain MicroFest
Big Mountain Ski Resort
Whitefish, MT 59937
(406) 862-1980
Late August, two days.

Nebraska

Nebraska Travel &
  Tourism
P.O. Box 94666
Lincoln, NE 68509-4666
(800) 228-4307
Tourist information, calendar
of events.

Breweries, Large

Falstaff Brewing Co.
3302 S 25th St.
Omaha, NE 68105
(402) 733-1920

Brewpubs

Crane River Brewpub &
  Cafe
200 N Eleventh
Lincoln, NE 68508
(402) 476-7766

Lazlo's Brewery & Grill
710 P St.
Lincoln, NE 68508
(402) 474-2337
Captain Donovan's Special
Amber, Creamator Stout.

Jaipur Restaurant &
  Brewpub
10922 Elm St.
Omaha, NE 68144
(402) 392-7331
Contact: Mark and Gary
  Herse
Tandoori and Northern Indian
cuisine, Open daily. Ten
bottled beers including Taj
Mahal, Golden Eagle from
India. Royal Golden Pale Ale,
Huntsman Brown Ale, Tusk
Dark Ale, Black Stripe Stout,
Pink City Weizen.

Johnny's Brewery &
  Cafe
Omaha, NE
(402) 895-1122

Jones St. Brewery
1316 Jones St.
Omaha, NE 68102
(402) 344-3858
Contact: Dean Dobmier,
  brewer
American pub fare and blues
music. Open daily. Ryan's
Stout, Harvester Wheat Beer,
Grand Slam Amber Ale, Patch
Pale Ale, Bolt, Nut and Screw.

Sharky's Brewery &
  Grill
Omaha, NE
(402) 390-0777

Places to Enjoy Beer

Billy Frogg's Grill & Bar
1120 Howard St.
Omaha, NE 68102
(402) 341-4427

Gallagher's Food &
  Spirits
Shaker Pl.
10730 Pacific St.
Omaha, NE 68114
(402) 393-1421

Momy Inn
1510 N Saddle Creek Rd.
Omaha, NE 68104

Howard St. Tavern
1112 Howard St.
Omaha, NE 68102
(402) 341-0433

Jams Bar & Grill
7814 Dodge St.
Omaha, NE 68114
(402) 399-8300

McKenna's Blues,
  Booze & BBQ
7425 Pacific St.
Omaha, NE 68114
(402) 393-7427

M's Pub
422 S Eleventh St.
Omaha, NE 68102
(402) 342-2550

Retail Stores

Baker's Supermarket
Various locations
Omaha, NE

Festivals and Events

Octoberfest
State College Campus
Chadron, NE 69337
(308) 432-6260
Contact: Dr. Shepherd, 10th
and Main Sts.
*October. German ethnic
festival.*

Czech Festival
Main St.
Clarkson, NE 68629
(402) 892-3431
Contact: Dick Moore, 611
Pine St.
*Late June, three days.
Celebration of Czech heritage,
with food and drink,
entertainment, crafts.*

Germanfest
Downtown
Fairbury, NE 68352
(402) 729-3000
Contact: Chamber of
Commerce, 515 Fourth St.
*Mid-September, three days.
German food and dance, bier
barrel race, arts, crafts,
entertainment.*

Minatare Tabor Days
Main St.
Minatare, NE 69356
(308) 783-2151
Contact: Mindy Corr, P.O.
Box 722
*Late July. Bed races, hog
wrestle, food, beer garden.*

St. Stanislaus Polish Festival
4002 J St.
Omaha, NE 68107
(402) 733-4886
Contact: Rita Stodolka,
4219 S 39th St.
*Mid-August. Traditional
foods, beer garden, events,
polka bands.*

Streetcar Days
City Park
Red Cloud, NE 68970
(402) 746-3238
Contact: Kay Jacoby, 1005
N Walnut St.
*Mid-August, two days.
Parade, air show, antique
cars, barbecue, beer garden,
dance.*

Oktoberfest
Legion Park
Sidney, NE 69162
(308) 254-2932
Contact: Judy Harris,
P.O. Box 91
*Early October, 3 days.
Entertainment, food,
biergarten, crafts, farmers
market.*

Oktoberfest
Mr. Tunes
South Sioux City, NE 68776
(402) 494-1614
Contact: Deb Hines, 100 S
Ridge Dr.
*Early October. Polka bands,
food and drink.*

Germanfest
Citywide
Syracuse, NE 68446
(402) 269-3352, 269-2464,
269-2346, or 269-2703
Contact: Jean Schulte, P.O.
Box 321
*Late September, three days.
Parade, food, beer garden,
crafts, dances.*

Nevada

Nevada Commission on Tourism
Capitol Complex
Carson, NV 89710
(800) 237-0774
*Tourist information, calendar
of events.*

Brewpubs

Carson Depot
Carson City, NV
(702) 884-4546

Holy Cow! Casino, Brewery & Cafe
2423 Las Vegas Blvd. S
Las Vegas, NV 89104
(702) 732-2697

Reno Brewing Co.
91 Bell St., #9
Reno, NV 89503
(702) 322-BREW

Great Basin Brewing Co.
846 Victorian Ave.
P.O. Box 2242
Sparks, NV 89432-2242
(702) 355-7711
Restaurant and brewery.

Union Brewery Co.
28 North C St.
Virginia City, NV 89440
(702) 847-0328

Festivals and Events

Oktoberfest
Wells, NV 89835
(702) 752-3504
October.

Of Historic Interest

Brewery Arts Center
449 W King St.
Carson City, NV 89701
(800) NEV-ADA1
Contact: Visitors' Bureau,
  (702) 687-7410
*Home of Tahoe Beer from
1864 to 1948, now an arts
center. Brewery memorabilia.*

New Hampshire

**Office of Travel &
  Tourism**
P.O. Box 856
Concord, NH 03302-0856
(603) 271-2343
Tourist information.

Breweries, Large

**Anheuser-Busch
  Brewery**
221 Daniel Webster Hwy.
Merrimack, NH 03054
(603) 889-6631
*Tours, Budweiser Clydesdales.
Budweiser, Busch, Michelob.*

Brewpubs

Italian Oasis
127 Market Pl.
Littleton, NH 03561
(603) 444-6995

**Martha's Exchange
  Restaurant**
183 Main St.
Nashua, NH 03060
(603) 883-8781

Portsmouth Brewery
56 Market St.
Portsmouth, NH 03801
(603) 431-1115
*Open daily. Wide selection of
brews, extensive menu. Tours
available: call for reservations.*

Smuttynose Brewing Co.
225 Heritage Ave.
Portsmouth, NH 03801
(603) 433-2337
Shoals Pale Ale.

Seven-Barrel Brewery
West Lebanon, NH 03784
(603) 298-5566

Places to Enjoy Beer

Kettle & Crane Inn
Rt. 3 and 4
Boscawen, NH 03303
(603) 796-2261

Red Parka Pub
Rt. 302
Glen, NH 03838
(603) 383-4344

Lamie's Inn & Tavern
490 Lafayette Rd.
P.O. Box 609
Hampton, NH 03842
(603) 926-0330
Fax (603) 929-0017

Murphy's Tavern
11 S Main St.
Hanover, NH 03755
(603) 643-4075
*Authentic tavern with 10 draft
beers.*

**176 Main Tavern &
  Restaurant**
176 Main St.
Keene, NH 03431
(603) 357-3100

**Granite Street Bar &
  Grille**
50 Phillippe Cote St.
Manchester, NH 03101
(603) 622-0900

**Abercrombie & Finch
  Restaurant**
219 Lafayette Rd.
North Hampton, NH 03862
(603) 964-9774
English pub setting.

Wolfe's Tavern
44 N Main St.
Wolfeboro, NH 03894
(800) 451-2389
in NH (603) 569-3016
*Authentic New England pub,
extensive beer list.*

Of Historic Interest

Wyman Tavern Museum
339 Main St.
Keene, NH 03431
(603) 352-1895
*Historic tavern, built 1770–
1820.*

**Sugar Hill Historical
  Museum**
Main St.
Sugar Hill, NH 03585
(603) 823-5336
*Reflecting life from 1780
through grand hotel era.
Stage coach tavern kitchen,
more. Open July to mid-
October.*

New Jersey

Breweries, Regional and Micro

**Saratoga Lager
  Brewing Co.**
412 Tenafly Rd.
Englewood, NJ 07632
(201) 568-0716
*Contract brewed by Cata-
mount, VT.*

Long Valley Pub & Brewery
P.O. Box 368
Long Valley, NJ 07853
(908) 876-5252
Contact: Geoffrey Price

The Ship Inn
Milford, NJ 08848
(908) 995-0188
Contact: David and Anne Hall
Microbrewery and restaurant.

Triumph Brewing Co.
138 Nassau St.
Princeton, NJ 08540
(609) 924-7855
Contact: Ray and Erica Disch, Adam Rechnitz

Places to Enjoy Beer

Andy's Corner Bar
265 Queen Anne Rd.
Bogota, NJ 07603
(201) 342-9887
Over 70 international and microbrew beers.

Jack O'Connor's
1288 Rt. 22 E
Bridgewater, NJ 08807
(908) 725-1500
Fax (908) 725-6633
Sixteen taps, good food, huge buffet.

Sam's
41 Union Ave.
Cresskill, NJ 07626
(201) 569-0556

> A quart of ale is a dish for a king
>
> —William Shakespeare, *The Winter's Tale*

Laughing Lion
40 N Sussex St.
Dover, NJ 07801
(201) 328-1800

The Front Porch
217 Wagaraw Rd.
Hawthorne, NJ 07506
(201) 427-4331

Hudson's
200 Hudson St.
Hoboken, NJ 07030
(201) 420-8686

McCormick's
266 Somerset Ave.
New Brunswick, NJ 08901

The Old Bay Restaurant
61–63 Church St.
New Brunswick, NJ 08901
(908) 246-3111
Sixteen taps, micros, seasonal specialties. Live music Wednesday to Sunday.

Basil T Leaf's
183 Riverside Ave.
Red Bank, NJ 07701
(908) 842-5990

Green Onion
15 Wallington Ave.
Wallington, NJ 07057
(201) 473-3677
Over three dozen micros and imports. Italian and grilled specialties.

Retail Stores

Supreme Liquors
112 S Washington St.
Bergenfield, NJ 07621
(201) 384-2230

Baumel's Exotic Beer
30 Westfield Ave.
Clark, NJ 07066
(908) 388-1905
Large selection of domestic and imported beers.

Clinton Wine & Spirits
57 Laneco Plaza
Clinton, NJ 08809
(908) 735-9655
Domestics, imports, micros. Free newsletter and price list: (800) 985-WINE.

Bayway World of Liquor
639 Bayway Ave.
Elizabeth, NJ 07201
(908) 353-6300

Grand Opening Liquors
408 Haledon Ave.
Haledon, NJ 07508
(201) 942-3312
Over 525 beers.

Leonia Wine & Spirit Shop
307 Broad Ave.
Leonia, NJ 07605
(201) 944-0956
Interesting selection of bottled beers, imported and domestic.

Grand Opening Liquors
1068 High Mountain Rd.
North Haledon, NJ 07508
(201) 427-4477
Over 525 beers.

Ramsey Liquors
47 W Main St.
Ramsey, NJ 07446
(201) 327-0353
Fax (201) 825-1108

Home Liquors
25 Valley St.
South Orange, NJ 07079
(201) 762-9682
*Over 200 varieties of domestic,
imported, and micros.*

Monaghan's Liquors
1617 Rt. 37 E and River Dr.
Toms River, NJ 08753
(908) 270-6060
Two hundred fifty beer brands.

**W Tuckerton Liquor
Store**
590 Rt. 9
Tuckerton, NJ 08087
(800) 572-9463
Two hundred ten beers.

Saddle River Liquors
380 Rt. 17
Upper Saddle River, NJ
07458
(201) 825-3161

Chestnut Wines & Spirits
Tice's Farm
327 Chestnut Ridge Rd.
Woodcliff Lake, NJ 07675
(201) 391-5171

Festivals and Events

**Long Valley Brewfest &
Street Fair**
Townwide
Long Valley, NJ 07853
(908) 832-9767
Contact: Geoffrey Price
*Mid-October. Beer tent with
many micros, crafts, food, live
bands.*

Octoberfest
Old Bay Restaurant
61–63 Church St.
New Brunswick, NJ 08901
(908) 246-3111
*Early October. Seasonal
micros, German-style buffet,
live blues.*

Of Historic Interest

Potter's Tavern
Broad St. W
Bridgeton, NJ 08302
(609) 455-5529
*1776 restored tavern. Home of
the state's first newspaper.
Tours weekends in summer by
appointment.*

Gabriel Davies Tavern
Fourth and Floodgate Rds.
P.O. Box 68
Glendora, NJ 08012
(609) 939-2699
*1756 tavern. Summer
concerts, tours by appointment.*

**Indian King Tavern
Museum**
233 Kings Hwy. E
Haddonfield, NJ 08033
(609) 429-6792
*Early American public house
from the time of Dolly
Madison.*

**Museum of American
Glass**
Glasstown Rd.
Millville, NJ 08332
(609) 825-6800
*In Wheaton Village. Over
9000 objects in collection.
1888 glass factory with
demonstrations.*

Golden Nugget Saloon
50 Lackawanna Dr.
Rt. 206, Byram
Netcong, NJ 07857
(201) 347-8900
Mail: P.O. Box 37
*Part of Wild West City. Food,
shows.*

Allen House
Rt. 34 and Sycamore Ave.
Shrewsbury, NJ 07702
(908) 462-1466
Mail: 70 Court St., Freehold
NJ 07728
*C18 tavern, rotating exhibits.
Open May–October.*

New Mexico

**New Mexico Department
of Tourism**
P.O. Box 2003
Santa Fe, NM 87503
Tourist information.

Breweries, Regional and Micro

Preston Brewery
P.O. Box 154
Embudo, NM 07531
(505) 852-4707

Santa Fe Brewing Co.
Flying M Ranch
HC 75, Box 83
Galisteo, NM 87540
(505) 466-3333
*Santa Fe Pale, Nut Brown,
and Fiesta ales; Old Pojoaque
Porter, Galisteo Weiss,
Chicken Killer Barley Wine,
Sangre de Frambuesa,
Maxwell's Dry Stout.*

Russell Brewing Co.
1242 Siler Rd.
Santa Fe, NM 87501
(505) 438-3138

The Chile Connection
MM #1, Ski Valley Rd.
Taos, NM 87525
(505) 776-8787

Sangre de Cristo Brewing
Taos, NM 87525
See Eske's Brewpub.

Brewpubs

Assets Grille & Brewery
6910 Montgomery Blvd. NE
Albuquerque, NM 87109
(505) 889-6400

Il Vicino
3403 Central Ave. NE
Albuquerque, NM 87106
(505) 266-7855

Rio Bravo Restaurant & Brewery
515 Central Ave. NW
Albuquerque, NM 87102
(505) 242-6800
Coronado Gold, High Desert Pale Ale, Esteban Dark.

Rio Grande Brewing
3760 Hawkins NE
Albuquerque, NM 87109
(505) 343-0903

Preston Brewing Co./ Embudo Station
Hwy. 68
P.O. Box 154
Embudo, NM 87531
(505) 852-4707

Organ Mountain Brewing Co.
O'Ryan's Tavern
700 S Telshore Blvd.
Las Cruces, NM 88001
(505) 522-8191

O'Ryan's Brewery & Tavern
700 S Telshore Blvd.
Las Cruces, NM 88001
(505) 522-8191

Eske's, a Brewpub
106 DeGeorges Ln.
Box 1572
Taos, NM 87571
(505) 758-1517
Six unfiltered, unpasteurized beers on tap. Southwest pubfare from the kitchen. Outdoor seating, music, smoke-free indoors.

Places to Enjoy Beer

Billy's Long Bar
4800 San Mateo
Albuquerque, NM 87109
(505) 889-0573

Brewster's Pub
312 Central Ave. SW
Albuquerque, NM 87102
(505) 247-2533

The Dingo Bar
313 Gold Ave. SW
Albuquerque, NM 87102
(505) 243-0663

Maria Teresa Restaurant & 1840 Bar
618 Rio Grande Blvd. NW
Albuquerque, NM 87102
(505) 242-3900

Oasis Restaurant & Lounge
5400 San Mateo NE
Albuquerque, NM 87109
(505) 884-2324

Saints & Sinners
2305 Riverside
Espanola, NM 87532
(505) 753-2757

Eddie's Bar & Grill
901 Av de Mesilla
Las Cruces, NM 88005
(505) 524-8603

Joe's Ringside
Hwy. 85
Las Vegas, NM 87701
(505) 425-7252

Evangelo's
200 W San Francisco St.
Santa Fe, NM 87501
(505) 982-9014

Murray's Delicatessen
115 E McCarthy Pl.
Taos, NM 87525
(505) 758-4205

Taos Inn
125 Paseo del Pueblo Norte
Taos, NM 87525
(505) 758-2233

Thunderbird Lodge
Taos Ski Valley
Taos, NM 87525
(505) 776-2280

Tim's Stray Dog Cantina
Taos Ski Valley
Taos, NM 87525
(505) 776-2894

Retail Stores

Kokoman Liquors
Hwy. 285
Pojoaque, NM 87501
(505) 455-2219

Festivals and Events

Fall Chili Fiesta
River Walk Park
Grants, NM 87020
(800) 748-2142
September.

Octoberfest
Haynes Park
Rio Rancho, NM 87124
(505) 892-1700
Late September, 3 days.
German dancing, entertain-
ment, food, drink.

Oktoberfest
Civic Events Center
Ruidoso, NM 88345
(800) 253-2255; in NM
   (505) 2577395
October.

New York

New York Division of
   Tourism
1 Commerce Plaza
Albany, NY 12245
(800) 225-5697
Tourist information.

Breweries, Large

Anheuser-Busch
   Brewery
2885 Belgium Rd.
Baldwinsville, NY 13027
(315) 635-4244
Free tours by appointment
only, Monday to Friday
September to April, Monday to
Saturday May to August, gift
shop. Budweiser, Busch,
Michelob.

Breweries, Regional and Micro

Brooklyn Brewery
118 N Eleventh St.
Brooklyn, NY 11211
(718) 486-7422
Contact: Steve Hindy
Brooklyn Lager, Brown.

Woodstock Brewing Co.
20 St. James St.
P.O. Box 1000W
Kingston, NY 12401
(914) 331-2810
Fax (914) 331-2950
Free tours, call for times.
Hudson Lager, St. James Ale,
Big Indian Porter, Roudout
Stout. Handicapped acces-
sible.

Buffalo Brewing Co.
1830 Abbott Rd.
Lackawanna, NY 14218
(716) 828-0004

Lake Titus Brewery
Malone, NY 12953

New Amsterdam
   Brewing Co.
257 Park Ave., S, 7th Floor
New York, NY 10010-7304
(212) 473-1100
Contract brewed by F X Matt.
New Amsterdam Amber, New
York Ale.

Riverosa Co.
New York, NY
Contract brewed.

Spring Street
   Brewing Co.
60 Spring St.
New York, NY 10012
(212) 226-9110

Genesee Brewing Co.
445 St. Paul St.
Rochester, NY 14605
(716) 546-1030
Genesee Cream and 12 Horse
ales; Koch's Golden Anniver-
sary Beer.

Shea's Brewery
445 St. Paul St.
Rochester, NY 14605
Michael Shea's Irish Amber
Beer.

Old Peconic Brewing Co.
Shelter Island, NY 11964
Contract brewed.

Old World Brewing Co.
2070 Victory Blvd., #4
Staten Island, NY 10314
(718) 370-0551
Fax (718) 370-0558
Contact: Sal Pennachio
New York Harbor Ale, NYH
Dark (porter style).

F X Matt Brewing Co.
811 Edwards St.
Utica, NY 13502
(315) 732-3181
One of America's oldest
breweries. Tours daily except
Sunday, holidays. Trolley
rides to 1888 tavern for
samples. Gift shop. Brews beer
for Dock Street, Harpoon,
Brooklyn, New Amsterdam,
Rhinos, Saranac, Matt's
Premium, and Freeport USA.

Brewpubs

Park Slope Brewing Co.
Sixth Ave. and Fifth St.
Brooklyn, NY
(718) 788-1756
Contact: Steve Deptula,
   Eugene Kaleniak.

Rochester Brewpub
800 Jefferson Rd.
Rochester, NY 14623
(716) 272-1550
Own brews, plus complete line
of Buffalo Brewing Co.

Chapter House Brewing Co.
400 Stewart Ave.
Ithaca, NY 14850
(607) 277-9782

Long Island Brewing Co.
111 Jericho Turnpike
Jericho, NY 11753
(516) 334-BREW
Contact: Mark Burford,
   brewmaster
*Brewery, restaurant, and
coffeehouse. Live entertainment.*

West Side Brewing Co.
340 Amsterdam Ave.
New York, NY 10023
(212) 721-2161

Yorkville Brewery & Tavern
1359 First Ave.
New York, NY 10021
(212) 517-BREW

Zip City Brewing Co.
3 W 18th St.
New York, NY 10011
(212) 366-6333
*Brews traditional European
style lager beers: Maerzen,
Pilsner, Dunkel. Upscale
American pub fare. Building
was once occupied by the
National Temperance Society.
Hah!*

James Bay Brewery & Restaurant
154 W Broadway
Port Jefferson, NY 11777
(516) 928-2525

Rohrbach's
315 Gregory St.
Rochester, NY 14620
(716) 244-5680
*Ales, lagers, seasonal
specialties.*

Mountain Valley Brewpub
122 Orange Ave.
Suffern, NY 10901
(914) 357-0101
Contact: Lon Lauterio,
   owner
*Extensive menu. Open daily.
Porter, Copper, Pale, Copper
Lyte.*

Syracuse Suds Factory
220 W Water St.
Syracuse, NY 13202
(315) 471-2253

Troy Pub & Brewery
417 River St.
P.O. Box 1629
Troy, NY 12180
(518) 273-BEER
Contact: Garry Brown
*Golden and Amber ales, Dark
Porter, Weizen Bier, Belgian
Cherry Ale, St. Nick's Nectar.*

Buffalo Brewpub
6861 Main St.
Williamsville, NY 14221
(716) 632-0552
*Own brews, plus complete line
of Buffalo Brewing Co.*

Places to Enjoy Beer

The Lionheart
258 Lark St.
Albany, NY 12210
*Smoke-free blues cafe with
good beers and gourmet food.*

Mahar's
1110 Madison Ave.
Albany, NY 12208
(518) 459-7868
Contact: Jim Mahar
*Small bar with huge selection
of over 600 beers. Live music
weekends.*

The Scrimshaw Tavern
660 Albany Shaker Rd.
Albany, NY 12211
(518) 452-5801

Washington Tavern
250 Western Ave.
Albany, NY 12203
*Draft and bottled beers, hand-
held food menu.*

Coopersmith's
615 E Main St.
Bayshore, NY 11706
(516) 666-0011

Henry's End Cafe
44 Henry St.
Brooklyn, NY 11201
(718) 834-1776

Mugs Ale House
125 Bedford Ave.
Brooklyn, NY 11211
(718) 384-8494

Teddy's Bar
96 Berry St.
Brooklyn, NY 11211
(718) 384-9787

Waterfront Ale House
136 Atlantic Ave.
Brooklyn, NY 11201
(718) 522-3794
*Large selection of tap beers.
Closed Monday. Comedy
night Tuesday.*

Croxley Ales
129 New Hyde Park Rd.
Franklin Square, NY 11010
(516) 326-9542
English/American cuisine,
27 taps.

Murph's
935 Hempstead Turnpike
Franklin Square, NY 11010
(516) 358-0548

Daytona House of Beer
345 Nesconset Hwy.
Hauppauge, NY 11788
(516) 366-3456

Tubby's
661 Old Willets Path
Hauppauge, NY 11788
(516) 234-2121
"Warm beer & lousy food."
Large selection of micros,
imports, cider.

Canterbury Ales
314 New York Ave.
Huntington, NY 11743
(516) 549-4404
English-type pub. Sixteen
taps, more bottled.

Conrad's Bar & Grill
W Jericho Turnpike
Huntington, NY 11743
(516) 427-9728

Raccoon Saloon
Main St., Rt. 9W
Marlboro, NY 12542-0477
(914) 236-7872
Goodly selection of micros and
imports.

Weepin' Willoby's
Rt. 17M
Monroe, NY 10950
(914) 783-2246

American Festival Cafe
Rockefeller Plaza
20 W 50th St.
New York, NY 10019
(212) 246-6699
Restaurant offering a number
of "boutique" beers. Monthly
Beermaker's Dinners.

Bell Cafe
310 Spring St.
New York, NY 10012
(212) 334-2355
Interesting beer selection,
good food, art shows.

The Brasserie
100 E 53rd St.
New York, NY 10022
(212) 751-4840
Restaurant open daily.

Brewsky's
41 E Seventh St.
New York, NY 10003
(212) 470-0671

Broome St. Bar
363 W Broadway
New York, NY 10013
(212) 925-2086

Chumley's
86 Bedford St.
New York, NY 10013
(212) 675-4449
Twenty-seven micros, lobster
specials.

East Side Ale House
51st St. and Second Ave.
New York, NY 10022
(212) 752-3615
Eight taps, large selection of
bottles.

Fraunces Tavern
54 Pearl St.
New York, NY 10004
(212) 269-0144
Historic tavern with museum
of early American history.

Jekyll & Hyde Pub
91 Seventh Ave. S
New York, NY 10014
(212) 255-5388

Jeremy's Ale House
254 Front St.
New York, NY 10038
(212) 964-3537

Jimmy Armstrong's
Saloon
875 Tenth Ave.
New York, NY 10023
(212) 581-0606
Bar with 12 taps, food, live
jazz and chamber music.

Kinsale Tavern
1679 Third Ave.
New York, NY 10021
(212) 348-4370

Manchester New York
920 Second Ave.
New York, NY 10017
(212) 223-7484
Fax (212) 223-7484
Sixteen taps, 42 bottles. Sports
bar.

McSorley's Ale House
15 E Seventh St.
New York, NY 10003
(212) 473-9148

North Star Pub
South St. Seaport
South St.
New York, NY 10038
(212) 509-6757
English style pub.

Nosmo King
54 Varick St.
New York, NY 10006
(212) 966-1239
Restaurant and bar. Six-course beer and food tasting menu.

Peculier Pub
145 Bleecker St.
New York, NY 10013
(212) 353-1327

Prince St. Bar
125 Prince St.
New York, NY 10012
(212) 228-8130

Riverrun
176 Franklin St.
New York, NY 10013
(212) 966-3894
Fifteen taps.

The Slaughtered Lamb
182 W Fourth St.
New York, NY 10012
(212) 627-5262

Tribeca Grill
375 Greenwich St.
New York, NY 10013
(212) 941-3900

White Horse Tavern
567 Hudson St.
New York, NY 10013
(212) 243-9260 or
(212) 989-3956

**Company B's Restaurant
& Pub**
206 Rt. 303
Orangeburg, NY 10962
(914) 365-6060
Fax (914) 365-6794
Twenty-six microbrews on tap, over 50 bottled. Full menu, including ale house favorites

and late-night dining. Live entertainment Tuesday to Saturday.

Slick's Tavern
Liberty and S Ferry Sts.
Schenectady, NY 12305
1804 building that has been a tavern since the turn of the century. Good selection, beer of the month special, huge sandwiches.

**Adobe Blues Old West
 Saloon**
63 Lafayette Ave.
New Brighton, Staten
 Island, NY 10301
(718) 720-BLUE
Contact: Jim Stayoch, Ken
 Tirado
Over 200 brands of beer from 32 countries. Southwestern food served in traditional pueblo style dining room. Also 17 tequilas, great margaritas, and jake, the one-eyed snake.

Clark's Ale House
122 W Jefferson St.
Syracuse, NY 13202
(315) 479-9859

**Coleman's Authentic
 Irish Pub**
Syracuse, NY 13204
(315) 476-1933
Pub restaurant, 10 taps.

**Horsefeathers
 Restaurant**
N Broadway
Tarrytown, NY 10591
(914) 631-6606

Holmes & Watson Ltd.
450 Broadway
Troy, NY 12180
(518) 273-8526
Twenty-three taps, over 200 brews, full lunch and dinner menu. Open daily from 11AM.

Tubby's
401 Sunrise Hwy.
West Islip, NY 11795
(516) 661-8976
"Warm beer & lousy food." Large selection of micros, imports, cider.

O'Brien's
605–607 Willis Ave.
Williston Park, NY 11596
(516) 746-9321
Draft Guinness and Bud. Woodpecker cider. Darts and pool.

Retail Stores

Cable Beverage
304 Rt. 304
Bardonia, NY 10954
(914) 623-7645

Cobble Heights
216 Pacific St.
Brooklyn, NY 11201
(718) 596-0871

Russin Thrifty
302–412 Meeker
Brooklyn, NY 11211
(718) 383-2200

**Thrifty American
 Beverage Center**
256 Court St.
Brooklyn, NY 11231
(718) 875-0226
Store with many microbrews.

Bargain Beverage
Rt. 17M
Chester, NY 10918
(914) 469-9955

Beverage Wagon
156–17 73rd Ave.
Flushing, NY 11367
(718) 969-0013 or
969-0178
Large import selection.

Beverageland
527 Rt. 111
Hauppauge, NY 11787

Big Z Beverage
1675 E Jericho Turnpike
Huntington, NY 11743
(516) 499-3479
Over 400 beers in stock.

Katonah Beverage Barn
24 Woodsbridge Rd.
Katonah, NY 10536
(914) 232-7842

Monarch Beverage
505 Long Beach Blvd.
Long Beach, NY 11561
(516) 432-6615
Fax (516) 432-6767
Free catalog.

Alex's Deli
95 MacDougal St.
New York, NY 10012
(212) 979-7826
Contact: Alex Anastiasiadis
*Four hundred kinds of exotic
beer.*

Festivals and Events

Old Songs Festival
Altamont Fairgrounds
Rt. 146
Altamont, NY 12009
(518) 765-2815
Contact: Andy Spence
*Late June. Folk music and
dancing, with beer on tap.
Fun for the whole family.*

New York Beer Festival
Under Brooklyn Bridge
Brooklyn, NY
Contact: Brooklyn Brewery
*Mid-September. Plenty of
beers to try, entertainment,
food from top NY restaurants,
other stuff.*

Oktoberfest
Cockaigne Ski Lodge
Cherry Creek, NY 14723
(716) 287-3500 or
287-3223
*Late September. German
music, wagon rides, products
from local Amish community.*

Oktoberfest
Hunter Mt.
Hunter, NY 12442
(518) 263-4223
*Early October. Mini German
Alps fest. Free pumpkins and
admission.*

Greater New York Beer Expo
NY Coliseum
10 Columbus Circle
New York, NY 10019
(908) 842-7507
*Late September. Run by Brew
Kettle Inc.*

St. Patrick's Day Parade
Fifth Ave.
New York, NY
*Mid-March. Bars tend to serve
beer colored green.*

Oktoberfest
Gore Mt. Ski Area
North Creek, NY 12853
(518) 251-2411
*Late September, 2 days.
Bavarian bands, dancers,
crafts, food and drink. Special
kids' korner.*

Of Historic Interest

Museum of Glass
Corning, NY 14830
(607) 937-5371
*The history of glass. Includes
drinking vessels from Roman
times on.*

Old Bethpage Village
Round Swamp Rd.
Old Bethpage, NY 11804
(516) 572-8400
*Living history pre-Civil War
village includes inn.*

Good ale, the true and proper drink of Englishmen. He is not deserving of
the name of Englishman who speaketh against ale, that is good ale.

— George Borrow (1803-1881)

Riley House Museum
Old Piseco Rd.
Speculator, NY 12164
(518) 548-6637
C19 tannery and tavern.
Local history.

North Carolina

North Carolina Travel &
Tourism
430 N Salisbury St.
Raleigh, NC 27611
(800) VISIT-NC
Tourist information.

Breweries, Large

The Stroh Brewery Co.
4791 Schlitz Ave.
Winston Salem, NC 27107
(910) 788-6710

Weeping Radish
Brewery #2
Duke St.
Durham, NC
(919) 688-2739

Gate City Brewing Co.
Greensboro, NC

Toisnot Brewing Co.
Wilson, NC 27893
The Spur Steakhouse &
Saloon.

Brewpubs

Tumbleweed Grill
122 Blowing Rock Rd.
Boone, NC 28607
(704) 264-7111
Mexican and Southwestern
cuisine. Open daily. Tum-
bleweed Amber, Gold Rush
Ale.

Dilworth Brewing Co.
1301 East Blvd.
Charlotte, NC 28203
(704) 377-2739
Reed's Gold, Albemarle Ale,
Dilworth Porter, Wild Wheat.

Mill Bakery, Eatery &
Brewery
122 W Woodlawn Rd.
Charlotte, NC 28217
(704) 525-2530
Fax (704) 525-5561
Serving breakfast, lunch, and
dinner 7 days a week. Ten
minutes from Charlotte
International Airport. Copper
Creek Ale, Red Oktober, 49er
Gold.

Spring Garden
Brewing Co.
714 Francis King St.
Greensboro, NC 27401
(910) 299-3649
Red Oak Lager, Hummin'
Bird, Blackbeard Bock,
Battlefield Black.

Weeping Radish
Restaurant & Brewery
Hwy. 64 E
Manteo, NC 27954
(919) 473-1157

Greenshields Brewery &
Pub
214 E Martin St.
Raleigh, NC 27601
(919) 829-0214

Places to Enjoy Beer

Sidewalk Cafe
110 Hardin
Boone, NC 28607
(704) 262-5142

Picasso's
1004 S Kings Dr.
Charlotte, NC 28207
(704) 333-2255

Bert's Seafood Grille
2419 Spring Garden St.
Greensboro, NC 27403
(910) 854-2314
Good variety of domestic and
imported beers.

Crocodile's Cafe
329 S Tate St.
Greensboro, NC 27403
(910) 274-5211
Live music, Italian food.

Harry's Shrimp & Oyster
Bar
1740 Battleground Ave.
Greensboro, NC 27408
(910) 273-8944
Draft beers and fresh seafood.

Southern Lights Bistro &
Bar
105 Smyres Pl.
Greensboro, NC 27403
(910) 379-9414

The Sunset Cafe
4608 W Market St.
Greensboro, NC 27407
(910) 855-0349
Draft beers, great food.

J Butler's Bar & Grille
2531 Eastchester Dr.
High Point, NC 27262
(910) 454-4398

J Butler's Bar & Grille
1106B S Main St.
High Point, NC 27262
(910) 861-5758

The Dog House
666 N Main St.
High Point, NC 27262
(910) 886-4953
Draft beer and hot dogs.

The Fox Bar & Grille
805 Westchester Dr.
High Point, NC 27262
(910) 882-0600
Lounge and grill.

Retail Stores

Peabody's
Hwy. 105
Boone, NC 28607
(704) 264-9476

The Warehouse
304 Howard St.
Boone, NC 28607
(704) 264-4935

Wellspring Grocery
81 S Elliott Rd.
Chapel Hill, NC 27514
(919) 968-1983

Jack Straws
1936A E Seventh St.
Charlotte, NC 28204
(704) 347-8960

**Mike's Discount
Beverage**
4620 Park Rd.
Charlotte, NC 28209
(704) 523-9748

Talley's Green Grocery
1408C E Blvd.
Charlotte, NC 28203
(704) 334-9200

Fowler's Gourmet Foods
905 W Main St.
Durham, NC 27701
(919) 683-2555

Festivals and Events

Oktoberfest
McGregor Village Shopping
Center
Cary, NC 27511
(919) 755-0382
Contact: J. Hammerle
*Mid-September. German food,
bands, folk dancing.*

**Oktoberfest
Internationale**
Fairgrounds
Ft. Bragg, NC 28307
(910) 396-3919
Contact: Chuck Dellinger
*Early October, 18 days. Inter-
national food, entertainment,
and more.*

Oktoberfest
Switzerland Inn
Little Switzerland, NC
28749
(800) 654-4026
*Late September, two days.
German and bluegrass music,
dance, and food.*

Oktoberfest
Parking lot across from
Ghost Town
Maggie Springs, NC 28751
(704) 926-1686
Contact: Carol Bennett
*Mid-September, 2 weekends.
Oompah bands, Alpenhorn
contest, German food.*

North Dakota

**North Dakota Parks &
Tourism**
604 E Blvd.
Bismarck, ND 58505
(800) 437-2077
*Tourist information, calendar
of events.*

Breweries, Regional and Micro

Dakota Brewing Co.
Grand Forks, ND
Contract brewed.

Places to Enjoy Beer

**Sergio's Mexican Bar &
Grill**
I-94 and Hwy. 22
Dickinson, ND 58601
(701) 264-1022

**Downtowner's Pub &
Grill**
301 Third Ave. N
Fargo, ND 58102
(701) 232-8851
Fourteen taps.

Beer Barrel
32 NE Third
Minot, ND 58702
(701) 839-9029

Liberty Tavern
600 Fourth Ave NE
Minot, ND 58702
(701) 852-5013

Ratch's Bar
100 NE Third
Minot, ND 58702
(701) 838-9312
Retail Stores

**Happy Harry's Bottle
Shop**
2215 Gateway Dr.
Grand Forks, ND 58201

**Happy Harry's Bottle
Shop**
2051 32nd Ave.
South Grand Forks, ND
58103

Festivals and Events

Octoberfest
Beulah, ND 58523
(701) 873-4585
Early October, two days.

Forx Fest
Downtown
Grand Forks, ND 58203
(701) 772-3152
Late July. Block party, dance, food, two beer gardens, kids' activities, entertainment.

Norsk Hostfest
North Dakota Fairgrounds
P.O. Box 2111
Minot, ND 58702
(701) 852-2368
Mid-October, tive days. Scandinavian fall festival, with arts, crafts, music, food and drink.

Oktoberfest
Main St.
New Leipzig, ND 58562
(701) 584-2920
Late September, three days.

Ohio

Ohio Travel & Tourism
P.O. Box 1001
Columbus, OH 43266-0001
(800) BUCK-EYE
Tourist information, calendar of events.

Breweries, Large

Anheuser-Busch Brewery
700 E Schrock Rd.
Columbus, OH 43229
(614) 847-6465
Tours Monday to Saturday. Gift shop. Budweiser, Busch, Michelob.

Breweries, Regional and Micro

Cincinnati Brewing Co.
22 E 12th St.
Cincinnati, OH 45210

Hudepohl-Schoenling
1625 Central Pkwy.
Cincinnati, OH 45214
(513) 241-4344
Fax (513) 241-2190
Ninth largest brewery in the U.S. by volume. Little Kings Cream Ale, Christian Moerlein Select, Mt. Everest Malt Liquor. Also importers.

Main Street Brewery
1203 Main St.
Cincinnati, OH 45210

Crooked River Brewing Co.
1101 Center St.
Cleveland, OH 44113
(216) 771-BEER

Columbus Brewing Co.
476 S Front St.
Columbus, OH 43215
(614) 224-3626
Fax (614) 241-2080
Contact: J. Scott Francis, brewmaster
Located in historic brewery district. Handcrafted award-winning ales and seasonal brews. Columbus Pale and Nut Brown ales, 1492 Lager.

Brewpubs

Capt Tony's Pizza & Pasta Emporium
23260 Chagrin Blvd.
Beachwood, OH 44122
(216) 464-TONY

Great Lakes Brewing Co.
2516 Market Ave.
Cleveland, OH 44113
(216) 771-4404
Historic building, outdoor beer garden, rustic beer cellar, Victorian tap. Good food, tours available. Dortmunder Gold, The Edmund Fitzgerald Porter (for fans of Gordon Lightfoot) Moon Dog Ale, Holy Moses Ale, The Eliot Ness, The Commander Perry IPA.

Barley's Brewing Co.
467 N High St.
Columbus, OH 43085
(614) 228-2537

Gambrinus Brewing Co.
Columbus, OH

Hoster Brewing Co.
550 S High St.
Columbus, OH 43216
(614) 228-6066
Restaurant has indoor and outdoor dining.

Melbourne's Brewing Co.
Strongsville, OH 44136
(216) 238-4677

Burkhardt's Brewing Co.
Uniontown, OH
(216) 896-9200

Places to Enjoy Beer

James Tavern Restaurant & Bar
160 W Wilson Bridge Rd.
Columbus, OH 43805
(614) 885-5050

Plank's Bier Garten
888 S High St.
Columbus, OH 43206
(614) 443-4570
*Oldest and biggest beer
garden in Columbus.*

Schmidt's Sausage Haus
240 E Kossuth St.
Columbus, OH 43206
(614) 444-6808
*German entertainment, food,
beer.*

Tanks Bar & Grill
2033 Wayne Ave.
Dayton, OH 45410
(513) 252-2249
Three taps, 70 bottles.

Brews Pub & Deli
Broadway
Granville, OH 43023
(614) 587-0249
Over 100 beers.

The Old Tavern
Rt. 84 and County Line Rd.
Unionville, OH 44088
(800) 782-8376
*Restaurant, built in 1798 as a
stagecoach stop.*

Festivals and Events

Old World Oktoberfest
Geauga Lake Park, SR 43
Aurora, OH 44202
(216) 486-3125
Contact: Old World Ventures
Late September, three days.

Oktoberfest
Bremen, OH 43107
(614) 569-7313
Contact: Jean Doan
*Late September, three days.
Parade, entertainment. Free.*

Oktoberfest
S Grant and E Livingston
Ave.
Columbus, OH
(614) 224-4300
Contact: Aaron Leventhal
*Mid-September, three days.
Continuous entertainment,
food, arts, crafts, special
events.*

Oktoberfest
1400 E Fifth St.
Dayton, OH 45402
(513) 293-3099
Contact: Liederkranz-Turner
Society
*Mid-September, two days.
German foods, drink, music.*

**German American
Festival Days**
531 E Wenger Rd.
Englewood, OH 45322
(513) 836-6889
Contact: German Club
Eidelweiss
*Mid-July, two days. German
bands, dancing, authentic
food and beer.*

Oktoberfest
531 E Wenger Rd.
Englewood, OH 45322
(513) 836-6889
Contact: German Club
Eidelweiss
*Early September, two days.
German Gemuetlichkeit, food,
bands.*

Oktoberfest
4 St. Parks
Minster, OH 45865
(419) 628-2433
Contact: Rolly Hausfeld
Early October, two days.
German heritage celebration.
Parade Sunday. Free.

Ohio Swiss Festival
P.O. Box 158
Sugarcreek, OH 44681
(216) 852-4113
Contact: Information Center
*Fourth Friday and Saturday
after Labor Day. Two days.
Swiss music, dancing,
yodelling, food, costumes,
Steintossen, Schwingfest,
crafts.*

Wooster Oktoberfest
141 N Walnut St.
Wooster, OH 44691
(216) 262-5735
*Late September, two days. Bier
Garten, ethnic foods, free
bandstand entertainment, arts
and crafts.*

Of Historic Interest

Brewery District
High and Front Sts.
Columbus, OH 43215
(614) 241-2070
*Renovated brewery buildings
housing restaurants, retail
shops, a winery, and several
microbreweries. Outdoor
concerts and events in
summer.*

Oklahoma

**Oklahoma Tourism &
Recreation Department**
Box 60789
Oklahoma City, OK 73145-
0789
(800) 652-6552
*Tourist information, calendar
of events.*

Brewpubs

Royal Bavaria
3401 S Sooner Rd.
Moore, OK 73160
(405) 799-7666

Interurban Brewery
Norman, OK

Norman Brewing Co.
102 W Main
Norman, OK 73069
(405) 360-5726

Bricktown Brewery
1 N Oklahoma
Oklahoma City, OK 73104
(405) 232-BREW
Fax (405) 232-0531
*Brewpub and restaurant, with
five handcrafted brews on tap.
Open all week, tours when the
brewmaster isn't busy.
Restaurant serves New Prairie
cuisine.*

Cherry St. Brewing Co.
1516 S Quaker
Tulsa, OK 74120
(918) 582-2739

Tulsa Brewing Co.
7277 S Memorial Dr.
Tulsa, OK 74133
(918) 459-2739

Flip's
5801 N Western
Oklahoma City, OK 73118
(405) 843-1527

Garfield's
7000 Crossroads Blvd.
Oklahoma City, OK 73149
(405) 634-6931

Bobo's Mexican Cantina
5020 W Sixth
Stillwater, OK 74601
(405) 372-9353

Eskimo Joe's
501 W Elm
Stillwater, OK 74074
(405) 372-8896

Full Moon Cafe
1525 E 15th
Tulsa, OK 74120
(918) 583-6666

Full Moon Cafe
6151 S Sheridan
Tulsa, OK 74133
(918) 492-1551

Festivals and Events

Oktoberfest
Fairgrounds
Muskogee, OK 74401
(918) 687-4406
*Early October, three days. Arts
and crafts, rodeo, German
food and music.*

Prague Kolache Festival
City Park, other locations
Prague, OK 74864
(405) 567-2616
Contact: P.O. Box 7
*First Saturday in May. Czech
heritage. Parade, costumes,
dancing, kolache baking,
wine, and beer brewing
contests, street dance. Coors is
the official beer of the festival.*

Oktoberfest
Downtown
Shawnee, OK 74801
(405) 273-1080
Mid-October, two days.

Oktoberfest
River West Festival Park
Tulsa, OK
(918) 596-2001
*Late October, three days.
Biergartens, complete with
German bands, dancing,
singalongs.*

Czech Festival
Downtown
Yukon, OK 73099
(405) 354-3567
*Early October. Over 70,000
visitors gather to celebrate
Czech heritage with polka
bands, costumes, arts and
crafts, and traditional foods.*

Of Historic Interest

The Dewey Hotel
Bartlesville, OK 74005
(918) 534-0215
*Built in 1900, hotel with
gambling room. Open Tuesday
to Saturday, April to October.*

Oregon

Oregon Tourism Division
775 Summer St. NE
Salem, OR 97310
(800) 547-7842
Tourist information.

Breweries, Large

**Blitz-Weinhard
  Brewing Co.**
1133 W Burnside St.
Portland, OR 97209
(503) 222-4351
*Henry Weinhard's Dark and
Light beers, Private reserve,
Weinhard's Ale, Weinhard's
Red Lager, Weinhard's Ice Ale.*

Breweries, Regional and Micro

**Oregon Trader
  Brewing Co.**
Albany, OR 97321
(503) 928-1931

Bandon Brewing Co.
Bandon, OR 97411

Deschutes Brewery & Pub
1044 NW Bono St.
Bend, OR 97701
(503) 382-9242 or
(503) 385-8606
Fax (503) 383-4505
Brewery now produces around
6000 barrels annually. Pub
serves food. Cascade Golden
Ale, Bachelor Bitter, Black
Butte Porter, other seasonal
and specialty brews.

Oregon Trail Brewing Co.
341 SW Second St.
Corvallis, OR 97330
(503) 758-3527

Mt. Hood Brewing Co.
Timberline Lodge
Government Camp, OR
  97028
(503) 272-3724

Full Sail Brewing Co.
506 Columbia St.
Hood River, OR 97031
(503) 386-2281
Fax (503) 386-7316
Largest micro in OR, located
in scenic Columbia Gorge.
Taste a variety of year-round
and seasonal brews. View the
Columbia River from the
White Cap Brewpub deck.
Full Sail Pilsner, WasSail
Winter Ale.

Saxer Brewing Co.
5875 SW Lakeview Rd.
Lake Oswego, OR 97034
(503) 699-9524

Rogue Ales
2320 OSU Dr.
Newport, OR 97365
(503) 867-3660
Fax (503) 867-3260
Shakespeare Stout,
Welcommen, Mexicali Rogue,
Old Crustacean, Newporter,
Imperial Stout, St. Rogue Red.
Also T-shirts, caps, glasses.

Bridgeport Brewing Co & Pub
1313 NW Marshall
Portland, OR 97209
(503) 241-7179

Full Sail Riverplace Brewery
307 SW Montgomery
Portland, OR 97201
(503) 222-5343
The Pilsener Room.

Hair of the Dog Brewing Co.
Portland, OR
(503) 232-6585

Multnomah Brewery
Portland, OR 97202
(503) 236-3106

Portland Brewpub #2
3015 NW Industrial St.
Portland, OR 97210
(503) 226-7623, 228-5269,
  or 222-5910
Open Fall '93. 3000 foot beer
hall and full service restau-
rant plus German beer house
of 140 bbl.

Riverplace Brewery
307 SW Montgomery
Portland, OR 97201

Star Brewing Co.
5231 NE Martin Luther
  King Blvd.
Portland, OR 97211
(503) 282-6003

Widmer Brewing Co.
929 N Russell St.
Portland, OR 97227
(503) 281-BIER

Willamette Valley Brewing Co.
66 SE Morrison
Portland, OR 97214
(503) 232-9771
Nor'Wester Pub.

Edgefield Manor & Gardens
2126 SW Halsey St.
Troutdale, OR 97060
(503) 669-8610
Brewery, inn, Power Station
Pub, winery. Historic building
and gardens. Open daily.

Brewpubs

Rogue River Brewing Co.
31B Water St.
Ashland, OR 97520
(503) 488-5061

McMenamin's
6179 SW Murray Rd.
Beaverton, OR 97005
(503) 644-4562

Pizza Deli & Brewery
249 N Redwood Hwy.
Cave Junction, OR 97526
(503) 592-3556
Wild River Brewing Co.
Family oriented pizza
restaurant with sun deck and
brewery. Award-winning
Original Oregon Steelhead
beers.

Eugene City Brewery
844 Olive St.
Eugene, OR 97401
(503) 345-8489
West Bros Bar-B-Q.

High Street Brewpub
1243 High St.
Eugene, OR 97440
(503) 345-4905

Steelhead Brewery & Cafe
199 E Fifth Ave.
Eugene, OR 97401
(503) 686-2739
Steelhead Amber, Oatmeal Stout, French Pete's Porter, Ginger Bells.

Blue Pine Brewpub
Grants Pass, OR 97526
(503) 476-0760

Highland Pub & Brewery
4225 SE 182nd St.
Gresham, OR 97030
(503) 665-3015

Cornelius Pass Roadhouse
Rt. 5, Box 340
Hillsboro, OR 97123
(503) 640-6174

White Cap Brew Pub
Hood River, OR 97031
(503) 386-2247
See Full Sail Brewing Co.

City Brewing Co.
140 S Oregon St.
Jacksonville, OR 97530

Lighthouse Brew Pub
4157 N Hwy. 101
Lincoln City, OR 97367
(503) 994-7238

Golden Valley Brewpub
980 E Fourth St.
McMinnville, OR 97128
(503) 472-1921

BayFront Brewpub
748 SW Bay Blvd.
Newport, OR 97365
(503) 265-3188

Fulton Pub & Brewery
618 SW Nebraska
Portland, OR 97201
(503) 246-9530

Hillsdale Brewery & Public House
1505 SW Sunset Blvd.
Portland, OR 97201
(503) 246-3938

Northwestern Brewpub & Cafe
Portland, OR
(503) 226-2508

Oak Hills Brewpub
14740 SW Cornell Rd.
Portland, OR 97223
(503) 645-0286

Portland Brewpub
1339 NW Flanders
Portland, OR 97209
(503) 222-3414
Fax (503) 228-7419
Seven beers on tap. Lunch available in beautiful mahogany paneled room with view of brewery. Portland Ale, Porter; McTarnahan's Ale.

Widmer Brewing Co.
1405 NW Lovejoy
Portland, OR 97209
(503) 281-BIER

Umpqua Brewing Co.
328 SE Jackson St.
Roseburg, OR 97470
(503) 672-0452
Fax (503) 672-0452
Brewpub with pizza and burgers. Open Wednesday to Saturday, lunch Thursday and Friday. Live music Saturday from 9PM to 1AM. Beers on tap and to go; seasonal specials. No Doubt Stout, Downtown Brown, Summer Wheat.

Thompson Brewery & Public House
3675 Liberty Rd. S
Salem, OR 97301
(503) 363-7286

Wilamette Brewpub
120 Commercial St. NE
Salem, OR 97301
(503) 363-8779

McMenamin's W Linn Pub & Brewery
2090 SW 8th Ave.
West Linn, OR 97005

Places to Enjoy Beer

Riverwood Pub
8136 SW Hall Blvd.
Beaverton, OR 97005
(503) 643-7189

Suds 'n Such
935 NW King
Corvallis, OR 97330
(503) 758-5200

Grub Street Grill
35 N Central Ave.
Medford City, OR 97501
(503) 779-2635

Coyotes
NE 28 and Sandy
Portland, OR
(503) 234-8573

Dublin Pub
6821 SW Beaverton-
Hillsdale Hwy.
Portland, OR 97225
(503) 297-2889

Horse Brass
4534 SE Belmont
Portland, OR 97215
(503) 232-2202
British style pub.

The Elusive Trout
39333 Proctor Blvd.
Sandy, OR 97055
(503) 668-7884

Retail Stores

Oasis Market
2849 Willamette
Eugene, OR 97405

Burlingame Grocery
8502 SW Terwilliger
Portland, OR 97219
(503) 246-0711

MT Bottle & Deli
11925 N Center
Jantzen Beach
Portland, OR 97217
(503) 289-0336

Festivals and Events

Blues & Brews Festival
Benton County Fairgrounds
110 SW 53
Corvallis, OR 97333
(503) 754-6624
*Mid-September. Blues bands,
microbrews from OR and WA.*

**Microbrew & Wine
Festival**
Eugene, OR
(503) 686-6648
Contact: Jim Jensen
*Late September, three days.
Over 20 breweries, 5 wineries.
Food, child care, live music.*

Hop Festival
City Park
Hubbard, OR 97032
(503) 981-9454 or
(503) 981-4249
Contact: Fire Department
*Mid-July. Parade with
antique hop-handling
equipment, beer garden.*

Oktoberfest
Mount Angel, OR 97362
(503) 845-9440
*Mid-September, four days.
Food, music, bier-, wein-, and
kindergartens.*

**Oregon Annual Brewers'
Festival**
Waterfront Park
Portland, OR
(503) 778-5917
*Mid-July. Largest gathering
of independent brewers in U.S.*

Rheinlander Oktoberfest
Portland, OR
(503) 778-5917
Late September, 4 days.

Oktoberfest
Umpqua Brewing
328 SE Jackson St.
Roseburg, OR 97470
(503) 672-0452
*September, last Saturday
weekend.*

**Summer Wheat Blues
Fest**
Umpqua Brewing
328 SE Jackson St.
Roseburg, OR 97470
(503) 672-0452
*July, fourth Saturday
weekend.*

Oktoberfest
Seaside, OR 97138
(503) 738-6391
Contact: Chamber of
Commerce, P.O. Box 7
*Mid-October, three days.
Bavarian festival.*

Of Historic Interest

Baldwin Hotel Museum
Klamath Falls, OR 97601
(503) 883-4208
Contact: Chamber of
Commerce, P.O. Box 1867
*1900s hotel filled with
originals.*

Pennsylvania

**Bureau of Travel
Marketing**
453 Forum Bldg.
Harrisburg, PA 17120
(717) 787-5453
Tourist information.

Breweries, Large

Stroh Brewery Co.
Lehigh Valley Brewery
P.O. Box 2568
Allentown, PA 18103
(610) 395-6811
*Free tours Monday to Friday,
10AM to 3PM. Gift shop.
Stroh's, Augsberger, Schlitz,
Schaefer, Old Milwaukee.*

Pittsburgh Brewing Co.
Pittsburgh, PA

Breweries, Regional and Micro

Stoudt Brewing Co.
Rt. 272, P.O. Box 880
Adamstown, PA 19501
(717) 484-4387
Award-winning microbrewery,
Black Angus restaurant,
Antiques Mall open Sunday.
Beer festival held weekends
early July to early September
with live music, German food.
Open daily, tours Saturady
and Sunday.

Neuweiler Brewing Co.
2310 SW 26th St.
Allentown, PA 18103
Brewed Porter, Black and
Tan, Traditional Lager, Stock
Ale.

Arrowhead Brewing Co.
1667 Orchard Dr.
Chambersburg, PA 17201
(717) 264-0101
Red Feathers Pale Ale.

Latrobe Brewing Co.
Latrobe, PA 15650

Red Bell Brewing Co.
Philadelphia, PA
Contract brewed.

Penn Brewery
800 Vinial St. at Troy Hill
Rd.
Pittsburgh, PA 15212
(412) 682-4441
Fax (412) 237-9406
Contact: Tom or Mary Beth
Pastorius
Brewery and authentic
German beer hall with food.
Open Monday to Saturday.
First micro in PA, and first
tied house since Prohibition.
Many special events. Penn
Pilsner, Dark, and Light
Lager; Oktoberfest; Kaiser
Pils.

Yuengling Brewery
Fifth and Mahantongo Sts.
Pottsville, PA 17901
(717) 622-4141
America's oldest brewery. Tours
Monday to Friday, closed
holidays.

Straub Brewery
303 Sorg St.
St. Marys, PA 15857
(814) 834-2875
Free tours Monday to Friday,
9AM to noon; gift shop with
shirts, caps, patches, etc;
"Eternal Tap" open Monday
to Saturday. Straub Beer,
Light.

Jones Brewing Co.
P.O. Box 746
254 Second St.
Smithton, PA 15479
(412) 872-6626
Stoney's Beer and Light Beer,
Esquire Extra Dry Beer.

Lion Brewing Co.
700 N Pennsylvania
Wilkes-Barre, PA 18703
Stegmaier 1857 Lager, Porter,
Gold Medal.

Brewpubs

Dock Street Brewing Co.
2 Logan Square
Philadelphia, PA 19103
(215) 496-0413
Fax (215) 496-0423
Contact: Nick Funnell,
brewmaster
City's only full grain brewery.
One of the country's largest
selection of freshly brewed on
premises classic beers and
ales. Open for lunch and
dinner 7 days. Live jazz and
Latin music; billiard room;
gift items. Tours available.

Philadelphia Brewing Co.
Philadelphia, PA
See Samuel Adams Brew-
house. Ben Franklin's Golden
Ale, George Washington's
Porter, Brew House Brown
Ale, and Cranberry Wheat.

Samuel Adams Brewhouse
1516 Sansom St., 2nd floor
Philadelphia, PA 19102
(215) 563-2326
Contact: Jim Pericles,
brewmaster
Beer is brewed behind large
windows: watch as you

I have fed purely upon ale; I have eat my ale, drank
my ale, and I always sleep upon ale.
— George Farquhar
(1678-1707)

*sample. Extensive menu,
frequent specials. Entertainment on weekends, closed
Sunday.*

Whitetail Brewing Co.
Cyber Center
1600 Pennsylvania Ave.
York, PA 17404
(717) 843-6520

Places to Enjoy Beer

Black Angus
Rt. 272
Adamstown, PA 19501
(717) 484-4385
*Restaurant, German-
American cuisine, serving
brews from Stoudt's Brewery.
Open daily for dinner.*

Buckingham Steakout
2559 Bogarts Tavern Rd.
P.O. Box 237
Buckingham, PA 18912
(215) 794-7784
*Steakhouse and English pub
fare. Twenty taps.*

10 Downing St.
10 Jefferson Bank Center
Downingtown, PA 19335
(610) 269-4579
*Restaurant with good beer
selection; local and imported.
Self-service beer center. Open
daily.*

The Farmhouse
1449 Chestnut St.
Emmaus, PA 18049
(610) 967-6225
Fax (610) 965-6225
*C18 farmhouse restaurant,
New American cuisine, large
selection of micros and
imports, many taps. Special
beer and whiskey dinners.
Beer gift baskets.*

Watney's Inn
2415 W Main St.
Ephrata, PA 17522
(717) 733-2014
*Built 1766. One hundred.
beers, food.*

Blue Parrot Bistro
35 Chambersburg Rd
Gettysburg, PA 17325

Chiodo's Tavern
107 and 109 W Eighth Ave.
Homestead, PA 15120
(412) 461-3113
*Restaurant with 120
worldwide bottled beers.*

Shank's Tavern
36 Waterford Ave.
Marietta, PA 17547
(717) 426-1205
*Established 1814. Micro on
tap.*

The Artful Dodger
Second and Pine Sts.
Philadelphia, PA
(215) 922-7880

Brigid's
726 N 24th St.
Philadelphia, PA 19130
(215) 232-3232
*Belgian and French cuisine,
Belgian beers.*

Cavanaugh's
119 S 39th St.
Philadelphia, PA 19104
(215) 386-4889

Copa, Too
263 S 15th St.
Philadelphia, PA 19102
(215) 735-0848
*Beer cuisine, good selection,
monthly beer tasting dinners.*

Cutter's
2005 Market St
Philadelphia, PA 19103
(215) 851-6262

Dickens Inn
Head House Square
Second and Pine Sts.
Philadelphia, PA
(215) 928-9307
*British style pub. Shepherds
pie, sherry trifle. Darts, beer
by the yard. Special events
and beer tastings.*

The Happy Rooster
118 S 16th St.
Philadelphia, PA 19102
(215) 563-1481

Khyber Pass
54 S Second St.
Philadelphia, PA 19106
(215) 440-9683
*Largest selection of beers in
town.*

Moriarty's
1116 Walnut St.
Philadelphia, PA 19107
(215) 627-7696

Odeon Restaurant
114 S 12th St.
Philadelphia, PA 19107
(215) 922-5875

Serrano
20 S Second St.
Philadelphia, PA 19106
(215) 928-0770

Tangier Cafe
1801 Lombard St.
Philadelphia, PA 19146
(215) 732-5006

Epicurean Restaurant & Bar
902–8 Village at Eland, Rt. 113
Phoenixville, PA 19460
(610) 933-1336
Seven taps, over 100 domestics and imports.

Cooper's Waterfront
304 Kennedy Blvd.
Pittston, PA 18640
(717) 654-6883
Large selection of bottled beers, great food.

Cooper's Seafood House
701 N Washington Ave.
Scranton, PA 18509
(717) 346-6883
Two hundred beers.

Deer Head Inn
RD 1
Spring Creek, PA 16436
(814) 563-9079
Open Tuesday to Saturday.

Zeno's Pub
Allen and College
State College, PA 16801
One hundred beers including taps.

Jefferson House & Pub
119 Market St.
Warren, PA 16365
(814) 723-2268
Restored Victorian mansion, pub fare and more. English ale on draft.

Mr. Dunderbak's
Lehigh Valley Mall
Whitehall, PA 18052
(610) 264-4963
German-American restaurant with over 100 imports, micros, beer gifts.

Retail Stores

Roxy Beverage
712 Fourth St.
Altoona, PA 16602
(814) 943-8181

Shangy's
601 State Ave.
Emmaus, PA 18049
(610) 967-1701
Over 700 labels from 60 countries.

Brandt Distributors
813 S 17th St.
Harrisburg, PA 17105
(800) 827-2638
Imports and micros.

Kunda Bev
349 S Henderson Rd.
King of Prussia, PA 19406
(610) 265-3113

Mt. Jewett Beverage
Rt. 6, Box BB
Mount Jewett, PA 16740
(814) 778-5421

Brandt Distributors
150 S 22nd St.
Pittsburgh, PA 15203
(412) 481-0310
Imports and micros.

Crescent Beer Distributors
1004 W Fourth Ave.
Warren, PA 16365
(814) 723-1344

Festivals and Events

Bavarian Beer Fest
Black Angus Complex
Rt. 272
Adamstown, PA 19501
(717) 484-4385
Late July to early September, weekends. Bands, entertainment, ethnic foods, beers, and wines, dancing.

Great Eastern Microbrewery Fest
Stoudt Hall
Black Angus Complex
Adamstown, PA 19501
(717) 484-4385
Mid-June, two days. Over 50 specialty beers from the eastern US. Includes Best of the Wursts buffet. Advanced ticket purchase recommended.

Stoudt's Beer Festival
Black Angus Complex
Rt. 272
Adamstown, PA 19501
(215) 484-4385
Early Jul to early September, Friday to Sunday. Held in the Brewery Hall. Music, German and American food, and beer.

Oktoberfest/Fall Fest
Indian Field
Carlisle Barracks
Carlisle, PA 17013
(717) 245-4332
Mid-September. Live entertainment, food, games.

Classic Beer Fest
Split Rock Resort
Lake Harmony, PA 18624
(800) 255-7625
in PA (717) 722-9111
  ext. 702
Late November, two days. Beer tasting, foods, entertainment.

Oktoberfest
New Castle, PA 16101
(412) 656-1200
Mid-September, four days.
Ethnic foods, drink, arts,
crafts, entertainment.

Brick Hotel Beer
Festival
State and Washington Ave.
Newtown, PA 18940
(215) 860-8313
Call for information.

Oktoberfest
Fairmount Park
Philadelphia, PA
(215) 496-0413
Contact: Dock St.
Brewing Co.
October.

Six Months 'til
Oktoberfest
Dock St. Brewing
2 Logan Square
Philadelphia, PA 19103
(215) 496-0413
Late April. Beers, food, and
music.

Oktoberfest
Station Square
Melody Tent
Pittsburgh, PA
(412) 682-4441
Mid-September, two weekends.
Entertainment, food, dance,
and a Bavarian Bazaar.

Oktoberfest
Penn Brewery
800 Vinial St.
Pittsburgh, PA 15212
(412) 682-4441
September, last two weekends.
Outdoor food, grill, entertain-
ment, authentic Munich
Oktoberfest Bier.

Oktoberfest
Shamokin, PA 17872
(717) 648-4675
Mid-October. Polka dancing
in the streets, over 100 craft
stands. Food, drink, enter-
tainment.

Oktoberfest
Shawnee Mt. Ski Area
Shawnee-on-Delaware, PA
18356
(717) 421-7231
Late October. Bavarian food,
drink, crafts, dancing.

Family Oktoberfest
Mill Bridge Village
Strasburg, PA 17579
(717) 687-6521
September and October,
weekends. German bands,
singers, costumed dancers.
Food and drink.

Of Historic Interest

Barns-Brinton House
U.S. 1
Chadds Ford, PA 19317
(610) 388-1120
Built as a tavern in 1714.
Open weekends May to
September.

Dickson Tavern
201 French St.
Erie, PA 16507
Oldest surviving building in
Erie. Tavern setting, rooms
furnished with C19 objects.

Penn's Tavern
Rt. 147
Fisher's Ferry, PA 17801
(717) 286-4913
Built in 1703 and still
operating. German and
American fare. Open Tuesday
to Sunday.

Witmer's Tavern
2014 Old Philadelphia Pike
Lancaster, PA 17602
(717) 299-5305
Historic 1725 inn. Guest
rooms.

Compass Inn Museum
Rt. 30 E
Laughlintown, PA 15655
(412) 238-4983
Restored 1799 stagecoach inn,
reconstructed cookhouse,
blacksmith shop, and barn.

Bube's Brewery
102 N Market St.
Mount Joy, PA 16830
(717) 653-2056
Intact 1800s brewery, with
tours daily Memorial Day to
Labor Day, now three
restaurants: The Bottling
Works, with Biergarten where
Bavarian Bierfests are held;
Alois's, fine dining; and The
Catacombs, dining in a vault,
with medieval feasts twice
monthly.

Golden Plough Tavern
157 W Market St.
York, PA 17401
(717) 845-2951
1741 tavern, now a museum.

Rhode Island

Rhode Island Tourism
7 Jackson Walkway
Providence, RI 02903
(800) 556-2484
Tourist information, calendar
of events

Brewpubs

Trinity Brewing Co.
Providence, RI
(401) 453-2337

**Union Station
Brewing Co.**
Providence, RI
(401) 274-BREW

Places to Enjoy Beer

Custom House Tavern
36 Weybosset St.
Providence, RI 02903
(401) 751-3630
*British-style pub. Guinness on
draft; large selection of
bottles. Music.*

Wickenden Pub
Wickenden St.
Providence, RI 02906

Festivals and Events

Oktoberfest
Yachting Center
4 Commercial Wharf
Newport, RI 02881
(401) 846-1600
*Early October. Authentic
German celebration: food,
oompah bands, huge steins of
German beer.*

Taste of Rhode Island
Yachting Center
4 Commercial Wharf
Newport, RI 02840
(401) 846-1600
*Late September, two days.
Sponsored by Guinness & Bass
Ale. Over 40 restaurants
participate. Arts and crafts,
music, kids' area.*

Octoberfest
Roosevelt Ave.
Downtown
Pawtucket, RI
(401) 728-0500
*Early October, two days.
German foods, Biergarten, live
entertainment.*

Rhode Island Beer Expo
Convention Center
Providence, RI
(401) 274-3234
Early October.

Of Historic Interest

White Horse Tavern
Marlborough and Farewell
Sts.
Newport, RI 02881
(401) 849-3600
*Oldest operating tavern in
America, built 1673.*

South Carolina

**South Carolina Division
of Tourism**
P.O. Box 71
Columbia, SC 29202
(803) 734-0122
Fax (803) 734-0138
*Tourist information, calendar
of events.*

Breweries

Palmetto Brewing Co.
289 Huger St.
Charleston, SC 29403
(803) 937-0903
Contact: Lewis Bruce, Ed
Falkenstein

Places to Enjoy Beer

Arizona's
14 Chapel St.
Charleston, SC 29403
(803) 577-5090

Back Market Cafe
61 State St.
Charleston, SC 29401
(803) 720-2114

Mike Calder's
288 King St.
Charleston, SC 29401
(803) 577-0123

Tommy Condon's
160 Church St.
Charleston, SC 29401
(803) 577-3818

Mediterranean Deli
S Windemere Shopping
Center
Charleston, SC
Bar and retail store.

Vickeries
15 Beaufain St.
Charleston, SC 29401
(803) 577-5300

Wild Wing Cafe
36 N Market St.
Charleston, SC 29401
(803) 722-9464

Nick's Tavern & Deli
107–2 Sloan St.
Clemson, SC 29631

Beulah's Bar & Grill
920C Gervais St.
Columbia, SC 29201
(803) 779-4655

Monterrey Jack's
733 Santee Ave.
Columbia, SC 29205
(803) 256-7764

Dempsey's
233 N Main St.
Greenville, SC 29601
(803) 271-1400

Henni's
103 N Main St.
Greenville, SC 29601
(803) 370-1090

Sophisticated Palate
34 S Main St.
Greenville, SC 29601
(803) 235-4202

Anchovies
4079 Hwy. 17 Business
Murrells Inlet, SC 29576
(803) 651-0664

Chairman's Corner
2002 N Kings Hwy.
Myrtle Beach, SC 29577
(803) 448-2512

Dead Dog Saloon
404 26th Ave. S
Myrtle Beach, SC 29577
(803) 626-8106

Doc Holiday's
1525 13th Ave. N
N Myrtle Beach, SC 29582
(803) 249-6111

Dunleavy's Pub
2213B Middle St.
Sullivan's Island, SC 29482

Retail Stores

Harris Teeter
290 E Bay St.
Charleston, SC 29401
Supermarket with good beer selection.

Green's Discount Beverage
400 Assembly St.
Columbia, SC 29201
(803) 799-9499

Frugal MacDougal's
3630 Festival Dr.
Ft. Mill, SC 29715
(803) 548-6634

Green's Discount Beverage
445 Congaree St.
Greenville, SC 29607
(803) 297-6353

Green's Discount Beverage
2850 N Kings Hwy.
Myrtle Beach, SC 29577
(803) 448-1623

South Dakota

South Dakota Department of Tourism
711 E Wells Ave.
Pierre, SD 57501-3369
(800) 952-3625
Fax (605) 773-3256
Tourist information.

Brewpubs

Firehouse Brewing Co.
610 Main St.
Rapid City, SD 57701
(605) 348-1915
Contact: Bob Fuchs
First brewpub in SD. Offers high-class pub fare. Buffalo Bitter, Brown Cow Ale, Rushmore Stout, and more.

Places to Enjoy Beer

Coolidge Inn
Hwy. 16A
Custer State Park, SD 57730
(605) 255-4515

Red Garter Saloon
Downtown
Keystone, SD 57751
(605) 666-4404
Fax (605) 666-4405
Jesse James' favorite saloon and casino.

Brandy's Restaurant & Lounge
1525 W Havens
Mitchell, SD 57301
(605) 996-5556

Brig Steak House & Lounge
N Hwy. 37
Mitchell, SD 57301
(605) 996-7444

Alpine Hotel
225 Main St.
Hill City
Rapid City, SD 57701
(605) 342-3701

Kelly's Stockman Pub
201 N Weber
Sioux Falls, SD 57101
(605) 331-4482

Lions Pub
1500 W Russell
Sioux Falls, SD 57101
(605) 334-7123

Skelly's Pub & Grill
105 N Main Ave.
Sioux Falls, SD 57101
(605) 334-8100

Carey's Bar
Vermillion, SD 57069
Around 20 taps.

Festivals and Events

German Schmeckfest
Eureka, SD 57437
(605) 284-2130
Late September.

Germanfest
Hill City, SD 57745
(800) 888-1798
In SD (605) 574-2538
Mid-September, two days.

Oktoberfest
Mt. Marty College
Yankton, SD 57078
(605) 668-1542
Late October, three days.

Of Historic Interest

Old Style Saloon #10
657 Main
Deadwood, SD 57732
(800) 952-9398
In SD (605) 578-3346
"The only museum in the world with a bar." Shows, gambling.

Tennessee

Tennessee Department of Tourism
P.O. Box 23170
Nashville, TN 37202
(615) 741-2159
Tourist information, calendar of events.

Breweries, Regional and Micro

Coors Brewery
5151 E Raines Rd.
Memphis, TN 38118
(901) 375-2000
Brewery tours, beer sampling in the Coors Belle, replica Mississippi River sternwheeler. Open Monday to Saturday,

free. *Coors, Killian's Red, Keystone.*

Bohannon Brewing Co.
134 Second Ave. N
Nashville, TN 37201
(615) 242-8223
Market St. Brewery & Pub, in historic building. Free tours and tastings Monday to Friday, 2PM. Open Monday to Friday, 10AM to 4PM. Market Street Pilsner, Oktoberfest, Wheat Beer, Golden Ale.

Brewpubs

Big River Grille & Brewing Works
222 Broad St.
Chatanooga, TN 37402
(615) 267-2739
Contact: Tim Hennen, Rob Gentry
In historic trolley barn. Angler's Amber Ale, Trolleyman Wheat, Imperial 375, Iron Horse Stout.

Bosco's Pizzeria & Brewery
7615 W Farmington, #30
Germantown, TN 38138
(901) 756-7310
Contact: Chuck Skypeck, brewer
Gourmet pizza, grill and rotisserie. Open daily. Tennessee Cream Ale, Neshoba Amber Ale, Germantown's Own, Boscos Holiday Ale.

Smoky Mountain Brewing Co.
424–426 Gay St.
Knoxville, TN 37902
(615) 673-8400
Contact: Ron Downer, brewmaster

Retail Stores

Allen Biermakers
4111 Martin Mill Pk.
Knoxville, TN 37920
(800) 873-6258
or (615) 577-2430

Sam's Party Store
605 15th St.
Knoxville, TN 37916
(615) 522-5056

Frugal MacDougal's
701 Division St.
Nashville, TN 37203
(615) 242-3863

Festivals and Events

Oktoberfest
Fairgrounds
Clarksville, TN 37040
(615) 645-3722
(615) 439-1958
Early October, two days. Traditional German food, festivities, costumes, dancing.

Oktoberfest
National Guard Armory
Crossville, TN 38555
(615) 484-9599
Early October, two days. Authentic German cuisine, live music.

Oktoberfest
7 Ave. N and Monroe
Nashville, TN 37208
(615) 256-2729
Early October. German music, crafts, food.

Of Historic Interest

Museum of Beverage Containers
1055 Ridgecrest Dr.
Goodlettsville, TN 37072
(615) 859-5236
Museum of beverage containers and advertising. Over 300,000 beer and soda cans. Gift shop.

Crockett Tavern Museum
2002 Morningside Dr.
Morristown, TN 37814
(615) 587-9900
Pioneer museum in a roadside tavern setting. The original tavern was burned after housing smallpox victims.

Texas

Texas Tourism
P.O. Box 12728
Austin, TX 78711
(512) 462-9191
Tourist information.

American Breweriana
P.O. Box 612169
Dallas, TX 75261
Contact: Jon Ruckstuhl
Texas Pride Chapter. For collectors of breweriana.

Breweries, Large

Anheuser-Busch Brewery
775 Gelhorn Dr.
Houston, TX 77029
(713) 675-2311
Tours Monday–Saturday. Budweiser, Busch, Michelob.

Stroh Brewery Co.
Longview Brewery
1400 W Cotton
Longview, TX 75604
(903) 753-0371
Tours Monday to Friday.

Pearl Brewing Co.
312 Pearl Pkwy.
P.O. Box 1661
San Antonio, TX 78215
Pearl Lager Beer.

Breweries, Regional and Micro

Celis Brewery
2431 Forbes Dr.
Austin, TX 78754
(512) 835-0884
Fax (512) 835-0130
P.O. Box 141636, zip 78714
Contact: Pierre Celis, brewmaster
Tours usually Tuesday to Saturday, 2 and 4PM. Celis White, Celis Pale Bock, Celis Golden.

Hill Country Brewing
730 Shady Ln.
Austin, TX 78702
(512) 385-9111

Old City Brewing Co.
603 W 13th St., #1A-345
Austin, TX 78701
(512) 472-2337
Pecan Street Lager (contract brewed).

Texas Brewing Co.
703 McKinney Ave.
Dallas, TX 75202
(214) 871-7990
Tours Monday–Saturday. Outback Lager, Cowboy, Westend, Dallas Gold, Bluebonnet.

St. Arnold Brewing Co.
2522 Fairway Pk.
Houston, TX 77092
(713) 686-9494
Fax (713) 686-9474
Amber Ale, Kristall Weizen.

Frio Brewing Co.
1905 N St. Mary's
San Antonio, TX 78215
(210) 225-8222

Spoetzl Brewery
603 E Brewery
Shiner, TX 77984
(512) 594-3852
Tours Monday to Friday, hours vary with season. Gift shop, museum.

Brewpubs

Armadillo Brewing Co.
419 E Sixth St.
Austin, TX 78701
(512) 322-0039
Roadkill Red, Axe's Pale.

The Bitter End
311 Colorado
Austin, TX 78701
(512) 478-2337

Copper Tank Brewing Co.
504 Trinity
Austin, TX 78701
(512) 478-8444
Contact: Davis Tucker
Copper Light, Copper Tank Raspberry Ale, White Tail Ale, Big Dog Brown Ale, Fire House Stout.

Waterloo Brewing Co.
Fourth and Guadalupe
Austin, TX
(512) 477-1836

Hubcap Brewing Co.
1701 N Market
Dallas, TX 75202
(214) 651-0808

**Yegua Creek
Brewing Co.**
2920 Henderson Ave.
Dallas, TX 75206
(214) 824-2739

**Fredericksburg
Brewing Co.**
245 E Main St.
Fredericksburg, TX 78624
(210) 997-1646
Fax (210) 997-8026
Contact: John Davies
*Restaurant, brewpub, beer
garden, and bed and brews.
Pedernales Pilsner, Edelweiss
Hefeweiss, Jailhouse Bock,
Round Bale Pale Ale,
Enchanted Rock Red, Ain't
So Dumb Blonde.*

Houston Brewing Co.
6228 Richmond Ave.
Houston, TX 77005
(713) 953-0101

**Market Sq. Brewpub &
Cafe**
Houston, TX
(713)222-6925
Contact: Tim Manchego,
Richard Coggins
*Own brews plus St. Arnold's
on tap.*

Rock Bottom Brewery
6111 Richmond Ave.
Houston, TX 77057
(713) 974-2739
Contact: Tim Case, brewer
*Palomino Pale, Rocket Red
Ale, Big Horn Brown Ale.*

The Village Brewing Co.
2415 Dunstan in the Village
Houston, TX
(713) 524-HOPS
Contact: Raju Lulla
*Houston Wheat, Village Pale
Ale, Amber Owl, Hampton
Brown Ale, Armadillo Stout.*

Bedrock Brewing Co.
Alamo Cement Lab
San Antonio, TX
(210) 822-1130
Contact: Richard Maddox

Boardwalk Bistro
4011 Broadway
San Antonio, TX 78209
(210) 824-0100
*Lager, ale, Bock, and stout.
Specialty beers. Live music.*

Joey's
217 N St. Mary's
San Antonio, TX 78205
(210) 733-9573
Contact: Joey Villareal
*Brewpub and bar with pub
food all night. Fifty brews.
Open Monday to Saturday.*

Cafe on the Square
San Marcos, TX
Contact: Gary Moore
*Beers use artesian well water
from a nearby spring.*

Places to Enjoy Beer

Crown & Anchor
2911 San Jacinto
Austin, TX 78705
(512) 322-9168
*Twenty taps, over 100 import
bottles.*

The Dog and Duck Pub
406 W 17th St.
Austin, TX 78701
(512) 479-0598
*Twenty-eight taps, seasonal
specials, over 60 bottled beers.*

Double Dave's
3000 Duval
Austin, TX 78759
(512) 441-DAVE

The Elephant Room
315 Congress Ave.
Austin, TX 78701
(512) 473-2279

Maggie Mae's
512 Trinity St.
Austin, TX 78701
(512) 478-8541

The Posse East
2900 Duval St.
Austin, TX 78705
(512) 477-2111

Scholtz Garten
1607 San Jacinto
Austin, TX 78701
(512) 477-4171

Shakespeare's Pub
314 E Sixth St.
Austin, TX 78701
(512) 472-1666

The Tavern
922 W 12th St.
Austin, TX 78703
(512) 474-7496

Texas Showdown Saloon
2610 Guadalupe
Austin, TX 78705
(512) 472-2010

The Texas Tavern
301 E 22nd St.
Austin, TX 78722
(512) 471-5651

Carney's Pub
3410 S College
Bryan, TX 77801

The Angry Dog
2726 Commerce St.
Dallas, TX 75226
(214) 741-4406

Flip's
1520 Greenville Ave.
Dallas, TX 75206
(214) 824-9944

The Gingerman
2718 Boll
Dallas, TX 75204
(214) 754-8771
*Wide selection of micros and
imports.*

The Green Elephant
2710 Boll St.
Dallas, TX 75204
(214) 750-6625

London Tavern
2001 Greenville Ave.
Dallas, TX 75206
(214) 823-7711

The Medieval Inn
7102 Greenville Ave.
Dallas, TX 75231
(214) 363-1118

Mimi's Pub & Cafe
5111 Greenville Ave.
Dallas, TX 75206
(214) 368-1994

Stan's Blue Note
2908 Greenville Ave.
Dallas, TX 75206
(214) 824-9653

The Tipperary Inn
2818 Greenville Ave.
Dallas, TX 75206
(214) 823-7167

Pig & Whistle Pub
5731 Locke Ave.
Ft. Worth, TX 76107
(817) 731-4938

Foam Depot
215 22nd St.
Galveston, TX 77550
(409) 762-8894
*Twenty-six taps, over 50
bottles, great pizza.*

The Ale House
2425 W Alabama
Houston, TX 77098
(713) 521-2333

The Ashford Arms
781 Dairy Ashford
Houston, TX 77079
(713) 497-5316

The Brewery Tap
717 Franklin
Houston, TX 77002
(713) 237-1537

The Crooked Ferret
11835 Jones Rd.
Houston, TX 77070
(713) 894-0055

The Gingerman
5607 Morningside
Houston, TX 77005
(713) 526-2770
*Wide selection of micros and
imports.*

The Hops House
2321A Hwy. 6
Houston, TX 77084
(713) 496-0623

Local Charm
1501 Telephone
Houston, TX 77023
(713) 237-0829

Mathias'
1960 FM 3755 W
Houston, TX
(713) 537-5837

Munchie's Cafe
1617 Richmond Ave.
Houston, TX 77006
(713) 528-3545

The Richmond Arms
5920 Richmond Ave.
Houston, TX 77057
(713) 784-7722

Shakespeare's Pub
14129 Memorial Dr.
Houston, TX 77079
(713) 497-4625

**Sherlock's Baker Street
  Pub**
10001 Westheimer
Houston, TX 77042
(713) 977-1857

Timber Wolf Pub
2511 Bissonnet at Kirby
Houston, TX 77005
(713) 526-1705
*Large beer selection, special
events.*

Buckhorn Saloon
600 Lone Star Blvd.
San Antonio, TX 78204
(210) 270-9467
Contact: Jerry Retzloff

Dick's Last Resort
406 Navarro
San Antonio, TX 78205
(210) 224-0026

Durty Nellie's
200 S Alamo Pl.
Palacio del Rio
San Antonio, TX 78733
(210) 222-1400

Hills & Dales Ice House
15403 White Fawn
San Antonio, TX 78255
(210) 695-8309

Kangaroo Court
102 W Crockett St., #800
San Antonio, TX 78205
(210) 224-6821

Mama's Hofbrau
9903 San Pedro
San Antonio, TX 78216
(210) 342-3219
*Open daily for breakfast,
lunch, and dinner. Large draft
beer selection.*

Retail Stores

Wheatsville Co-op
3101 Guadalupe
Austin, TX 78705
(512) 478-2667

Whip In
1950 S I-35
Austin, TX
(512) 442-5337
*Over 200 import and domestic
beers.*

Wines, Etc.
17050 Hwy. 3
Webster, TX 77598
(713) 338-2241

Festivals and Events

Texas Brewers Festival
Downtown on Fourth St.
Austin, TX
(512) 462-1855
Early November.

Of Historic Interest

Landmark Inn
Florence and Florella Sts.
Castroville, TX 78009
(210) 931-2133
*State historic structure.
Originally a stagecoach inn,
now restored to 1940s era.
Some rooms available for rent.*

**Nutt House Hotel &
Dining Room**
Town Square
Granbury, TX 76048
(817) 573-5612
*Restored country inn dated
1983. Now a noted restaurant,
8 guest rooms.*

**Kreische Brewery
Historic Site**
Monument Hill Site
La Grange, TX 78945
*Guided tours of ruined
brewery, one of the first in
Texas.*

Lobster in Weissbier

½ lb cooked lobster meat, cut in
  small chunks
½ cup lobster stock or water
2 tbsp butter
2 shallots, minced
2 tbsp flour

¼ tsp salt
¼ tsp crushed fennel seeds
3 or 4 caraway seeds
1 cup Weissbier
1 egg yolk
Minced parsley to garnish

Cook shallots in butter until soft. Stir in flour, stock, and fennel, cook until flour bubbles.
Add caraway seeds, then slowly stir in beer and rest of stock. Simmer until well blended
and slightly thickened. In a double boiler, add 2 tbsp of the hot sauce to the egg yolk.
Using wire whisk, stir in the rest of the sauce, and whisk, heating slowly, until thick and
creamy. Add lobster, cook for two minutes, sprinkle with parsley, and serve over pasta.
Serves 3 or 4.

— German recipe

**Stonewall Saloon
  Museum**
Town Square
St. Jo, TX 76265
*Restored saloon displays
historic items relating to cattle
drive era. Open daily except
January and February.*

Stagecoach Inn
Salado, TX 76571
*Former guests include
Generals Custer and Lee, Sam
Houston, and Jesse James.
Now a restaurant.*

Utah

Utah Travel Council
Council Hall, Capitol Hill
Salt Lake City, UT 84114-
  7420
(801) 538-1030
Fax (801) 538-1399
Tourist information.

Breweries, Regional and
Micro

Telluride Beer Co.
Moab, UT 84532
Contract brewed.

**Schirf Brewing Co./
  Wasatch Brewpub**
250 Main St.
Park City, UT 84060
(801) 645-9500
Brewery and brewpub.

**Uinta Brewing Co./Lazy
  Moon Pub**
32 Exchange Pl.
Salt Lake City, UT 84112
(801) 467-0909

Brewpubs
Eddie McStiff's Brewpub
57 S Main
Moab, UT 84532
(801) 259-4282
*Brewpub and restaurant with
extensive menu. Saloon bar,
front counter store with beer,
T-shirts, etc. Locality contains
national and state parks that
are worth a visit. Amber Ale,
Raspberry Wheat, Extra
Special Bitter.*

**Ebenezer's Restaurant
  Brewery**
4266 Riverdale Rd.
Riverdale, UT 84405
(801) 394-0302

Red Rock Brewing
254 S 200 W
Salt Lake City, UT 84110
(801) 521-7446

Salt Lake Brewing Co.
147 W Broadway
Salt Lake City, UT 84101
(801) 328-2329
Fax (801) 575-7139
*And Squatter's Pub Brewery.
Emigration Amber Ale,
Parley's Porter, Rocky
Mountain Wheat, Cole's
Special Bitter.*

Vermont

Vermont Travel Division
134 State St.
Montpelier, VT 05602
(802) 828-3236
*Tourist information, calendar
of events.*

Breweries, Regional and
Micro

The Mountain Brewers
Rt. 4 Marketplace
P.O. Box 140
Bridgewater, VT 05034
(802) 672-5011
*Tours and tastings daily.
Long Trail Ale, India Pale
Ale, Stout, Light Ale, Kolsch.*

Magic Hat Brewing Co
180 Flynn Ave.
Burlington, VT 05401
(802) 658-2739
*Microbrewery. Call for curent
tour and beer information.*

**Otter Creek Brewing
  Co.**
74 Exchange St.
Middlebury, VT 05753
(800) 473-0727
in VT (802) 388-0272
*Tours Friday, 4:30 and
5:30PM. Brewery store open
most days.*

Catamount Brewing Co.
58 S Main St.
White River Junction, VT
  05001
(802) 296-2248
Fax (802) 296-2420
Contact: Philip Gentile
*Opened 1986. Tours: July to
October all week; November to
June Saturday. Call for times.
Famous for award-winning
handcrafted ales and lagers.
Store open all week. Cata-
mount Amber, Gold, Porter.
Seasonal: Octoberfest,
Christmas Ale, Bock,
American Wheat.*

Brewpubs

McNeill's Brewery
90 Elliot St.
Brattleboro, VT 05301
(802) 254-2553
Contact: Reagin and
    Holiday McNeill
Good food, darts, ales, cider.
Open daily, tours available by
appointment. Extra Pale, Nut
Brown, Duck's Breath Bitter,
Firehouse Pale, Slopbucket
Brown, Dead Horse IPA, Pale
Bock.

Windham Brewery
6 Flat St.
Brattleboro, VT 05301
(802) 254-4747
Brewery and restaurant,
Latchis Grille. Tours Wednes-
day. Moonbeam Pale Ale,
Whetstone Golden Lager,
Windham Porter.

Vermont Pub & Brewery
144 College St.
Burlington, VT 05401
(802) 865-0500
Fax (802) 658-4112
Pub seats 150, serves
traditional American and
British fare. Regular beers:
Burly Irish Ale, Dogbite
Bitter, VT Smoked Porter,
Mild Ale, Best Bitter/SPA,
Smoked Beer. Many seasonal
and special brews.

Jasper Murdoch's
    Alehouse
Norwich Inn
Main St.
Norwich, VT 05055
(802) 649-1143

Places to Enjoy Beer

Bromley View Inn
Rt. 30
Bondville, VT 05340
(802) 297-1459

Old Red Mill
Rts. 9 and 100
Wilmington, VT 05363
(802) 464-3700

Festivals and Events

Sugarbush Brewers
    Festival
RR1, Box 350
Warren, VT 05674-9500
(800) 537-8427
Fax (802) 583-6303;
in VT (802) 583-2381
Mid-September, two days. At
Sugarbush resort. Beers from
northeast microbrewers, live
music, food by local restau-
rants, crafts, foliage chairlift
rides.

Oktoberfest and Folk
    Music Festival
Grunberg Haus
Waterbury, VT 05676
(802) 244-7726
Mid-September, two days.
German food, music, and
dancing.

Of Historic Interest

Tour of Historic Inns
Manchester, VT 05255
(802) 362-1792
Early December, two weekends.

Virginia

Virginia Tourism
1021 E Cary St., Tower II
Richmond, VA 23219
(804) 876-4484
Fax (804) 786-1919
Tourist information.

Breweries, Regional and Micro

Old Dominion
    Brewing Co.
44633 Guilford Dr.
Ashburn, VA 22011
(703) 689-1225
Dominion Lager, Stout, Ale;
Hard Times Select.

Potomac River
    Brewing Co.
14141-A Parke Long Ct.
Chantilly, VA 22021
(703) 631-5430
Tours Saturday, 1–3PM.
Specializes in ales, including
Patowmack and
Rappahannock Red, and Mt.
Vernon Porter.

Steamship Brewing Co.
415 West 24th St.
Norfolk, VA 23517
(8045) 623-3430
Contact: Lee Scanlon
Captain's Lager, Raspberry
Ale. Tours by appointment.

Brewpubs

Bardo Rodeo
2000 Wilson Blvd.
Arlington, VA 22201
(703) 527-9399
Contact: Bill Stewart
Huge: 900 seats inside, 300 in
outdoor beer garden. 108 taps,
including 10 or more house
brews. Ales and lagers includ-
ing Alt, White, seasonal, and
Chang, Tibetan beer.

Blue Ridge Brewing Co.
709 W Main St.
Charlottesville, VA 22901
(804) 977-0017
Hawksbill Lager, Piney River
Lager, Afton Ale, Humpback
Stout.

Legend Brewing Co.
321 W Seventh St.
Richmond, VA 23224
(804) 232-8871
Small taproom serves food.
Tours by request.

Richbrau Brewery
1214 E Cary St.
Richmond, VA 23219
(804) 644-3018
Brews are served at next door
Queen Anne's Pub, Shockoe
Slip area. Big Nasty Porter,
Old Nick Pale and Golden
Griffin ales.

Places to Enjoy Beer

Bilbo Baggins
208 Queen St.
Alexandria, VA 22314
(703) 683-0300
Fax (703) 683-1857

Bullfeathers
112 King St.
Alexandria, VA 22314
(703) 836-8088

Calvert Grill
3106 Mt. Vernon Ave.
Alexandria, VA 22305
(703) 836-8425
Good micro selection.

Murphy's Pub
713 King St.
Alexandria, VA 22314
(703) 548-1717
Features Murphy's Stout, from
Cork, Ireland, Mooney's Stout,
VA, and Guinness. National
and local sports via satellite.

Cellar Restaurant
302 N Main St.
Blacksburg, VA 24060
(703) 953-0651

Old Brouge
760 C Walker Rd.
Great Falls, VA 22066
(703) 759-3309

Hero's American Restaurant
9412 Main St.
Manassas, VA 22110
(703) 330-1534
Restaurant with 16 taps.
Lunch and dinner daily.

Bavarian Inn Restaurant
5541 Iowa Ave.
Norfolk, VA 23513
(804) 858-2758
German foods, beers. Open
Tuesday to Sunday.

Reggie's
333 Waterside Dr.
Norfolk, VA 23510
(804) 627-3575
British pub. Food, live
entertainment.

Carlyle Grand Cafe
400 S 28th St.
Shirlington, VA
(703) 931-0777

Retail Stores

King Street Gourmet Cellar
210 King St.
Alexandria, VA 22314
(703) 683-5439

Sutton Place Gourmet
600 Franklin St.
Alexandria, VA 22314
(703) 549-6611
Micros and imports.

Fern St. Gourmet
6025A Burke Center Pkwy.
Burke, VA 22015
(703) 425-9463

Festivals and Events

Oktoberfest
Town Point Park
Norfolk, VA 23607
(804) 441-2345
Early October, two days.
German music, foods,
beverages, kid's events. Free.

Oktoberfest
Strawberry Hill Convention
Center
Richmond, VA
(804) 228-3200
Mid-October.

Of Historic Interest

Gadsby's Tavern Museum
134 N Royal St.
Alexandria, VA 22314
(703) 383-4242
Tavern dating back to the time
of George Washington. Tours.
Closed Monday. Sorry, no
beer.

Historic Michie Tavern
Thomas Jefferson Pkwy.
Charlottesville, VA 22902
(804) 977-1234
C18 tavern, now a museum,
also serving food.

Rising Sun Tavern
1306 Caroline St.
Fredericksburg, VA 22401
(703) 371-1494
1760 home of George
Washington's brother George,
later a tavern. Open daily.

Colonial Williamsburg
P.O. Box 1776
Williamsburg, VA 23187-
1776
(800) HIS-TORY
in VA (804) 220-7645
Restored C18 community,
including: Raleigh Tavern,
where Virginians gathered to
discuss political events
leading to independence;
Wetherburn's Tavern, learn
about 1750s tavern keeper's
family, slaves, and business
practices.

Washington

Washington State
Tourism
P.O. Box 42513
Olympia, WA 98504-2513
(800) 544-1800
Tourist information, calendar
of events.

Breweries, Large

Rainier Brewing Co.
3100 Airport Way S
Seattle, WA 98134
(206) 622-2600

Breweries, Regional and Micro

Northern Lights
Brewing Co.
Airway Heights, WA 99001
(509) 244-4909

Kelly Creek Brewing Co.
Bonney Lake, WA 98390

Hart Brewing Co.
176 First St.
Kalama, WA 98625
(206) 673-2121
Tours available. Pyramid
Ales: Pyramid Pale, Best
Brown, Snow Cap, Wheaten™

and Spring Seasonal Wheaten
Bock Ales; Hefeweizen; Sphinx
Stout; Amber Wheat Beer.

Hale's Ales
109 Central Way
Kirkland, WA 98033
(206) 827-4359

Whidbey Island
Brewing Co.
Langley, WA 98260
(360) 221-8373

Fish Brewery & Pub
515 Jefferson
Olympia, WA 98501
(206) 943-6480

Onalaska Brewing Co.
Onalaska, WA 98570
(206) 978-4253

Thomas Kemper
Brewing Co.
22831 Foss Rd. NE
Poulsbo, WA 98370
(360) 697-7899
Fax (360) 697-6867
Tours, tastings. Tap Room
serves food all day. Beer
Garden. Various special events
such as Oktoberfest. Only
Northwest micro dedicated to
brewing lager beers. Owned by
Hart Brewing Co. Pale Lager,
Poulsbo Pilsner, Integrale,
Oktoberfest, Winterbrau.

Roslyn Brewing Co.
Roslyn, WA 98941
(509) 649-2232

Jet City Brewing Co.
Seattle, WA
(206) 392-5991
Contract brewed.

Maritime Pacific
Brewing Co.
1514 NW Leary Way
Seattle, WA 98107
(206) 782-6181

Pike Place Brewery
1432 Western Ave.
Seattle, WA 98101
(206) 622-3373
Microbrewery in the Public
Market. Free tours, tastings
Monday to Saturday, gift
shop.Pike Place Pale and
East India Pale ales; Pike
Place XXXXX Stout; Old
Bawdy Barley Wine.

Redhook Ale Brewery
3400 Phinney Ave. N
Seattle, WA 98103
(206) 548-8000
And Trolleyman Pub. Redhook
ESB, Ballard Bitter,
Blackhook, Wheathook.

Seattle Brewers
530 S Holden
Seattle, WA 98108
(206) 762-7421

Hale's Ales
E 5634 Commerce St.
Spokane, WA 99212-1307
(509) 534-7553

Olympia Brewing Co.
Tumwater, WA 98502
(206) 754-5000

Smith & Reilly
Vancouver, WA
Contract brewed.

Redhook Ale Brewery
Woodinville, WA 98072
(206) 483-3232

Yakima Brewing & Malting Co.
8513 NE Hwy. 99
P.O. Box 9158
Yakima, WA 98909-0158
(509) 575-1900
Producers of Grant's ales, stouts, and beers.

Brewpubs

The Anacortes Brewhouse
320 Commercial St.
Anacortes, WA 98221
(360) 293-2444

Leavenworth Brewery
Leavenworth, WA 98826
(509) 548-4545

Front St. Ale House
San Juan Island, WA
(206) 378-BEER
San Juan Brewing Co.

Big Time Brewing Co.
4133 University Way NE
Seattle, WA 98105
(206) 545-4509
Coal Creek, HefeRyzen, Atlas Amber, Old RIP, Old Wooly, Prime Time, Bhagwans Best.

California & Alaska St. Brewery
4720 California Ave. SW
Seattle, WA 98116
(206) 938-2476

Pacific Northwest Brewing Co.
322 Occidental Ave. S
Seattle, WA 98104
(206) 621-7002

Birkebeinder Brewing Co.
Spokane, WA
(509) 458-0854

Ft. Spokane Brewery
W 401 Spokane Falls Blvd.
Spokane, WA 99201
(509) 838-3809

Hazel Dell Brewpub
8513 NE Hwy. 99
Vancouver, WA 98665
(360) 576-0996

Winthrop Brewing Co.
155 Riverside
Winthrop, WA 98862
(509) 996-3183

Grant's Brewery Pub
32 N Front St.
Yakima, WA 98901
(509) 575-2922
A non-smoking pub with music, food, and Grant's beers: Scottish, Celtic, and Spiced ales, Imperial Stout, IPA, Wheat Beer, and Yakima Cider.

Places to Enjoy Beer

Archer Ale House
1212 Tenth St.
Bellingham, WA 98225
(360) 647-7002
Ten taps, two cask-conditioned pumps. Smokefree.

Rico's Pub
Main St.
Pullman, WA 99163
Twelve taps.

Blue Star Cafe & Pub
4512 Stone Way N
Seattle, WA 98103
(206) 548-0345

Cutters Bayhouse
2001 Western Ave.
Seattle, WA 98121
Restaurant and bar featuring Pike Place Pale Ale.

74th St. Ale House
7400 Greenwood Ave. N
Seattle, WA 98103

Conley's Place
E 12622 Sprague,
Spokane, WA 99216
(509) 924-5411
Restaurant featuring Northwest beers.

Engine House No. 9
611 N Pine
Tacoma, WA 98406
(206) 272-3435
Historic building. around 30 taps plus bottles.

Retail Stores

Larry's Markets
12321 120 Pl. NE
Kirkland, WA 98033
(206) 820-2300

Larry's Markets
10008 Aurora Ave. N
Seattle, WA 98133
(206) 527-5333

Louie's on the Pike
1924-26 Pike Pl. Market
Seattle, WA 98101
(206) 443-1035

Festivals and Events

Oktoberfest
Bainbridge Island, WA 98110
(206) 692-7293
Mid-September

Northwest Microbrewery Festival
Herb Farm
Fall City, WA 98024
Mid-June (Father's Day).

Maifest
Leavenworth, WA 98826
(509) 548-5807
Early May, three days.
Bavarian village welcomes
spring with maypole dance,
oompah bands, music, arts
and crafts, food and drink.

Deutsches Fest
Odessa, WA 99159
(509) 982-0049
Mid-September, three days.
German festival with food,
music, costumes, ugly beard
contest, arts and crafts.

Great NW Microbrew
 Invitational
Seattle, WA
(206) 232-2982
Contact: Michael Piazza
Late September, three days.

Northwest Folklife
 Festival
Seattle Center
Seattle, WA
(206) 684-7300
Contact: 305 Harrison St.,
 Seattle, WA 98109
Memorial Day weekend.
Traditional music, dance,
crafts, and food of 100
countries. Folklife Brewpub
co-sponsored by Thomas
Kemper Brewing and Hart
Brewing/Pyramid Ales.

Northwest Ale Festival
Seattle, WA
(206) 527-7331
Contact: Microbrew
 Appreciation Society
Early September, six days.

Oktoberfest
Stevenson, WA 98648
(509) 427-5588
Early October, three days.

Museum of Brewing
Merchant du Vin
140 Lakeside Ave.
Seattle, WA 98122
(206) 322-5022
Brewing memorabilia.

American Hop Museum
E Toppenish Ave. and B St.
Toppenish, WA 98948
Opens late 1993 or early
1994. In old Hop Growers
Supply Bldg. Hop memora-
bilia, equipment, gift shop.

Old Timers Plaza
Toppenish, WA 98948
Mural by Robert Thomas,
"When Hops were Picked by
Hand."

West Virginia

West Virginia Tourism
2101 Washington St.
East Charleston, WV 25305
(800) 225-5982
Tourist information.

Cardinal Brewing Co.
Charleston, WV

Brewpubs

West Virginia
 Brewing Co.
1291 University Ave.
Morgantown, WV 26505
(304) 296-BREW
Gourmet menu. Open Monday
to Saturday. A J Gold, Fennen
Celtic Ale, Cameron Scottish
Stout, Gabriel's Wheat.
Formerly One Onion
Brewpub.

Places to Enjoy Beer

Tari's
123 N Washington St.
Berkeley Springs, WV
 25411
(304) 258-1196

Cliffside Inn
Rt. 340 W
Harpers Ferry, WV 25425
(304) 535-6302

Festivals and Events

Octoberfest
Weston, WV 26452
(304) 269-2608
October, Columbus Day
weekend. Area's Swiss,
German, and Austrian
heritage. Dance, food, drink,
yodelling, oompah bands.

Of Historic Interest

The Old Mill
Harman, WV 26270
Water-powered grist mill.

Drover's Inn
Millers Tavern
Historic district
Wellsburg, WV 26070
(304) 737-0188
Drover's Inn, built in 1848,
now a restaurant. Millers Inn
built in 1798.

Wisconsin

Wisconsin Tourism
123 W Washington Ave.
P.O. Box 7606
Madison, WI 53707
(800) 432-TRIP
Tourist information, including
brewery tours. In WI and
neighboring states, call (800)
372-2737.

Breweries, Large

G. Heileman Brewing Co.
1111 S Third St.
La Crosse, WI 54601
(608) 782-BEER

Miller Brewing Co.
3939 W Highland Blvd.
Milwaukee, WI 53201
(414) 931-2000
*Free tours and samples
Monday to Saturday. Includes
outside walking: dress
accordingly. Group reservations advised. Gift store.
Miller, Lowenbrau.*

Pabst Brewing Co.
917 W Juneau Ave.
Milwaukee, WI 53233
(414) 223-3500
*Free tours and tastings: June
to August, Monday to
Saturday; September to May,
Monday to Friday. Gift store.
Pabst, Olympia, Hamm's.*

Breweries, Regional and Micro

**Jacob Leinenkugel
Brewing Co.**
1–3 Jefferson Ave.,
Hwy 123 N
Chippewa Falls, WI 54729
(715) 723-5558
*Tours weekdays June to
December by appointment.
Hospitality Center open all
year Monday to Saturday.
Subsidiary of Miller Brewing
Co. Leinenkugel's,
Leinenkugel's Light and
Limited.*

Walter Brewing Co.
Eau Claire, WI 54701
Contract brewed.

Gray Brewing Co.
Janesville, WI 53545

Lone Star Brewing
100 Harborview Plz.
La Crosse, WI 54601
*Subsidiary of G Heileman.
Lone Star, Lone Star Light,
Lone Star Bock.*

Rainier Brewing Co.
100 Harborview Plz.
La Crosse, WI 54601
*Rainier Ale, Dry, Light, Draft,
Draft Light.*

Capitol Brewing Co.
7734 Terrace Ave.
Middleton, WI 53562
(608) 836-7100
*Tours year round; call for
times. Museum, Gift Haus
open Monday to Friday; Beer
Garden open in summer.
Garten Braeu Special,
Oktoberfest, Dark, Weizen;
Wisconsin Amber.*

Falstaff Brewing Co.
P.O. Box 766
Milwaukee, WI 53201
*Ballantine Ale and India Pale
Ale.*

Lakefront Brewery
818A E Chambers St.
Milwaukee, WI 53212
(414) 372-8800
Contact: Russ Klisch,
  president
*Following the tradition of
early Milwaukee brewers.
Riverwest Stein Beer, Klisch*

*Lager, East Side Dark, Cream
City Pale Ale. Tasting room
and tours on Saturday at
1:30, 2:30, and 3:30PM.*

Specialty Brewing Co.
P.O. Box 766
Milwaukee, WI 53233
*Subsidiary of Pabst. Old
Tankard Ale, Milwaukee
Germanfest Bier.*

Sprecher Brewing Co.
701 W Glendale Ave.
Glendale, WI 53209
(414) 964-BREW
*Retail sales. Tours Saturday,
call for information. Also
contract brewing co.*

**Joseph Huber
  Brewing Co.**
1208 14th Ave.
Monroe, WI 53566
(608) 325-3191

New Glarus Brewing Co.
P.O. Box 328
New Glarus, WI 53574

Mid-Coast Brewing
35 Wisconsin St.
Oshkosh, WI 54901
Chief Oshkosh Red Lager.

Stevens Point Brewery
2617 Water St.
Stevens Point, WI 54481-
  5248
(715) 344-9310
*Free tours and Brewery Store
Monday to Saturday: call for
hours. Catalog of collectibles:
call (800) 369-4911.*

Brewpubs

Appleton Brewing Co.
1004 S Olde Oneida St.
Appleton, WI 54915
(414) 735-0507
*Open Monday–Saturday, 11
to 7. Two brewpubs: Dos
Bandidos and Johnny O's
Pizza. Adler Brau Light,
Lager, Oktoberfest, Bock, and
more.*

Rowland's Calumet Brewery & Brewpub
25 N Madison St.
Chilton, WI 50314
(414) 849-2534
*Smallest brewery in WI,
housed in town's first
firehouse. Four or 5 beers on
tap. Tours available when time
permits. Open Tuesday to
Sunday. Hosts WI Micro-
brewers' Beer Fest in late May.*

Brewmaster's Pub and Brewery
4017 80th St.
Kenosha, WI 53142
(414) 694-9050
*Tours available. Open daily,
11AM to midnight. Restau-
rant too. Brewmasters'
Kenosha Gold, Johnson's
Honey Lager, Amber Vienna
Style, Oktoberfest.*

Water St. Brewery
1101 N Water St.
Milwaukee, WI 53202
(414) 272-1195
*Brewery and restaurant.
Continuous variety of seasonal
and specialty brews. Open
daily.*

Cherryland Brewery & Pub
341 N Third Ave.
Sturgeon Bay, WI 54235
(414) 743-1945
*Housed in an old railroad
station. Tours daily, 11AM to
4 PM. Silver Rail, Golden
Rail, Cherry Rail, Apple Bock,
and various seasonal brews.
Also contract brewing co.*

Randy's Fun Hunters Brewery
841 E Milwaukee St.
Whitewater, WI 53190

Places to Enjoy Beer

Kneisler's on KK
2900 S Kinnickinnic Ave.
Bay View, WI 53207
(414) 483-2900
*Imports, outdoor patio,
volleyball.*

Essen Haus
514 E Wilson
Madison, WI 53703
*Restaurant with German beers
on tap.*

Quivey's Grove Stable Tap & Grill
6261 Nesbitt Rd.
Madison, WI 53719
(608) 273-4900

Barrel Riders Pub
1132 E Wright
Milwaukee, WI 53212
(414) 372-2929

Begga's Pub
2479 N Framey St.
Milwaukee, WI
(414) 264-7735

Brown Bottle Pub
221 W Galena
Milwaukee, WI 53212
(414) 271-4444
*In historic Schlitz Brewery
Park complex. Large selection
of international brews.*

Cactus Jack's
Hwy. 100
251 N Mayfair Rd.
Milwaukee, WI 53226
(414) 475-6611
*Open daily, over 40 beers,
food. Live music Tuesday to
Saturday.*

Grady's Saloon
3101 W Lincoln
Milwaukee, WI 53215
(414) 643-9819

John Hawk's Pub
100 E Wisconsin Ave.
Milwaukee, WI 53202

Landmark 1850 Inn
5905 S Howell
Milwaukee, WI 53207
(414) 769-1850

Mel's Corner Tap
158 E Jeaueau
Milwaukee, WI 53202
(414) 274-7201

Polish Falcon's Nest 725
801 E Clark
Milwaukee, WI 53212
(414) 264-0680

Riverwest Tavern
900 E Auer
Milwaukee, WI 53212
(414) 265-8389

Suds Tavern
2979 N Bremen St.
Milwaukee, WI 53212
(414) 263-7837

Tony's Tavern
412 S Second St.
Milwaukee, WI 53204
(414) 273-6321

Tracks Tavern
1020 E Locust St.
Milwaukee, WI 53212
(414) 562-2020

Von Trier
2235 N Farwell Ave.
Milwaukee, WI 53202
(414) 272-1775
*Fifteen imported draft beers,
beer garden. Open daily from
4:30PM.*

Old Saloon
145 S Knowles
New Richmond, WI 54017

Lizard Lounge
141 High St.
Oshkosh, WI 54901
(414) 426-1290

Sir James Pub
316 N Franklin St.
Port Washington, WI 53074
*Large selection of imports and
domestic beers.*

Retail Stores

Sting Ray Liquors
3628 Spooner Ave.
Altoona, WI 54720

The Market Basket
14835 W Lisbon Rd.
Brookfield, WI 53005-1510
(800) 824-5562
Fax (414) 783-5203
in WI (414) 783-5233
*Large selection of specialty
and import beers.*

Star Liquor
1209 Williamson St.
Madison, WI 53703

Avenue Wine & Liquor
4075 S Howell Ave.
Milwaukee, WI 53207

Discount Liquors
4530 W Forest Home Ave.
Milwaukee, WI 53219

Gilbert's Liquor
2853 N Oakland
Milwaukee, WI 53211

**North Shore Wines &
Spirits**
5544 N Point Washington Rd.
Milwaukee, WI 53217

**Oklahoma Liquor &
Beer**
933 W Oklahoma Ave.
Milwaukee, WI 53215
(414) 744-2444

Siegel's Liquor
3476 N Oakland
Milwaukee, WI 53211

Wick's Beer & Liquor
4496 N Oakland Ave.
Milwaukee, WI 53211
(414) 332-3600

Festivals and Events

Belgian Days
Town Park
Brussels, WI 54204
(414) 825-1244
*Mid-July, two days. Belgian
food, games, arts and crafts.*

**WI Microbrewers' Beer
Festival**
Rowland's
25 N Madison St.
Chilton, WI 53014
(414) 849-2534
*Late May. Twenty to 25
different beers, served by their
brewers and brewmasters.*

Oktoberfest
Fennimore, WI 53809
(608) 822-3599
*Late September, 2 days.
Entertainment, arts and
crafts, beer and brats garden.*

Maifest
Marketplace Mall
Germantown, WI 53022
(414) 255-2590
*Mid-May, two days. Celebra-
tion of spring with arts and
crafts, live music, traditional
food and beverages.*

Bavarian Volkfest
Old Heidelberg Park
Glendale, WI 53209
(414) 462-9147
*Late June two days. Authentic
Bavarian festival with food,
beverages, entertainment.
Beer drinking contest.*

Gemutlichkeit Days
Jefferson County Fair-
grounds
Jefferson, WI 53549
(414) 674-3392
*Mid-September, three days.
German heritage celebrations
with polka music, food,
drinks, entertainment.
Contests include beer keg
tossing.*

Great Taste of the Midwest
Lakefront
Madison, WI
August. Brews from over 30 breweries. Sells out early.

Quivey's Grove Beer Fest
6261 Nesbitt Rd.
Madison, WI 53719
(608) 273-4900
Early October.

German Fest
Henry W. Maier Festival Park
Milwaukee, WI
(800) 837-FEST
In WI (414) 464-9444
Late July, three days. German music, food, drinks, entertainment.

International Beer Tasting
Mayfair Mall
Milwaukee, WI
(414) 297-8011
Early April. Run by Channel 10/36 Friends. One hundred fifty brands from over 20 countries, plus local microbrews. Food, live music.

Oktoberfest
Old Heidelberg Park
Milwaukee, WI
(414) 462-9147
Mid-September, three weekends. Plenty of food, beer, and gemutlichkeit.

Fall Fest
County Fairgrounds
Shawano, WI 54166
(715) 524-2139
Late September, two days. German music, dancing, food, and drink.

Of Historic Interest

Brewery Works Fine Arts Complex
W62 N718 Riveredge Dr.
Cedarburg, WI 53012
(414) 377-7220
1843 brewery, now studio of sculptor Paul J. Yank and Ozaukee Art Center, with exhibits of arts and crafts.

Wade House Inn
Hwy. 23
Greenbush, WI 53026
(414) 526-3271
Restored 1850 stagecoach inn, home of WI Carriage Museum, over 100 horsedrawn vehicles. Open daily May to October.

Milton House Museum
18 S Janesville St.
Milton, WI 53563
(608) 868-7772
1844 stagecoach inn, once a station on the underground railway, now a museum.

Jack Pandl's Whitefish Bay Inn
1319 E Henry Clay St.
Milwaukee, WI 53217
(414) 964-3800
Inn and restaurant with enormous collection of antique beer steins.

Pabst Mansion
2000 W Wisconsin Ave.
Milwaukee, WI 53233
(414) 931-0808
Built in 1893 by Capt Frederick Pabst, founder of Pabst Brewery. Restored interior. Guided tours daily, seasonal events. See what all those pints bought. He also built the Pabst Theater, 144 E Wells.

Wyoming

Wyoming Division of Tourism
I-25 at College Dr.
Cheyenne, WY 82002
(800) 225-5996
Tourist information.

Breweries, Regional and Micro

Otto Brothers' Brewing Co.
1295 Northwest St.
Wilson, WY 83014
(307) 733-9000
Mail: P.O. Box 4177,
Jackson, WY 83001
Call for tours. Annual Oktoberfest. Teton and Old Faithful ales, Moose Juice Stout.

Brewpubs

Medicine Bow Brewing
115 17th St.
Cheyenne, WY 82001

Jackson Hole Pub & Brewery
265 Milward
Jackson Hole, WY 83001
(307) 739-BEER
Contact: Albert Upsher
Snake River Brewing Co.

Places to Enjoy Beer

Murf the Surf's Bar & Cafe
Box 3
Centennial, WY 82055
(307) 742-6047
Beer garden, food.

Trading Post Restaurant & Saloon
Box 248
Centennial, WY 82055
(307) 721-5074

Pine Lodge Bar
520 McCaffery
Encampment, WY 82325
(307) 327-5203

Mingles Lounge &
  Liquor Store
3206 E Grand Ave.
Laramie, WY 82070
(307) 721-2005
Ten beers on tap, food, games.
Open daily.

Hotel Wolf
101 E Bridge
Saratoga, WY 82331
(307) 326-5525
Restaurant and lounge.

Alpenhof
Teton Village, WY 83025
(307) 733-3242

Retail Stores

Spirits of the West
385 W Broadway
Jackson, WY 83001
(307) 733-3854

The Still
1602 Spring Creek Dr.
Laramie, WY 82070
(307) 742-4321
Domestic and imported beers.

Festivals

Oktoberfest
Rock Springs, WY 82902
(307) 362-3771
Late October.

Marshall Islands

Marshall's Best
  Microbrewery
Majuro

Puerto Rico

Puerto Rico Tourism
Box 4435
2 La Princesa Dr.
San Juan, PR 00902
(809) 721-2400
Fax (809) 725-4417
Tourist information, calendar
of events. Publishes monthly
Que Pasa? guide to what's
on.

Breweries, Regional and Micro

Cerveceria India
Post Center N
P.O. Box 1690
Mayaguez, PR 00681

Places to Enjoy Beer

Shannon's Irish Pub
Calle Loiza 1503
Santurce, PR 00911
(809) 728-6103

U.S. Virgin Islands

Tourist information (800) USVI-INFO

Island Brewing &
  Malting Co.
P.O. Box 5310
St Thomas, VI

Places to Enjoy Beer

Antoine's
58A King St.
Christiansted
St. Croix, VI 00820
(809) 773-0263

Oskar's Bar &
  Restaurant
4A La Grand Princess
Christiansted
St. Croix, VI 00820
(809) 773-4060

Cruz Inn
P.O. Box 566
Cruz Bay
St. John, VI 00830
(809) 776-7688

Mongoose Restaurant,
  Cafe & Bar
Mongoose Junction
St. John, VI 00830
(809) 776-7586

Pusser's
Wharfside Village
Cruz Bay
St John, VI 00830
(809) 774-5489
Store and pub serving English
fare.

Dungeon Bar
Bluebeard's Hill
Charlotte Amalie
St. Thomas, VI 00801
(809) 774-1600

Greenhouse
Veterans Dr.
Charlotte Amalie
St. Thomas, VI 00802
(809) 774-7998
On the waterfront. Live
entertainment, meals.

Retail Stores

Spigot Liquor Store
59 King's Wharf
Christiansted
St Croix, VI 00820
(809) 778-8400

Africa and the Middle East

Listings by Country

Algeria

Brasseries Glacieres
Lotissement Industriel
Algiers

Brasserie la Gauloise
Rte. Nationale 5
Reghaia

Benin

Societe Nationale des Brasseurs
Zi Rte. de Porto Dovd
BP 135
Cotonou

Botswana

Kgalagadi Brewers
N Mandela Dr.
Gaberone

Places to Enjoy Beer

Grand Hotel
Francistown
Bull & Bush Pub
Gaberone

Burkina Faso

Brasseries de Haute-Volta
P.O. Box 345
Quagatdougou

Cameroon

Nobra
BP 2280
Douala
Tel 42 05 03

Brasserie dle Pellas
Douala
Tel 42 22 44

UCB
BP 638
Douala
Tel 42 62 18

Les Brasseries du Cameroun
BP 496
Yaounde
Tel 22 39 03
Marketers of Tuborg.

Guinness Cameroun
BP 242
Yaounde
Tel 22 47 56

International Brasserie
BP 4237
Yaounde
Tel 42 72 73

Central African Republic

Ocatour
Ave. de la Victoire
BP 655
Bangui
Tel 614366
Tourist information.

Brasserie Motte Cordonnier Afrique
Ave. du Pres D'Estang
BP 806
Bangui

Chad

Brasseries de Logone
P.O. Box 170
Moundou

Congo

Brasserie de Brazzaville
Rue de Nouveau Port
BP 105
Brazzaville

Societe des Brasseries Kronenbourg
P.O. Box 1147
Pointe Noire

Egypt

Egyptian Tourist Authority
Misr Travel Tower
Abbassia Square
Cairo
Tel (02) 823510
Fax (02) 830844
Tourist information.

Places to Enjoy Beer

Monty's Bar
Cecil Hotel
Alexandria
Open 24 hours.

Audio 9
33 Kasr an-Nil St.
Cairo

New Arizona Bar
Alfa St.
Cairo

Omar Khayam Restaurant & Cafe
An-Nasr Way
Hurghada
Bar and liquor store.

Liquor Store
Ramses St.
Luxor

Ethiopia

Addis Ababa Brewery
Ras Abebe Aragay St.
Addis Ababa Shewa

Meta Brewery
Addis Ababa

St. George Brewery
Addis Ababa

Melotti Brewery
Asmara

Gabon

Societe des Brasseries de Haut Ognoue
Franceville
Brews Biere Regab.

Ghana

Gulder International Brewery

Accra Brewery
P.O. Box 351
Accra
Brews Club Mini.

Guinness Ghana
P.O. Box 1536
Kumasi

Kumasi Brewery
Lake Rd.,
P.O. Box 848
Kumasi
Star brand.

Guinea

Brasseries de Guinea
Km 7, 5 rte. de Coyah
Conakry

Iraq

Eastern Brewing Co.
Mirjan Bldg.
Southgate
Baghdad

Iraqui Brewery
293/1 Ras El-Qaria
Rashid St.
P.O.B. 29021
Baghdad

Israel

Israeli Government Tourist Office
24 King David St.
Jerusalem
Tel 02-754863
Tourist information.

Breweries

Tempo Beer Industries
P.O. Box 127
New Industrial Zone
IL-42101 Metanya
Tel 53 358131
Fax 53 358165
Maccabi, Gold Star.

Places to Enjoy Beer

Petra Pub
Under Lake Center Hotel
Galilee
Tel 72 11 75

Pub Carlsberg
Promenade
Galilee

London Price
85 Ha'Atamaut Rd.
Haifa

The Pub
102 Ha'Atamaut Rd.
Haifa

Arizona
37 Jaffa Rd.
Jerusalem

Champs Pub
5 Yoel Solomon St.
Jerusalem

Glasnost
15 Heleni haMalka St.
Jerusalem
Tel 25 69 54

Mad Hatters Pub
6 Yosef Rivlin St.
Jerusalem

Mike's Place
14 Harkness St.
Jerusalem
Tel 10 49 30

Sergey
Heleni haMalka St.
Jerusalem
Tel 25 85 11

Tavern Pub
16 Rivlin St.
Jerusalem
Tel 24 45 41

Ego Trip
7 Mendele St.
Tel Aviv

Gordon's Pub
17 Gordon St.
Tel Aviv
Tel 522 2128

Kassit
117 Dizengoff St.
Tel Aviv

Long John Silver's
Off Dizengodd Square
Tel Aviv
Tel 528 5084

Jordan

Arab Breweries Co.
Prince Mohammed St.
P.O. Box 168
Amman

General Investment Co.
Amman
Brews Amstel under license.

Places to Enjoy Beer

Castle Hotel
Moi Ave.
P.O. Box 84231
Mombasa
Tel 23403

Kenya

Kenya Breweries
Thika Rd.
Ruaraka
P.O. Box 30161
Nairobi
Tel 8027 01
Tusker.

Places to Enjoy Beer

Laikipia Bar
Galole Rd.
Eastleigh

Octopus Bottoms Up
P.O. Box 1329
Kisumu
Tel 40835
*Barbecue and dart board on
the roof.*

Istanbul Bar
Moi Ave.
Mombasa

Buffalo Bill's
Heron Ct. Hotel
Milimani Rd.
Nairobi
Tel 720 740

The Pub
Standard St.
Nairobi

Thorn Tree Cafe
New Stanley Hotel
Kimathi St.
Nairobi
Tel 333 233
*Named after the central thorn
tree, with travelers' message
board.*

Zanze Bar
5th floor, Kenya Cinema
  Plz.
Moi Ave.
Nairobi

Liberia

Monrovia Breweries
Monrovia
*Brewery currently closed (it
was blown up), but there are
hopes of its reopening.
Monrovia Lager, Club, Dark.*

Malawi

**Carlsberg Malawi
  Brewery**
Blantyre

Mali

**Societe Malienne de
  Boissons Gazeuses**
Rue Moussa Travele
Barnako

Mauritius

Mauritius Breweries
Phoenix
*Stella Pils, Guinness Foreign
Export Stout.*

Morocco

**Moroccan National
  Tourist Office**
BP 19
98 Blvd. Mohammed V
Rabat
Tel 22 05 77
*Tourist information, festival
calendar.*

Breweries

**Societe de Boissons
  Gazeuses de Souss**
Km 12, Rte de Marrakesh
Agadir

**Societe des Brasseries
  du Maroc**
Av. Pasteur Lalla Arita
Casablanca

Places to Enjoy Beer

Dailla
17 bd Mohammed V
Fes

Es Saada
Av. Mohammed es Slaoui
Fes

Many bars
Av. Mohammed V
Gueliz
Marrakesh

Club de Nuit
Corner Av. Hassan II and
  Av. des FAR
Meknes

Hotel Miramar
Av. des FAR
Tangier

Tanger-Inn
rue Magellan
Tangier
Tel 09 93 53 37

Namibia

Hausa Breweries
P.O. Box 11
Swakopmund

Namibia Breweries
P.O. Box 206
Windhoek 9000
Tel (061)6 2915

Places to Enjoy Beer

Crayfish Bar
Bismarck St.
Luederitz

Kuecki's Pub
Swakopomund

Western Saloon
Swakopomund

Thueringer Hof Hotel
Kaiser St.
Windhoek
Tel 061 220631
Beer garden.

Festivals

Oktoberfest
Windhoek
Late October.

Niger

Societe des Brasseurs
BP 11245
Rte. de Dasso
Niarney

Nigeria

Guinness Nigeria
Akran Way
P.O. Box 17
Ikeja
Lagos

Nigerian Breweries
Iganmu Ho
Abebe Village
P.O. Box 545
Lagos
Guilder, Star.

West Africa Breweries
121 Western Ave.
Iponri
P.O. Box 2246
Lagos

Senegal

**Societe des Brs de
  l'Ouest Afrique**
Rte. des Brasseries
Dakar

Sierra Leone

Sierra Leone Brewery
Wellington Ind Estate
P.O. Box 721
Freetown

South Africa

Breweries

**South African Tourism
  Board**
Private Bag X164
Pretoria 0001
TVL
Tel (012) 347 0600
Fax (012) 45 4889.
Tourist information.

South African Breweries
Alrode Brewery
P.O. Box 3913
Alrode 1450
Tel (011) 864 2014
Fax (011) 908 4540

St. George's Brewery
P.O. Box 38210
Boosyens 2016
Tel (011) 493 8640

South African Breweries
Ohlsson's Brewery
P.O. Box 166
Butterworth, Transkei
Tel (0474) 62 0221
Fax (0474) 62 0333

Mitchell's Waterfront Brewery
Victoria and Albert
  Waterfront
Cape Town, CP

South African Breweries
Ohlsson's Cape Brewery
P.O. Box 23012
Claremont 7735
Tel (021) 64 2000
Fax (021) 61 0567
Tours Available.

South African Breweries
Prospecton Brewery
P.O. Box 833
Durban 4000, Natal
Tel (031) 902 1243
Fax (031) 910 1494
Tours Available.

Crawford Breweries
P.O. Box 20441
Durban North 4016, Natal
Tel (031) 84 4721

South African Breweries
United Breweries
P.O. Box 196
Ga-Rankuwa,
  Bophuthatswana
Tel (01461) 33 331
Fax (01461) 33 331, ext. 206

South African Breweries
Chamdor Brewery
P.O. Box 1781
Krugersdorp 1740
Tel (011) 951 2600
Fax (011) 762 7884

Mitchell's Kynsna Brewery
P.O. Box 1220
Kynsna 6570
Tel (0445) 2 4685
Tours with tastings. Weekdays 10:30AM.

South African Breweries
Pietersburg Brewery
P.O. Box 2056
Pietersburg 0700
Tel (01521) 93 8401
Fax (01521) 93 8209

South African Breweries
P.O. Box 98
Port Elizabeth 6000
Tel (0474) 56 2222
Fax (041) 55 8220

Sterling Breweries
P.O. Box 40132
Redhill 4071
Tel (031) 503 1231

South African Breweries
Rosslyn Brewery
P.O. Box 911/087
Rosslyn 0200
Tel (012) 52 999
Fax (012) 541 2522
Tours Available.

South African Breweries
P.O. Box 782178
Sandton 2146
Tel (011) 881 8111
Fax (011) 881 8030
Central office.

Places to Enjoy Beer

Pig & Whistle
Kowe Rd.
Bathurst, CP
Tel 0464 25-0732
Built in 1831.

Plaka Tavern
Longmarket St.
Bloemfontein, Natal

Polo Tavern
West St.
Bloemfontein, Natal

Bertie's Landing
Victoria and Albert
  Waterfront
Cape Town, CP

Brass Bell
Kalk Bay
Cape Town, CP

Ferryman Tavern
Victoria and Albert
  Waterfront
Cape Town, CP
Next to Mitchells Brewery.

Heidelberg Hotel
Station Station Observatory
Cape Town, CP

Perseverance Tavern
83 Buitenkant St.
Cape Town, CP
Tel 021 461-2440
Built in 1836.

Stag's Head
Hope St. Gardens
Cape Town, CP

Cockney Pride
Marine Parade and W Mall
  St.
Durban, Natal

Finnegan's
Rutherford St.
Durban, Natal

London Tavern
Tyzack St.
Durban, Natal
A bar in a bus.

Finnegan's
Terminus St.
East London, CP

Jekyll & Hyde
Lock St. Jail Complex
East London, CP

Breakaway Tavern
Savoy Hotel
Jeffreys Bay, CP

Brewpub
Gold Reef City
Johannesburg, TVL
Tel 011 496-1600

Radium Beer Hall
282 Louis Botha Ave.
Johannesburg, TVL

Yard of Ale
Market Theatre Complex
Johannesburg TVL

**Halfway House Hotel
Drive-In Pub**
Kimberley
*Order a drink without leaving
your car.*

Star of the West Pub
Kimberley
*Established 1870, the oldest
continuously functioning bar
in the country.*

Mountainside Hotel
Lower Quthing
Tel 75 0257

The Godfather
61 Voortrekker
Oudtshoorn
Tel 0443 22-5404

De Acker, Dorp & Herte
Stellenbosch, CP

De Kelder
63 Dorp St.
Stellenbosch, CP

**Legends Restaurant &
Pub**
Du Toit and Bird
Stellenbosch, CP

Orange River Hotel
Upper Quthing
Tel 75 0252

Miles Kitchen
Sanlam Plz.
Welkom, OFS

Sudan

Blue Nile Brewery
P.O. Box 1405
Khartoum
Camel lager.

Swaziland

Places to Enjoy Beer

Prince Velebantfu Hotel
Mbabane Rd.
Manzini
Tel 46415

Ikhwezi Bar
Johnstone St.
Mbabane
Tel 45011

Syria

Al-Chark Brewery
State owned.

Tanzania

Arusha Brewery
P.O. Box 3014
Arusha

Tanzania Breweries
Uhuru St.
P.O. Box 1854
Dar es Salaam

Moshi Brewery
P.O. Box 714
Moshi

Togo

Brasserie de Kara
Kara
Tel 60 60 12

**Societe Togolaise des
Boissons**
Zone Industrielle du Port
BP 2239
Lome
Tel 27 58 80

Brasseries du Benin
47 rue du Grand Marche
BP 896
Lorne
Tel 21 50 62

Tunisia

Brasseries de Tunisia
Rte. de l'Hospital Militaire
Tunis

Uganda

Nile Breweries
P.O. Box 54 and 75-62
Jinja

Zaire

Tourzaire
Res de la Rwindi
Blvd. du 30 Juin
Kinshasa
Tel 25858
Tourist information.

Breweries

**Co Africaine des
Boissons**
P.O. Box 280
Kinshasa Fed. District

Bralima
Av. du Flambeau 912
BP 7246
Kinshasa 1

**Societe de Boissons de
Kinshasa**
Rte. do Poid Lourd
BP 10661
Kinshasa Fed. District

Unibra
Av. Col Ebeya
BP 10199
Kinshasa Fed. District

Places to Enjoy Beer

**Ave. des Martyrs de la
Revolution**
Bukava
*This street is lined with bars,
many of which have live
music.*

Zambia

Zambia Breweries
P.O. Box 1293
Lusaka
Tel 74381

Zimbabwe

Chibuku Breweries
Chibuku Ho
H Chitepo Ave.
P.O. Box 3004
Harare

National Breweries
Manchester Rd.
Southerton
P.O. Box 699
Harare

Places to Enjoy Beer

Alabama
Bulawayo Sun Hotel
Bulawayo

Shumba Bar
Main St.
Bulawayo

Bird & Bottle
Ambassador Hotel
Union Ave.
Harare

Old Crow Bar
Eighth St. and Selous Ave.
Harare

Terreskane Hotel
Harare

Your Place
99 Robt Mungabe Rd.
Harare

What's in a Name?

You can be sure your ancestors had something to do with making beer if your surname is Brauer, Breuer, Brewer, Brewster, Brouwer, Brosterman, or Brower. Maltas, Malter, Maltser, Malthouse, and Malthus all derive from malt. A cooper makes barrels, hence the surname. Inman, Tapster, and Tapper were innkeepers. Goodale, Goodall, Godhale, and Gaudale were names given to brewers whose ales were good.

If your name is Beerman, or Beery, maybe your ancestors were just good customers for the brew.

ASIA AND THE PACIFIC

Listings by Country

China

China International Travel Service
Chongwenmen Hotel
2 Quianmen Dong Daije
Beijing
Tel 755017
Responsible for looking after foreign tourists in China. Arranges tours for groups and individuals.

Breweries

Beijing Brewery
Beijing

Yanjiang Brewery
Beijing

Shengli Beer Co.
Guangzhou

Heineken Brewery
Hainan Island
Tiger Beer.

Huizhou Brewing Co.
Huizhou

Jinan Brewery Group
Jinan

Golden Key Brewery
Putian
Licensed producers of Beck's.

Qianjiang Brewery Group
Qianjiang

Qingdao Brewery
Qingdao Shandong
Also spelled Tsingtao. Tours available.

Shenyang Brewery
Shenyang
Snowflake.

Donghu Brewing Group (East Lake)
Wuhan

Pabst Brewery
Zhaoqing

Zhujiang Brewery (Pearl River)
Zhujiang

Places to Enjoy Beer

Bars can be found in all major hotels, which are mostly foreign/Chinese joint ventures.

Brauhaus
Jianguomenwa
Beijing

Pig & Whistle
Holiday Inn Lido
Jichang Lu Jiangtai Lu
Beijing

Trader's Pub
JC Mandarin Hotel
1225 Nanjing Xilu
Shanghai
Tel 279 1888 ext. 5307

Cook Islands

Cook Islands Tourist Authority
Main Rd.
Avarua
P.O. Box 14
Rarotonga
Tel 682 29435
Fax 682 21435
Tourist information and Visitors Center.

Places to Enjoy Beer

Crusher Bar
Aitutaki
Tel 682 31283

Ralphie's Bar & Grill
P.O. Box 24
Aitutaki
Tel 682 31418

Metua's Restaurant & Bar
Browns Arcade
P.O. Box 928
Rarotonga
Tel 682 20850
Open daily. Live band Friday and Saturday. Charter fishing trips: catch your own meal.

Fiji

Fiji Visitors Bureau
Thompson St.
G.P.O. Box 92
Suva
Tel 679 302433
Fax 679 300970
Tourist information.

Carlton Brewery
122–164 Foster Rd.
Walu Bay
P.O.B. 696
Suva
Tel 679 31 5811
Fax 679 30 0408
G.P.O. Box 696
Tours weekdays, 3PM.

Places to Enjoy Beer

Farmer's Club
Main St.
Nandi

Flight Deck
Box 9246
Airport
Nandi
Tel 72 444

Johai's Bar
Box 213
Nandi
Tel 72 192

Sandalwood Inn
Box 445
Nandi
Tel 72 553
Contact: John and Ann Birch

Royal Suva Yacht Club
Suva

Traps
305 Victoria Parade
Suva

Tavua Hotel
Tavua
Tel 91 122
Mail: Box 47
Mba, Fiji

Hong Kong

Hong Kong Tourist Association
35/F, 1 Connaught Pl.
Central
Tel (852) 801 7111
Tourist information. Multi-lingual telephone hotline: 801 7177.

Carlton & United Breweries
3A Chater Rd.
Central
Tel (852) 848 8300
Fax 852 868 4762

Carlsberg Brewery
1 Dai Kwai St.
Tai Po Ind Est
Tai Po, New Territories
Tel (852) 667 3788
Fax (852) 896 7600

Hong Kong & San Miguel Breweries
13 Miles Castle Peak Rd.
Sham Tseng, New Territories
Tel (852) 491 04 11
Fax 852 491 7237
Sun Lik beer.

Places to Enjoy Beer

Bull & Bear
Hutchinson Ho
Lambeth Walk
Central
Tel 525 7436

Dragon Boat Bar
2 Queen's Rd.
Central
Tel 233-1111
Fax 845-2590
In HK Hilton.

Kangaroo Pub
35 Haiphong Rd.
Tsimshatsiu
Tel 376 0786

Ned Kelly's Last Stand
11A Ashley Rd.
Tsimshatsiu
Tel 366 0562

Old China Hand Tavern
104 Lockhart St.
Wanchai
Tel 865 7362

Wanch
54 Jaffe Rd.
Wanchai
Tel 861 1621

India

Government Tourist Office
88 Jan Path
Delhi
Tel 332-0005
Tourist information.

Breweries

High Range Breweries
24 Grant Rd.
Bangalore

Khoday Breweries
9 Seshadri Rd.
Bangalore 560 009

Mysore Breweries
Jalahalli
Camp Rd.
Yeswantpur
Bangalore

United Breweries
24 Grant Rd.
P.B. 5104
Bangalore 560 001

Kesarval Breweries
P Bag 3
Bethora Ponda
Goa

Associated Breweries
15 Cawasji Patel St.
Fort
Bombay 400 001

Doburg Lager Breweries
82 Nagindas Master Rd.
Bombay 400 001

Skol Breweries
Chandra Mukhi
Nariman Point
Bombay 400 021

Jupiter Breweries
109 E/i-A
Biplabi Rashbehari
Bose Rd.
Calcutta
W Bengal

Kalyani Breweries
6 Old Court House St.
P.B. 56
Calcutta

East Coast Breweries
12 Cantonment Rd.
Cuttack

Narang Breweries
3 Cavalry Lines
Delhi 7

Arlem Breweries
Chowgule Ho
Mormugoa Harbour
Goa

Lilasons Breweries
Industrial Area
Govindpura
Bhopal 23

United Breweries
Nacharan Ind. Area
Hyderabad
Andhra Pradesh

Mohan Gold Water Breweries
P.B. 200
Lucknow

Punjab Breweries
P.B. 167
Ludhiana
Punjab

Mohan Meakin Breweries
Mohan Nagar
Ghaziabad
Kingfisher brand.

Mohan Rocky Spring Water Breweries
P.O. Khopali
Mohanwadi
Kolaba

Haryana Breweries
49 KM Stone
GT Road
Murthal
Haryana

Hindustan Breweries
21a Barakhambu Rd.
New Delhi 110 001

Indo Lowen Brau Breweries
E1 and 2
S Extension II
New Delhi

Mt. Shivalik Breweries
Prabhat Kiran, 3rd floor
7 Rajendra Pl.
New Delhi 110 008

MP Beer Products
New Ind. Area 12
Sanwar Rd.
Palasia
Indore

Premier Breweries
Kanji Kode St.
Palghat 678 623 Kerala

Sica Breweries
Avy-Ankuttipalayam
Muthirapalayam
Pondicherry 605 010

Artos Breweries
Ramachandrapuram 533 255

Mohan Meakin Breweries
Solan
Simla Hills
Kingfisher

**Drvans Modern
Breweries**
Bohri P.O.
Talab Tillo Jammu 2

Indonesia

Indonesian Tourism
81 Jalan Kramat Raya
Jakarta
Java
Tourist information.

Breda Brewing Co.
Jakarta
Java

P T Delta
Jakarta
Java

**Brasseries de
l'Indochine**
Medan
Sumatra

George & Dragon Pub
Behind Hotel Indonesia
Jakarta
Java
Tel 345625

Garuda Bar
72 Jalan Malioboro
Yogyakarta
Java
Tel 2113

Japan

Organizations

**Japan National Tourist
Organization**
6–6, Yurakucho 1-chome
Chiyoda-ku
Tokyo
Tel (03) 3502-1461
Tourist information.

**Brewers Association of
Japan**
2–8–18, Kyobashi
Chuo-ku
Tokyo 104
Tel (03) 3561 8386
Fax (03) 3561 8380
Contact: Akira Yoshizumi,
Manager
*Industry association that
lobbies the authorities,
promotes orderly drinking and
recycling, technical activities,
cultivates raw materials.*

**Brewing Society of
Japan**
6–30, Takinogawa 2-chome
Kita-ku
Tokyo 114
Tel (910) 3853

**National Research
Institute of Brewing**
2–6–30 Takinogawa
Kita-ku
Tokyo 114

Breweries

Sapporo Beer Brewery
2 Takasecho
Funabashi City Chiba Pref
Tel (0474) 37 3591
*Brewery with tours, beer
garden, beer hall. Tours in
English and German,
weekdays, reservations*

*necessary. Also has breweries
in Sapporo, Hokkaido, Sendai,
Gunma, Saitama, Shizuoka,
Nagoya, Osaka, and Kyushu.*

Orion Breweries
1985–1 Gusukuma
Orasoe City
Okinawa 901–21
Tel (0988) 77 1133
Fax (0988) 78 7044
Brewery in Nago.

Suntory
2–1–40 Dojimahama
Kita-ku
Osaka 530
Tel (03) 3470 1131
*Head office. Breweries in
Tonegawa, Musashino, and
Katsura.*

**Hokkaido Asahi
Breweries**
Minami 1–1
Nangodori 4-chome
Shiroishi
Sapporo 062
Tel (011) 861 9311
Fax (011) 861 8094

Sapporo Brewery
Kita-Shichijo
Higashi-ku
Sapporo
Tel 011 743 4368
*Founded in 1876. Visitors by
appointment.*

Kirin Brewery Co.
6–26–1 Jingu-Mae
Shibuya-ku
Toyko 150
Tel (03) 5499 6111
Fax (03) 5499 6578
Head office.

Sapporo Breweries
7–10–1 Ginza
Chuo-ku
Toyko 104
Tel (03) 3572 6111
Fax (03) 3574 2438
Head office.

Kirin Brewery
1–17–1 Namamugi
Tsurumi-ku
Yokohama Kanagawa Pref
Tel (045) 503 8250
Open Tuesday to Sunday.
Group tours in Japanese. Also
has breweries in Chitose,
Sendai, Tochigi, Takasaki,
Toride, Tokyo, Nagoya,
Hokuriku, Shiga, Kyoto,
Amagasaki, Okayama,
Hiroshima, and Fukuoka.

Places to Enjoy Beer

Kirin City Beerhall
8–8 Ginza
Chuo-ku
Tokyo
Tel (03) 3571 2590

Levanti Beerhall
2–8—7 Yuraku-cho
Chiyoda-ku
Tokyo
Tel (03) 3571 2661
Beer and oysters.

Sapporo Lion Beerhall
6–10—12 Ginza
Chuo-ku
Tokyo
Tel (03) 3571 2590
Beer, snacks.

Of Historic Interest

**Kikumasamune
Shiryokan**
1–9–1 Ozaki Nishimachi
Higashi-nada-ku
Kobe
Tel (078) 854 1029
Sake museum in historic
brewery district. Tours, video
on sake productions, tastings.

Korea

**Tourist Information
Center**
10 Ta-dong
Chung-go
Seoul 100-180
Tel (02) 757-0086
Fax (02) 757-5997
Tourist information. Travelers'
phone service, hotel reserva-
tions, small theater with
informative films on Korea.

Oriental Brewery
Incheon

Oriental Brewery
Kwangju

Chosun Brewery
Seoul

Oriental Brewery
582 Yongdungpo-Dong
Youngdungpo-gu
Seoul

Places to Enjoy Beer

Blue Villa
Near South Gate
Seoul
Tel 23 3694
Beer hall.

Green Villa
Behind Tiffany
Seoul
Tel 777 4728
Beer hall.

OB's Cabin
Behind UNESCO Bldg.
Seoul
Tel 776 4784
Beer hall.

Sansoo Gapsan
Behind Tiffany
Seoul
Tel 777 3125
Beer hall with music.

Of Historic Interest

Korean Folk Village
Suweon
Living history village with
traditional architecture,
crafts, includes a brewery.

Macau

**Government Tourist
Office**
Travessa do Paiva
Tel (853) 77218
Tourist information.

Malaysia

Malayan Breweries
95–97 Jalan Yew
55100 Kuala Lumpur
Tel 603 221 4033
Fax 603 221 7915

Guinness Anchor Berhad
Sungei Way Brewery
P.O. Box 144
46710 Petaling Jaya
Selangor
Tel 603 776 3022
Fax 603 774 0986

**Carlsberg Brewery
   Malaysia Berhad**
55 Persiaran Selangor
Sec. 15
40000 Shah Alam Selangor
Tel 603 559 1621
Fax 603 559 1931

Places to Enjoy Beer

Beers
Parkroyal Hotel
Batu Ferringhi

FMS Bar
Jalan Sultan Yusof
Ipoh

The Pub
11 Jalan Sultan Ismail
Kuala Lumpur
Tel 2322377
Fax 2301514
In the Shangri-La Hotel.

Hong Kong Bar
371 Lebuh Chulia
Penang

Sumi's Bar
22 Lebuh Pantai
Penang

Tiger Bar
108 Lebuh Muntri
Penang

20 Leith Street
20 Leith St.
Penang

Myanmar

Myanmar Brewery
Thuyezay Quarter
P.O. Box 2
Mandalay

Nepal

**Tourist Information
   Center**
Gangapath
Kathmandu
Tel 229818
Tourist information.

Gorkha Brewery

Nepal Brewery
Hetauda

Everest Brewery
Kathmandu

Himalayan Brewery
Kathmandu

Places to Enjoy Beer

Spam's Place
N Thamel
Kathmandu

Tom & Jerry's Pub
N Thamel
Kathmandu

Yak Horn Pub
Chhetrapati Thamel
Kathmandu

Pakistan

**Tourism Development
   Corp.**
P.O. Box 1465
H-2, St. 61, F-7
Islamabad 44000
Tel 811001-4
Tourist information.

Quetta Brewery
Quetta

Muree Brewery Co.
P.O. Box 13
Rawalpindi

Papua New Guinea

**Papua New Guinea
   Tourism**
P.O. Box 7144
Boroko
Tel 675 272521
Fax 675 259119
Tourist information.

South Pacific Brewery
P.O. Box 6550
Boroko
Port Moresby

Philippines

Department of Tourism
T M Kalaw St.
Ermita
Manila
Tel 59 90 31
Fax (632) 501567
Tourist information.

Asia Brewery
Allied Bank Bldg.
Manila
Tel 02 810 2701

San Miguel Corp.
710 Aurora Blvd.
Quezon City
Tel 02 721 8720

Polo Brewery
Valenzuela
Tel 361 2534
San Miguel Corp.

Places to Enjoy Beer

Braukeller
Holiday Inn
3001 Rotas Blvd.
Manila
Tel 59 79 61

Hobbit House
1801A Mabini St.
Ermita Manila
Bar with folk music.

Singapore

Singapore Tourist Board
250 North Bridge Rd.
Singapore 0617
Tel (65) 339 6622
Fax (65) 339 9423
Tourist information.

Asia Pacific Breweries
459 Jalan Ahmad Ibrahim
Singapore 2263
Tel 861 6200
Fax 862 1648
Contact: Ms Teo Li Hiang
   860 6482
*Tours for groups of 10 to 30,
Monday to Friday. Includes
visit to souvenir shop and
Tiger Tavern for tasting. Tiger,
Anchor Pilsener beers, ABC
Extra stout.*

Malayan Breweries
948 Alexandria Rd.
Singapore 0511
Tel 473 3533

**Orang Utan Brewery
   & Pub**
17 Jink Kim St.
Singapore
Contact: Pail Lawhon,
   chairman
*Brewpub that helps support
endangered wildlife.*

Places to Enjoy Beer

Bierstube
31 Marina Pk.
Singapore
German bar, Guinness on tap.

Dukes Tavern
80 Marina Parade Rd.
Singapore
Tel 440 0215

Jim's Pub
15 Claymore Dr.
Singapore
Tel 737 0811

Festivals

Food & Hotel Asia
World Trade Center
Tel 65 388 4747
Fax 65 339 5651
Contact: Singapore Exhibi-
   tion Services
*Mid-April, 4 days. Trade show
for food, beverages, and hotel
industry.*

Sri Lanka

McCallum Breweries
299 Union Pl.
P.O. Box 74
Colombo 2

Ceylon Brewery
Nuwara
Eliya

Tahiti

Tourist Bureau
Blvd. Pomare
Papeete
Tourist information.

Hinano Brewery

Places to Enjoy Beer

Le Pub
Av. Bruat
Papeete

Taiwan

Taiwan Tourism Bureau
280 Chunghsaio E Rd.
Sec. 4, 9th floor
Taipei
Tel 721 8541
Tourist information.

**Taiwan Tobacco & Wine
   Bureau**
4 Nanchang Rd.
Sec. 1
Taipei
Tel 321 4567
*Government bureau that
oversees tobacco and alcoholic
beverages.*

Places to Enjoy Beer

Pig & Whistle Pub
394 Ying Tsai Rd.
Taichung
Tel 04 322 6555
British pub and music cellar.

Barleyfield Pub
1 Fuchou St.
Taipei
Tel 392 3958
Cheap!

The Horseshoe
2 Ln. 28
Shuang Cheng St.
Taipei
Tel 591 6856
*English-style pub restaurant.
Draft beer, live jazz.*

Pig & Whistle Pub
78 Tienmou E Rd.
Taipei
Tel 874 0630
British pub and wine bar.

Ploughman Pub
9 Ln. 25
Shuang Cheng St.
Taipei
Tel 594 9648
Merry England: darts, draft beer.

Waltzing Matilda Inn
3 Ln 25
Shuang Cheng St.
Taipei
Tel 594 3510

Zum Fass
55 Basement Ln.
Lin Shen N Rd.
Taipei
Tel 531 3815
Swiss/German atmosphere, cuisine, beer.

Thailand

**Tourism Authority of
Thailand**
Ratchadamnoen Nok Ave.
Bangkok 10100
Tel (02) 282-1143
Fax (02) 280-1744
Tourist information.

Breweries

Boon Rawd Brewery Co.
999 Samsen Rd.
Dusit
Bangkok 10800
Tel 2411360
Fax 2431740

Kloster Thailand
113–115 Sukhumvit Rd.
Bangkok 10110
Tel 2537647
Fax 2539693

**Rajavithi International
Co.**
293/2 Rajavithi Rd.
Bangkok 10300
Tel 2537647
Fax 2434377, 2432397

Thai Amarit Brewery Co.
369/1 Pracharaj 1 Rd.
Bangsue
Dusit
Bangkok 10800
Tel 5850222
Fax 5878785

Places to Enjoy Beer

Bobby's Arms
Soi Charuwan
Bangkok
English pub.

George & Dragon Pub
Soi 23 Sukhumvit
Bangkok
English pub.

Alter Bier Garten
Soi 7
Pattaya Beach Rd.
Pattaya
German and Thai specialties.

Alt Heidelberg
273 Beach Rd.
Pattaya
German specialties.

Festivals

Thailand Food Fair
Queen Sirikit National
  Convention Center
Bangkok
Tel 279 4721
Fax 02 271 3223
Contact: Bangkok Exhibi-
  tion Services
*Mid-October, 4 days. Trade
show for the food, beverage,
and catering industries.*

Tonga

Tonga Visitors Bureau
P.O. Box 37
Vuna Rd.
Nuku'alofa
Tongatapu Is.
Tel 676 21733
Fax 676 22129
Tourist information.

Vanuatu

National Tourism Office
P.O. Box 209
Port Vila
Tel 678 22685
Fax 678 23889
Tourist information.

National Breweries
P.O. Box 169
Port Vila
Tel 678 22435
Fax 678 22152
Vanuatu Premium Bitter.

Places to Enjoy Beer

Club Vanuatu
Port Vila
Tel 678 22615
*Inexpensive food and drinks.
Poker machines, darts,
snooker, squash, etc.*

Duke of Windsor Pub
Port Vila
Tel 678 24808
*Old English pub with draft
beer, garden restaurant, darts,
sports TV.*

Rossi
Port Vila
Tel 678 22528
*Bar and beer garden with
harbor view.*

Scooter's Beer 'n'
   Burger Bar
Port Vila

Vietnam

South East Asia Brewery
Hanoi
*Joint venture between Viet Ha
and Carlsberg.*

Viet Ha Brewery
Hanoi

Hue Brewery
Hue

Places to Enjoy Beer

Piano Restaurant
Hang Vai St.
Hanoi
*Some imported beers, seafood
specialties, live music.*

The Hop

*"Turkeys, heresies, hops and beer
All came to England in one year."*

The hop, which gives beer its characteristic bitter flavor, grows wild in much of Europe. It's a climbing plant, and is cultivated to grow up hop poles placed tepee-like in the fields. There are male and female plants. The "head" is actually a collection of bracts, a cluster of modified leaves beneath the small, drooping flowers. The true fruit of the hop is a small nut. Hops are now cultivated for commercial use in brewing by many countries, including England, Germany, Czechoslovakia, and the USA.

Young hop tops, cut in spring and boiled in broth, can be eaten like asparagus. Hops can be used to flavor pea soup, or to make a sauce to accompany fish or chicken.

Before automated picking machinery was introduced, many Londoners would spend their summers in the hop-fields of Kent. Whole families would pick by day, and live in dormitory-like cabins at night. Fresh air, good company, and a chance to earn some money — what more could you want from a holiday?

Traditionally, a bunch of hops, placed above the mantelpiece and renewed each year, brings luck into a house. Pillows stuffed with hops promote sleep and pleasant dreams.

According to Nicholas Culpepper (1616–1654) in his Complete Herbal, hops "open obstructions of the liver and spleen, cleanse the blood, loosen the belly, cleanse the reins from gravel [kidney-stones], and provoke urine. . .cure the venereal disease, and all kinds of scabs, itch. . .tetters, ringworm, the morphew, and all discolorings of the skin. They purify the blood, and keep the body gently open."

— Heather Wood

AUSTRALIA AND NEW ZEALAND

National Listings

Listings by State

Note: In Australia, "hotel" does not necessarily imply lodgings. Sometimes it's just a pub.

National Listings

The Institute of Brewing
P.O. Box 229
Brooklyn Park
SA 5032
Tel 08 356 0996
Fax 08, 235 1061
Contact: J. V. Harvey,
Secretary, Australian and
New Zealand section
Association of breweries.

**Australian Beer
Magazine**
9 Rose Terr.
Paddington
NSW 2021

**National Festival of
Beers**
Story Bridge Hotel
200 Main St.
Kangaroo Point
QLD 4169
Early July. Over 50 Australian beers on tap.

Listings by State

Australian Capital Territory

**Australian Pizza
Kitchens**
P.O. Box 961
Fishwyck
ACT 2609

**Eagle Hawk Village
Brewing Co.**
P.O. Box 82
Watson
ACT 2602

New South Wales

**Brewers' Association
of NSW**
95 York St.
Sydney
NSW 2000
Tel 02 290 1422
Fax 02 262 2658

Breweries

Hahn Brewing Co.
101 Pyrmont Bridge Rd.
Camperdown
NSW 2050
Tel 02 519 3733
Fax 02 516 2504
Hahn's Sydney Bitter.

Goulburn Brewery
Bungonia Rd.
Goulburn
NSW 2580

Toohey's
29 Nyrang Rd.
P.O. Box 58
Lidcombe
NSW 2141
Tel 2648 8611
Fax 2647 9456

**Queen's Wharf Brewery
Hotel**
150 Wharf Rd.
Newcastle
NSW 2300

Scharer's Little Brewery
180 Old Hums Hwy.
Picton
NSW 2571

Balmain Brewery
18 Hornsey Rd.
Rozelle
NSW
Tel 02 810 8900

**Lord Nelson Brewery
 Hotel**
corner Kent and Argyle Sts.
The Rocks
Sydney
NSW 2000
*Oldest continually licensed
pub in Sydney.*

**Tank Stream
 Brewing Co.**
17 Little Pier St.
Sydney
NSW 2000
Tel 02 268 5055
Fax 02 267 6132

Diggers Rest Hotel
Lightning Ridge
NSW
Outback watering hole.

Craig Brewery
Darling Harbourside
Sydney
NSW
Aussie barbecue.

Pumphouse Brewery
17 Little Pier St.
Darling Harbour
Sydney
NSW
Tel 02 29 1841
Brewpub with beer garden.

Cidermakers

Bulmer Australia
Lot 1, Badgally Rd.
Campbelltown
NSW 4560
Tel 046, 258 711
Fax 046, 284 566

Places to Enjoy Beer

Victoria Hotel
Keppel St.
Bathurst
NSW

Thurless Castle Hotel
200 CLeveland St.
Chippendale
NSW

Castlereagh Hotel
Talbregar St.
Dubbo
NSW

Glengarry Castle Hotel
Lawson St. and
 Abercrombie Rd.
Redfern
NSW

Fortune of War
137 George St.
The Rocks
Sydney
NSW

Hero of Waterloo
Lower Fort St.
The Rocks
Sydney
NSW
*Great old pub that still has the
trapdoor used to shanghai
unsuspecting sailors. Has
American beers.*

Ox on the Rocks
155 George St.
The Rocks
Sydney
NSW
Good pub food.

Of Historic Interest

Powerhouse Museum
Sydney
NSW
Tel 02 217 0111
*Has a wonderful computer
that allows you to "brew your
own beer," selecting the
quantities of ingredients,
controlling the times and
temperatures. If you get it
wrong, the figure on the screen
spits it out.*

Northern Territory

Breweries

**Australian Frontier
 Holidays**
G.P.O. Box 4665
Darwin
NT

**Carlton & United
 Breweries**
14 Winnellie Rd.
Winnellie
NT 0821
Tel 089 84 3066
Fax 089 47 2173

Places to Enjoy Beer

Humpty-Doo Hotel
Arnhem Rd.
Darwin
NT 88 1372
*Pub with a bull that drinks
beer.*

Of Historic Interest

Beer Can Regatta
Darwin
NT
June. All entrants must make their boats out of beer cans.

Queensland

Breweries

Eumindi Brewery
Memorial Dr.
Eumundi
QLD 4562
Tel 074 428 600
Fax 074 428 063
Eumundi Lager, Premium Light.

Carlton & United Breweries
18 Malt St.
Fortitude Valley
QLD 4006
Tel 07 253 0311
Fax 07 252 5593

Power Brewing Co.
66 River Terr.
Kangaroo Point
QLD 4169
Tel 07 891 6899
Fax 07 391 8511
P.O. Box 621
Beenleigh
QLD 4207
Powers Bitter, Light.

Castlemaine Perkins
11 Finchley St.
Milton
QLD 4064
Tel 07 361 7400
Fax 07 369 3584
G.P.O. Box 44
Brisbane
QLD 4001

Kelly's Brewery & Brasserie
521 Stanley St.
South Brisbane
QLD 4101
Tel 08 844 9777

Sanctuary Cover Brewery
P.O. Box 3074
Southport
QLD 4215

Power Brewing Co.
Corner Mules Rd. and
  Pacific Hwy.
Yatala
QLD
Tel 07 807 3633

Places to Enjoy Beer

Lake Eacham Hotel
Atherton
QLD

Crown Hotel
Cairns
QLD

Story Bridge Hotel
200 Main St.
Kangaroo Point
QLD 4169

Bottom Pub
Kuranda
QLD
Garden bar, good grub, live music at night.

Frogs
Kuranda
QLD
Beer and Devonshire cream teas.

Manly Hotel
Manly
QLD

Town & Country Pub
Eachan Hotel
Yungabarra
QLD

South Australia

Breweries

Elders Ltd.
27 Currie St.
G.P.O. Box 551
Adelaide
SA 5000
Tel 08, 218 4511
Fax 08, 231 1910
Head office.

SA Brewing Co.
69 Quay West Ave.
Birkenhead Pt.
Drummoyne
SA 819 6755

Kent Town Brewery
2 Rundle St.
Kent Town
SA 5067

Coopers Brewery
9 Statenborough St.
Leabrook
SA 5068
Tel 08 332 5088
Fax 08 332 9618
P.O. Box 46
Kensington Park
SA 5068
Brand is XXXX (Fourex), the answer to the question "How does an Aussie spell beer?"

Loaded Dog Pub
North Fitzroy
Melbourne
SA
Brewpub and restaurant.

Lion Brewing &
  Malting Co.
163 Melbourne St.
North Adelaide
SA 5006

**Port Dock Brewery
  Hotel**
10 Todd St.
Port Adelaide
SA 5016

**South Australian
  Brewing Co.**
107 Port Rd.
Thebarton
SA 5031
Tel 08 354 8888
Fax 08 43 6281
Mail: G.P.O. Box 1472,
  Adelaide, SA 5001
*Tours Monday to Wednesday,
by appointment. Labels: West
End Premium, Export Dry,
Draught, Export, Light; Eagle
Super, Bitter, Blue; Southwark
Premium, Bitter, Special; Kent
Town Real Ale, more.*

**Carlton & United
  Breweries**
34–36 Rosberg Rd.
Wingfield
SA 5013
Tel 08 262 7488

Places to Enjoy Beer

Old Spot Hotel
Gawler
SA

Old Mill Restaurant
Hahndorf
SA
*The oldest German settlement
in Australia.*

Tasmania

Breweries

**Carlton & United
  Breweries**
Port Tower Bldg.
Evans St.
Hobart
TAS 7000
Tel 002 31 2133

St. Ives Pub Brewery
86 Sandy Bay Rd.
Hobart
TAS 7150

Tasmanian Breweries
Cascade Brewery
156 Collins St.
Hobart
TAS 7000
Tel 002 30 9111
Fax 002 23 5378
G.P.O. Box 88A
Hobart
TAS 7001
*Historic brewery, tours
available, museum. Labels:
Huoncry, Mercury (cider).*

Boag's Brewery
P.O. Box 8791
Launceston
TAS 7251

Victoria

Breweries

Alehouses of Australia
85 Auburn Rd.
Auburn
VIC 3123

**Rifle Brigade Pub
  Brewery**
137 View St.
Bendigo
VIC 3550

Leyah
18 McLean Ave.
Bentleigh
VIC 3204

**Linden Natural
  Brewing Co.**
8/20 Broadway
Bondbeach
VIC 3196

**Carlton & United
  Breweries**
16 Bouverie St.
Carlton
VIC 3053
Tel 03 342 5511
Fax 03 347 6341
Head office.

Kiewa Brewing Co.
P.O. Box 595
Croydon
VIC 3136
Tel 03 720 5422

**Carlton & United
  Breweries**
G.P.O. Box 753F
Melbourne
VIC 3001
Tel 8356 0996
Fax 8235 1061

**Lederberger
  Brewing Co.**
391 Inkerman St.
Melbourne
VIC
Tel 03 525 8000

**Grand Ridge
  Brewing Co.**
Main St.
Mirboo North
VIC 3871

Geelong Brewing Co.
Point Henry Rd.
Moolap
VIC 3221

Redback Brewery
75 Flemington Rd.
North Melbourne
VIC 3051

Bell's Hotel & Brewery
157 Moray St.
South Melbourne
VIC 3205
Tel 03 690 4511

Foster's Brewing Group
1 Garden St.
South Yarra
VIC 3141
Tel 03 828 2424
Fax 03 826 9310
Head office.

South Seas Brewery
478 Toorak Rd.
Toorak
VIC
Tel 03 826 1328

Places to Enjoy Beer

Young & Jackson's Hotel
1 Swanston St.
Melbourne
VIC

Mac's Hotel
Penda Rd.
Mount Gambier
VIC

Western Australia

Breweries

**Elizabethan Village Pub
& Brewery**
Canns Rs.
Armadale
WA
Tel 09 399 4537

Swan Brewery Co.
25 Baile Rd.
Canning Vale
WA 6155
Tel 09 350 0222
Fax 09 455 1138
G.P.O. Box 176D, Perth,
WA 6000.

Good on Yer
Freo
Fremantle
WA
Brewpub since 1952.

**The Sail & Anchor Pub
Brewery**
Esplanade
Fremantle
WA 6009
*English-style brewpub.
Occasional tours.*

Moonshine Brewery
Wildwood Rd.
Margaret River
WA 6285

Matilda Bay Brewing Co.
130 Stirling Hwy.
North Fremantle
WA 6159
Tel 09 430 6222
Fax 09 430 5344

Fremantle Brewing Co.
7 Blarney Pl.
O'Connor
WA 6163
Tel 09 337 7377
Fax 09 337 7069

Beer Sauce

1 pint lager	1 bayleaf
1 tsp vinegar	1 tsp butter
1 tsp brown sugar	2 tbsps potato flour
2 tbsps chopped onion	Cinnamon
1 clove garlic	Salt and pepper

Put beer into a pan with vinegar, sugar, onion, garlic, bayleaf, and cinnamon. Season with salt and pepper. Simmer for 15 minutes, then strain. Mix potato flour with a little cold water, add to the sauce, and cook until it thickens. Serve with baked fish.

— Swiss recipe

Elders International
72–82 Welshpool Rd.
Welshpool
WA 6106
Tel 09 472 2211

Margaret River
  Brewing Co.
c/o Sundance Store
Witchcliffe
WA 6286

Blarney Castle
Newcastle St.
North Perth
WA

New Zealand

Carlton & United
  Breweries
60 Khyber Pass Rd.
Auckland
Tel 09 309 3738
Fax 09 302 1813

Dominion Breweries
P.O. Box 1659
Auckland
*Also in Mangatainoka and
Timaru. DB Export Beer,
Lager, Dry Lager; DB
Draught Bitter Beer, Double
Brown Beer, Kiwi Lager.*

Independent Breweries
6 Lorian Pl.
E Tamaki
Auckland
*Labels: Nighthawk Dark Ale,
Panther Premium Lager,
Bighorn Blue.*

Mac's Brewhouse
Great South Rd.
Takanini
Auckland

The Malthouse
Auckland
Contact: Tod McCashin,
  brewmaster

Metro Brewery
13 Bruce McLaren Rd.
Henderson
Auckland

Newbegin Breweries
2 Miami Rd.
Te Papapa
Auckland
*Microbrewery. Labels: Old
Thumper Porter, Silver Fern
Natural Lager.*

New Zealand Breweries,
P.O. Box 23
Auckland
*Also in Christchurch,
Dunedin, Hastings, and
Wellington. Labels: Steinlager
NZ Lager Beer, Rheineck,
Blue Lager, Dry Beer, Lion
Red Beer.*

Shakespeare Tavern &
  Brewery
61 Albert St.
Auckland
*Labels: King Lear Old Ale,
Barraclough Lager, Falstaff's
Real Ale, Macbeth's Red Ale,
Willpower Stout.*

Stockan Brewery
P.O. Box 21–257
Henderson
Auckland

Tamstone Holdings
P.O. Box 76–467
Manukua City
Auckland

Three Crowns
  Brewing Co.
Studio X
Auckland
Contact: Rachel Wood,
  brewer
*Brewery in a movie theme
park promoted by Mickey
Rooney that includes a
restaurant, video games,
disco, rides, etc.*

The Loaded Hog
Christchurch

The Brewer's Arms
Ferrymead
Christchurch
*Brewpub. Labels: Merivale
Lager, Canterbury Ale, Classic
Dark.*

The Brewer's Arms
Merivale
Christchurch
*Brewpub. Labels: Merivale
Lager, Canterbury Ale, Classic
Dark.*

Canterbury Independent
  Brewers
Christchurch

Dux de Lux Tavern
P.O. Box 13–289
Christchurch
*Brewpub. Labels: De Luxe
Lager, Hereford Bitter, Blue
Duck Draught.*

Harrington's
Christchurch

Hororata Brewery
Hororata
Christchurch

Karmac Enterprises
Christchurch

Roc Mac
Merriville
Christchurch

Emerson's Brewery
Dunedin
Contact: Richard Emerson

Otago Brewery
P.O. Box 188
Dunedin

Speights Brewery
Dunedin
*Tours, free samples. Book
through the Visitors Center,
477-4176.*

Sunshine Brewing Co.
109 Disraeli St.
Gisborne
*Labels: Gisborne Gold, Bitter;
Sundowner, Moonshine Strong
Pilsener.*

Westland Breweries
Greymouth
*Labels: Monteith's Extra Bitter
Brown Beer.*

Pritz Investments
Hamilton

Settlers Brewing Co.
Henderson
*Microbrewery. Labels: Stockan
Draught Ale, Munich Lager.*

**Marlborough
  Brewing Co.**
Marlborough
*Microbrewery. Labels:
Marlborough Draught.*

Renwick Breweries
P.O. Box 10
Renwick
Marlborough

Burbridge's Brewery
Masterton

**McCashin's Brewery &
  Malthouse**
Nelson
Contact: Terry McCashin
Labels: Mac's Ale, Black Mac.

Pink Elephant Brewery
Nelson

Roc Mac
610 Main Rd.
Stoke
Nelson

Newman's Brewery
333 Frankton Rd.
Queenstown

White Cliffs Brewing Co.
RD 44
Uranui
Taranaki

Tauranga Brewing Co.
Tauranga

The Loaded Hog
Timaru

Anchor Brewing Co.
P.O. Box 50–477
Porirua
Wellington

The Loaded Hog
Wellington
*Brewpub. Live music Friday
and Saturday. Labels: Port
Nick Lager, Red Dog
Draught, Hogs Head Dark
Ale.*

**Parrot & Jigger Brewery
  Bistro Bar**
Wellington

Strongcroft Brewery
1 Jackson St.
Petona
Wellington

Places to Enjoy Beer
Twin Pines Tavern
Haruru Falls
Aaihia
*Good beer, good music, good
food, and great scenery.*

Cactus Jack's
96 Albert St.
Auckland
Tel 09 302 0942

London Bar
1 Wellesley St.
Auckland
Tel 09 373 3684

St. George Hotel
Willis and Boulcott Sts.
Wellington
Tel 04 473 9139

Retail Stores
Beer Essentials
O'Connell's Pavilion
Queenstown
*T-shirts, hats, etc. with various
Kiwi beer logos.*

CANADA

National Organizations

Importers of Beer

Magazines

Listings by Province

National Organizations

CAMRA Canada
1440 Ocean
Victoria
BC V8P 5K7
(604) 595-7728
Contact: John Rowling

**Brewing and Malting
  Barley Research**
206 167 Lombard Ave.
Winnipeg
MAN R3B 0T6

Importers of Beer

Imported Beer Co.
2410 Duncom Dr.
Missisauga
(905) 828-6288

**Premier Brands
  Beverage Importers**
101 Burnside Dr.
Toronto
(416) 588-7082

Stroh
1 Yonge St.
Toronto
(416) 366-7876

Magazines

Canada's Beer Magazine
102 Burlington Ct.
Ottawa
ONT K1T 3K5
(613) 737-3715
Contact: Mario D'Eer,
  Publisher
*Covers Canadian brewing,
micro and amateur. 4/year.*

What's Brewing
CAMRA
P.O. Box 2036
Station D
Ottawa
ONT K1P 5W3

Listings by Province

Entries are alphabetical by city.

Alberta

Alberta Tourism
10155 102nd St.
Edmonton
ALTA T5J 4L6
(800) 661-8888
*Tourist information, calendar
of events.*

Breweries

Big Rock Brewery
6403 35th St. SE
Calgary
(403) 279-2917

Drummond Brewing Co.
7016 30th St. SE
Calgary
(403) 236-5335

Molson Breweries
1892 15th St. SE
Calgary
(403) 233-1786

Labatt Alberta
P.O. Box 1818
Edmonton
ALTA T5J 2P2
(709) 579-0121
Fax (709) 578-2018

Drummond Brewing Co.
2210 50th Ave.
Red Deer
ALTA T4R 1W5
(403) 347-6633

Brewpubs

**Brewsters Brewpub &
Brasserie**
834 11th Ave. SW
Calgary
(403) 261-2739
Brewpub and restaurant.

Brewsters Brewpub #2
176 755 Lake Bonavista Dr.
SE
Calgary
(403) 225-2739

Places to Enjoy Beer

**Bottlescrew Bill's Old
English Pub**
First St. and 10th Ave. SW
Calgary
ALTA
*Large beer selection including
Big Rock on draught.*

Fox & Hounds Pub
7304 Macleod Tr. S
Calgary
(403) 258-2553

North Centre Inn
1621 Centre St. NW
Calgary
(403) 230-5950

Olde Manor Pub
11213 30th St. SW
Calgary
(403) 251-2029

Bryan's Pub
12904 97th St.
Edmonton
(403) 457-4633
Fax (403) 457-4634

Mickey Finn's Tap House
10511A 82nd Ave., 2nd
Floor
Edmonton
(403) 439-9852

Retail Stores

Beer Land
415 Fourth Ave. SE
Calgary
(403) 266-3344

La Beer Store
3620 17th Ave. SE
Calgary
(403) 235-0414

Liquor Barn
4880 32nd Ave. NW
Calgary
(403) 296-0740

OK Liquor Store
Bay H
3515 32nd St. NE
Calgary
(403) 250-1502

Royal Liquor Merchants
526 Fourth Ave. SW
Calgary
(403) 531-2770

Wine Cottage
319 4625 Varsity Dr. NW
Calgary
(403) 247-8900
Fax (403) 247-8900

Chateau Louis
11727 Kingsway
Edmonton
(403) 452-BEER

Southpark Liquor
174 3803 Calgary Trail S
Edmonton
(403) 437-BEER
Fax (403) 437-1534

**Yellowhead Cold Beer
Outlet**
15030 Yellowhead Trail
Edmonton
(403) 447-2691

British Columbia

**Tourism British
Columbia**
Parliament Bldgs.
Victoria
BC V8V 1X4
(800) 663-6000
*Tourist information, calendar
of events.*

CAMRA Victoria
P.O. Box 30101
Saanich Center Post Outlet
Victoria
BC V8X 5E1
(604) 386-2818
Magazine: *What's Brewing*
(Victoria).

Breweries

Columbia Brewing Co.
1220 Erickson
P.O. Box 1950
Creston
BC V0B 1GO
(604) 428-9344
Fax (604) 428-3433

**Horshoe Bay
  Brewing Co.**
6695 Nelson Ave.
Horshoe Bay
BC

Nelson Brewing Co.
512 Latimer St.
Nelson
BC V1L 4T9
(604) 352-3582
Fax (604) 354-1242
*Group tours by appointment
only.*

**Bowen Island
  Brewing Co.**
Bowen Island
North Vancouver
(604) 947-0822

Steveston Brewing Co.
3131 Chatham
Richmond
BC

**Granville Island Brewing
  Co.1**
1441 Cartwright St.
Granville Island
Vancouver
BC V6H 3R7
(604) 688-9927
Fax (604) 685-0504
*Free tasting tours daily, call
for reservations. Store with
beer, wines, and gift items.*

Anthony Mark Group
1290 Homer St.
Vancouver
BC V6B 2Y5
(604) 687-2444
Fax (604) 687-7555

**Pacific Western
  Brewing Co.**
3454 Loughead Hwy.
Vancouver
BC V5M 2A4
(604) 255-2510
Fax (604) 255-5077
*Tours and tastings daily.
Retail store open 11AM to
6PM.*

Shaftesbury Brewing Co.
1973 Pandora St.
Vancouver
BC V5L 5B2
(604) 255-4550
Fax (604) 255-8213
*Tours Monday to Friday or by
appointment, tastings. T-shirts
etc. for sale.*

**Okanagan Spring
  Brewery**
2801 27A Ave.
P.O. Box 1660
Vernon
(604) 542-2337

**Vancouver Island
  Brewing Co.**
Unit 4
 6809 Kirkpatrick Center
Victoria
BC V8X 3X1
(604) 652-4722
Fax (604) 652-5238
*Tours and tastings, end of
week is best. Retail store open
Monday to Friday, some
Saturdays in summer.*

Whistler Brewery
1209 Alpha Lake Rd.
Whistler
(604) 932-6185

Brewpubs

Sailor Hagar's Pub
235 W First St.
North Vancouver
(604) 984-7669

**Prairie Inn Cottage
  Brewery**
7806 E Saanich Rd.
Saaitchton
(604) 652-1575

Spinnakers Brewpub
308 Catherine St.
Victoria
BC V9A 3S8
(604) 386-BREW
Fax (604) 384-3246
*Lunch and dinner, brewery
tours, live afternoon and
evening entertainment, dart
boards. Great view of Lime
Bay.*

Swans Hotel, Pub & Cafe
506 Pandora Ave.
Victoria
BC V8W 1K8
(604) 361-3310
Fax (604) 361-3491
*Hotel, with restaurant, pub,
and Buckerfield's Brewery
right on the premises, brewing
traditional ales. Tours
available by appointment.*

Cider Manufacturer

Wyder's Cider
Richmond
(603) 778-1737
Contact: Iain Wyder
*Dry Draft and Traditional
English ciders, Dry Pear and
Dry Peach.*

Places to Enjoy Beer

Fogg n Suds
7090 Lougheed Hwy.
Burnaby
(604) 421-7837

Mountain Shadow
7174 Barnett Dr.
Burnaby
(604) 291-9322

Stone's Throw
1601 Burnwood Ave.
Burnaby
(604) 421-1092

John B
1001 Austin Ave.
Cocuitlam
(604) 931-5515

Two Parrots
170 Golden
Cocuitlam

Delta Lion
11161 84th Ave.
Delta
(604) 591-2111

Sundowner
1970A 64th Ave.
Delta
(604) 591-7974

Witch of Endor
22648 Dewdney Tpke. Rd.
Maple Ridge
(604) 467-5355

Jolly Alderman
500 W 12th
Vancouver
(604) 873-8111

Rose & Thorn
757 Richards
Vancouver
(604) 683-2821

Squires Four
6301 Sickle Rd.
Vernon
(604) 549-2144

Barley Mow Inn
2581 Penryhn
Victoria
(604) 477-4712

Black's Pub
Whistler
(604) 932-6945

Festivals

Octoberfest
German Canadian Club
Evergreen
Chilliwack
(604) 858-1701
Early October.

October Festival
Platzl
Kimberley
(604) 427-3666
Early October, 3 days.

Octoberfest
Lake la Hache
(604) 395-5353
October, Saturdays.

Bavarian Fest
Edgemont Village
North Vancouver
(604) 988-6328
Mid-September.

**International
    Brewmasters' Festival**
Enterprise Hall
Expo '86 site
Vancouver
(604) 732-3377
*Early August. Breweries from
Canada, Pacific NW, and CA.*

Oktoberfest
Commodore Ballroom
Vancouver
(604) 925-3333
Mid-October, 2 weekends.

**Victoria Microbrewery
    Festival**
Conference Center
720 Douglas St.
Victoria
(604) 595-7729
Contact: CAMRA Victoria
*Late October. Canadian and
U.S. micros.*

Oktoberfest
Whistler Village/Conference
    Center
Whistler
(604) 932-2394
Mid-October, 4 days.

Oktoberfest
Various locations
Williams Lake
(604) 392-7204
October.

Manitoba

Manitoba Tourism
#104
1670 Portage Ave.
Winnipeg
MAN R3J 0C9
(204) 774-8406
*Tourist information, calendar
of events.*

Travel Manitoba
7–155 Carlton St.
Winnipeg
MAN R3C 3H8
(204) 945-3796
Fax (204) 945-2302
*Events calendar, travel
information.*

Breweries

Labatt Manitoba
1660 Notre Dame
P.O. Box 776
Winnipeg
MAN R3C 2N3
(204) 697-5100
Fax (204) 632-9088

Molson Breweries
77 Redwood Ave.
Winnipeg
(204) 586-8011
Fax (204) 586-4853

Places to Enjoy Beer

Bailey's
185 Lombard Ave.
Winnipeg
(204) 944-1180

Carlos & Murphy's
129 Osborne St.
Winnipeg
(204) 284-3510
Mexican food.

Eastside Exchange
177 Lombard Ave.
Winnipeg
(204) 943-2368

Prairie Oyster Cafe
The Forks Market
Winnipeg
(204) 942-0918
Eclectic menu.

The Round Table
800 Pembina Hwy.
Winnipeg
(204) 453-3631
*Restaurant like an English
pub, serving shepherd's pie,
plowman's lunch, etc.*

Stars Bar & Grill
169 McDermott Ave.
Winnipeg
Live music some nights.

Tap & Grill
137 Osborne St.
Winnipeg
(204) 284-7455

Toad in the Hole
112 Osborne St.
Winnipeg
(204) 284-7201
*Selection of imports, pub grub.
Toad in the hole translates
into French as crapaud dans
le trou. Feel any better?*

New Brunswick

Tourism New Brunswick
P.O. Box 12345
Fredericton
NB E3B 5C3
(800) 561-0123
*Tourist information, calendar
of events.*

Breweries

Moosehead Breweries
49 Main St.
St. John
NB E2M 3H2
(506) 635-7000
Contact: the Oland family
*Canada's oldest independent
brewery (1867). Tours by
appointment. Store open
Monday to Saturday.*

Places to Enjoy Beer

River Room
659 Queen
Fredericton
(506) 455-3371

Fat Frank's Bar
58 Festival
Moncton
(506) 532-5952

Callahan's Sports Bar
122 Prince William
St. John
(506) 634-0366

Of Historic Interest

Bell Inn
Rt. 6
Village Square
Dorchester
(506) 379-6237
Historic site.

Newfoundland

**Newfoundland/Labrador
  Tourism**
P.O. Box 8730
St. John's
NFLD A1B 4K2
(800) 563-6353
*Tourist information, calendar
of events.*

Breweries

Labatt Newfoundland
Leslie St.
St. John's
NFLD A1E 3Y4
(709) 579-0121

Molson Newfoundland
131 Circular Rd.
St. John's
NFLD A1C 5W1
(709) 726-1786

Places to Enjoy Beer

Bartlett's Landing
P.O. Box 239
Middle Ridge Rd.
Brigus
NFLD A0A 1K0
(709) 528-1019
Fax (709) 528-1603
*Victorian restaurant and
village pub.*

Erin's Pub
184 Water
St. John's
(709) 722-1916

**Trapper John's Museum
& Pub**
2 George
St. John's
(709) 579-9630

Windsock Lounge
161 Water
St. John's
(709) 722-5001

Nova Scotia

Nova Scotia Tourism
P.O. Box 130
Halifax
NS B3J 2M7
(800) 565-0000
*Tourist information, calendar
of events.*

Breweries

Keith's Brewery
3055 Agricola Way
Halifax
NS B3K 4G2
(902) 455-1474

Moosehead Brewery
656 Windmill Rd.
Halifax
(902) 468-7040
Tours June 14 to August 27,

*Monday to Friday, 11AM and
1PM, holidays excluded.*

Oland Breweries
3055 Agricola Way
Halifax
NS B3K 4G2
(902) 453-1867

Granite Brewery
1222 Barrington St.
Halifax
(902) 423-5660
English-style brewpub.

Places to Enjoy Beer

Elbow Room Pub
1725 Market
Halifax
(902) 425-8696

Lawrence of Oregano
1726 Argyle
Halifax
(902) 422-6907

Midtown Tavern & Grill
Grafton
Halifax
(902) 422-5213

Split Crow Pub
1855 Granville
Halifax
(902) 422-4366

Bottoms Up Pub & Grill
252 Commercial St.
N Sydney
Cape Breton Island
(902) 794-7149

Blaster's Lounge
126 Main St.
Sydney Mines
Cape Breton Island
(902) 736-2365

Old Orchard Inn
Box 1090
Wolfville
NS B0P 1X0

Retail Stores

**Moosehead Cold Beer
Store**
650 Windmill Rd.
Halifax
(902) 468-2337

**Moosehead Country
Store**
1645 Barrington St.
Halifax
NS B3J 1Z9
(902) 422-5353
Moosehead collectibles.

Northwest
Territories

**Northwest Territories
Tourism**
Box 1320
Yellowknife
NT X1A 2L9
(800) 661-0788
Fax (403) 873-0294
*Tourist information, calendar
of events.*

Breweries

Arctic Brewing Co.
3502 Wiley
Yellowknife
NT X1A 2L5
(403) 920-2739
Fax (403) 920-BEER
Bush Pilots' Brewpub.

Places to Enjoy Beer

Nahanni Inn
Box 248
Ft. Simpson
NT X0E 0N0
(403) 695-2201
Fax (403) 695-3000

Ed's Place
Box 1612
Hay River
NT X0E 0R0
(403) 984-3181

Mackenzie Hotel
Box 1618
Inuvik
NT X0E 0T0
(403) 979-2861
Fax (403) 979-3317
Pub with entertainment.

Nanook Lounge
Eskimo Inn
Box 1740
Inuvik
NT X0E 0T0
(403) 979-2801
Fax (403) 979-3234

Bayshore Hotel
Bldg. 1060
Box 1240
Iqaluit
NT X0A 0H0
(819) 979-4210
Fax (819) 979-4210

Nanuq Inn
Box 175
Rankin Inlet
NT X0C 0G0
(819) 645-2513

Ontario

Ontario Travel
Queen's Park
Toronto
ONT M7A 2E5
(800) 668-2746
Tourist information, calendar of events.

Breweries

Labatt Hull
250 Deveault
Hull
(613) 777-5050

Labatt Breweries
London
ONT N6A 4M3

Labatt
60 Bristol Rd. E
Mississauga
(905) 568-0662

Labatt Breweries
181 Bay St., #200
P.O. Box 786
Toronto
ONT M5J 2T3
(416) 361-5294
Fax (416) 361-5197

Labatt Ontario
50 Resources Rd.
Toronto
(416) 248-0751

Molson Breweries
175 Bloor St. E
North Tower
Toronto
ONT M4W 3S4
(416) 975-1786
Fax (416) 966-6136

Hart Breweries
175 Industrial Ave.
Carleton Place
(613) 253-4278

Creemore Springs Brewery
Creemore
(705) 466-2531

Great Lakes Brewing Co.
Etobicoke
(416) 451-0073

Algonquin Brewery
Formosa
ONT

Sleeman Brewing & Malting Co.
551 Clair Rd. W
Guelph
ONT N1H 6H9
(519) 822-1834

Wellington County Brewery
55 Clair Rd. W
Guelph
(519) 837-2337
Tours by appointment. Arkell Best Bitter, County, Iron Duke, Imperial Stout.

Lakeport Brewing Corp.
201 Burlington St. E
Hamilton
(416) 360-5653
Contact: Bill Sharpe, President
Master Choice Cold Filtered Pilsener and Strong Cold Filtered Pilsener.

Glatt Bros. Brewing Co.
London

Hometowne Breweries
1 Adelaide N
London
(519) 432-1344

Thames Valley Brewing Co.
1764 Oxford E
London
(519) 457-2023

**Canadian National
  Brewers**
7030 Woodbine Ave., #500
Markham
ONT L3R 1A2
(416) 475-0139
Fax (416) 889-8890

Angel Brewing Co.
6 Queen W
Mississauga
(905) 274-9662

Conners Brewing Co.
6 Owen St. W
Mississauga
ONT

Firkin Brewing Co.
100 Matheson Blvd. E
Mississauga
ONT

Choice Brewing
6 Bexley Pl.
Nepean
(613) 829-5617

**Niagara Falls
  Brewing Co.**
6863 Lundy's Ln.
Niagara Falls
(416) 374-1166
Tours available.

Trafalgar Brewing Co.
Oakville
Contact: Mike Arnold

Conners Brewing Co.
1335 Lawrence Ave. E
St. Catherines
(416) 449-6101

Northern Breweries
P.O. Box 280
Sault Ste. Marie
ONT P6A 5L0
(705) 254-7375
Fax (705) 254-4482

**Upper Canada
  Brewing Co.**
2 Atlantic Ave.
Toronto
(416) 534-9281
Fax (416) 534-6998
Tours available.

Victoria St. Brewery
Victoria St.
Toronto
ONT M4W 3S4

Brick Brewing Co.
181 King St. S
Waterloo
(519) 576-9100
Fax (519) 576-0470
Tours by appointment.

Canada's Finest Beers
Wheatley

Brewpubs

Lighthouse Brewpub
Bowmanville

Tracks Brewpub
Brampton

**Elora Brewing/Taylor &
  Bate**
Elora

**Marconi's Steak & Pasta
  House**
Etobicoke

**Heidelberg Restaurant &
  Brewery**
P.O. Box 116
Heidelberg

Kingston Brewing Co.
34 Clarence St.
Kingston
Dragon's Breath Ale.

**The Lion Brewery
  Museum & Brewpub**
59 King St. N
Kitchener
(519) 886-3350

CC's Brewpub
6981 Millcreek Dr.
Meadowvale
London
(519) 542-0136

CEEPS Barney's
671 Richmond
London
(519) 432-1425

Blue Anchor Brewery
Orillia

The Master's Brewpub
Queen St.
Ottawa

**Port Arthur Brasserie &
  Brewpub**
901 Red River Ave.
Thunder Bay
(807) 767-4415

**Amsterdam Brasserie &
  Brewpub**
133 John St.
Toronto
(416) 595-8201
Open daily.

C'Est What?
67 Front St. at 19 Church
Toronto
ONT M5E 1BS
(416) 867-9499
*Pub, club, and cafe. Twenty
local brews on tap. Live music.*

Denison's Brewing Co.
75 Victoria St.
Toronto
(416) 360-5877
And Growler's Restaurant.

Granite Brewery
245 Eglington E
Toronto
(416) 322-0723

James Gate
Toronto

O'Toole's
1189 King W
Toronto
(416) 534-3666

Quinn's on the Danforth
Toronto

Rotterdam Brewing Co.
600 King St. W
Toronto
(416) 868-6882
Brewpub and restaurant.
Rotating selection of house
brews plus 250 bottles, 28
taps.

Spruce Goose Brewing
Co.
130 Eglington E
Toronto
(416) 485-4121

Tapster's Brewhouse &
Restaurant
100 Brittania Rd. E
Toronto

Union Station Brewpub
Toronto

Vinefera Bar & Grille
150 Eglington E
Toronto
(416) 487-9281

Winchester Brew Pub
255 Dundas St. W
Toronto

Charley's Tavern
Windsor

U-Brew Stores

A rapidly growing phenomenon, caused
in part by high liquor taxes. You brew
your own beer, but on their premises.
Ingredients are purchased from the
store, which also offers advice and takes
care of some of the brewing processes.
The store becomes something of a social
scene, as people swap recipes, etc.

Midtown U-Brew
151 Thompson
London
(519) 668-6203

Mr. Beer U-Brew
1072 Hyde Park Rd.
Hyde Park
London
(519) 657-1302

Mr. Beer U-Brew
1560 Dundas
London
(519) 457-6744

Dundas Custom Brewery
1825 Dundas St. E, #12
Missisauga
(905) 629-2739

The Brew Store
780 Burnhamthorpe Way
Mississauga
(905) 270-4677

Greensides & Sons
3075 Ridgeway, #25
Mississauga
(905) 607-2337

Brewing Station
2400 Bank
Ottawa
(613) 736-0121

U B Brewmaster
883 Tungsten St.
Thunder Bay
(807) 344-2337

Brewmore's Natural
Brewery
618 Gordon Baker
Toronto
(416) 490-6868

Select Brewing Services
85 Mowat
Toronto
(416) 531-2013

York Towne U-Brew
1335 Lawrence Ave.
Toronto
(416) 510-1010

Places to Enjoy Beer

Chester's
60 King St. E
Hamilton
Large selection of imports.

The Pilot House
King and Johnson Sts.
Kingston
Pub and restaurant. Draught
imports.

The Wellington
Wellington St.
Kingston
Pub and restaurant. Occa-
sional live entertainment.

York Tavern
24 Kent St. W
Lindsay

Blue Cactus Bar & Grill
2 Byward
Ottawa
(613) 238-7061

Mayflower II
201 Queen
Ottawa
(613) 238-1138

Rasputin's
696 Bronson Ave.
Ottawa
(613) 230-5102
Restaurant and bar.

Allen's Bar & Restaurant
143 Danforth Ave.
Toronto
Restaurant and bar.

Bow & Arrow
1954 Yonge St.
Toronto
Wellington County on draught.

Diplomat Tavern
3622 Dufferin St.
Toronto
(416) 635-6163

Duke of Kent
2315 Yonge St.
Toronto
Pub restaurant.

The Feathers
962 Kingston Rd.
Toronto
Serves Publican Ale from Upper Canada Brewery.

Horseshoe Tavern
368 Queen St. W
Toronto
ONT M5V 2A3
(416) 598-4753

Trotters
244 Adelaide St. W
Toronto
Pub with restaurant upstairs.

Atlas Hotel
35 Southworth St. N
Welland

Retail Stores

Premium Beer Co.
3131 Pepper Mill Ct.
Mississauga
(905) 828-6288
Ale, cider, lager.

Prince Edward Island

Prince Edward Island Tourism
P.O. Box 940
Charlottetown
PEI C1A 7M5
(800) 565-0267
Tourist information, calendar of events.

Quebec

Tourisme Quebec
P.O. Box 20
000
Quebec City
QUE G1K 4Y3
(800) 363-7777
Tourist information, calendar of events.

Association des Brasseurs de Quebec
1981 av. McGill College
Montreal
QUE H3A 2W9
(514) 284-9199
Fax (514) 294-0817
Contact: Yvon Millette, President
Quebec Brewers Association.

Breweries

Brasseries Labatt
50 Labatt
Montreal
(514) 366-5050

Unibroue
80 des Carrieres
Chambly
QUE J3L 2H6
(514) 658-2838
Contact: Andre Dion
Refermented beer.

Golden Lion Brewery
P.O. Box 474
Lennoxville
QUE J1M 1Z6
(819) 562-4589

La Brasserie Broubec
33 Windsor
Lennoxville
(819) 564-2441

Brasal Brasserie Allemande
8477 rue Cordner
Lasalle
Montreal
QUE H8N 2N2
(514) 365-5050
Fax (514) 365-2954

Les Brasseurs GMT
5710 Garnier
Montreal
QUE H2G 2Z7
(514) 274-4941

La Brasserie McAuslan
4850 St Ambroise, #100
Montreal
QUE H4C 3N8
(514) 939-3060
Fax (514) 939-6136
Tours Wednesday evening and occasional other times. Call for information.

Brasserie Molson O'Keefe
1555 Norte Dame E
Montreal
(514) 521-1786

**La Brasserie
  Portneuvoise**
225 rue Hardy
St. Casimir
QUE G0A 3L0
(418) 339-3242

Les Brasseurs du Nord
18 Kennedy, #3
St. Jerome
QUE J7Y 4B4
(514) 438-9060

Brewpubs

Mon Village Brewery
Hudson

La Cervoise
4457 St. Laurent
Montreal
843-6586
Brewpub and restaurant.

Le Cheval Blanc
809 Ontario St. E
Montreal

Le Crocodile
5414 Gatineau St.
Montreal

La Taverne du Sergeant
Montreal

L'Inox
37 rue St-Andre
Vieux-Port
Quebec
QUE G1K 8T3
(418) 692-2877
*European-style hot dogs. Free
parking at night.*

Places to Enjoy Beer

Zuma's Cantina
1130 blvd. Maloney
Gatineau
(819) 246-0325
Tex-Mex food.

Aux Quatre Jeudis
44 rue Laval
Hull
(819) 771-9557

Brasserie les Raftsmen
60 St.-Raymond
Hull
(819) 777-0924

**La Maison des Bieres
  Importees**
1418 Cartier
Montreal
Domestic and imports. Food.

Berthelot Bistro
1135 rue Berthelot
Quebec
QUE G1R 3G2
(418) 649-1806
*Restaurant, imported beers.
Terrace garden.*

Moss Bistro Belge
255 rue St.-Paul
Quebec
QUE G1K 3W5
(418) 692-0233
*Belgian cuisine, imported
beers.*

St. Alexandre Pub
1087 rue St.-Jean
Quebec
QUE G1R 1S3
(418) 694-0015
*Two hundred domestic and
imported beers, Twenty taps.
English style pub with meals.*

Turf Pub
1179 av. Cartier
Quebec
QUE G1R 2S1
(418) 522-9955
*Open daily. English-style pub,
smoked meats, darts. Imported
beers.*

Le Village Pump
801 3rd Ave.
Quebec
(418) 649-8577

Manhattan Grill
2635 blvd. Hochelaga
Ste.-Foy
QUE G1V 4T3
(418) 657-1670
*Large selection of draught
and bottled beers.*

Brasserie Olympique
2700 blvd. Laurier
Ste.-Foy
QUE G1V 2L8
(418) 658-6373
*Restaurant with French
cuisine and draught beer.*

Saskatchewan

Tourism Saskatchewan
1919 Saskatchewan Dr.
Regina
SASK S4P 3V7
(800) 667-7191
*Tourist information, calendar
of events.*

**Saskatchewan Brewers
  Association**
380 Dewdrey Ave. E
P.O. Box 3057
Regina
SASK S4P 3G7
(306) 525-0377
Fax (306) 352-3574
Contact: Larry Kitz, GM

Breweries

Labatt Saskatchewan
1401 Herman Ave.
Saskatoon
(306) 653-1611

Molson Breweries
6–701 Second Ave. N
Saskatoon
(306) 653-7976
Fax (306) 652-7900

Canadian Brewery
P.O. Box 7541
Saskatoon
SASK S7K 4L4

**Great Western
  Brewing Co.**
519 Second Ave. N
Saskatoon
SASK S7K 2C6
(306) 653-4653
Fax (306) 653-2166

Brewpubs

Brewsters Brewpub #3
Cornerstone Inn
Moose Jaw.

Bonzzini's Brewpub
4634 Albert St.
Regina
(306) 586-3553

Barley Mill Brewing Co.
6807 Rochdale Blvd.
Regina
(306) 949-1500

**Brewsters Brewpub &
  Brasserie #1**
1832 Victoria Ave. E
Regina
(306) 761-1500

Bushwakker Brewing Co.
Strathdee Mall
Regina
(306) 359-7276

The Last Straw
127 Albert St. N
Regina
(306) 543-3311

**Cheers Brewpub &
  Restaurant**
32–2105 Eighth St. E
Saskatoon
SASK S7K 0T8
(306) 955-7500
Fax (306) 955-8144
*Cajun and Italian specialties,
smoked prime rib.*

**Clark's Crossing
  Brewpub**
3030 Diefenbacker Rd.
Saskatoon
(306) 384-6633

**Fox & Hounds Pub &
  Brewery**
Canarama Shopping Center
Saskatoon
(306) 664-2233

Saskatoon Brewing Co.
32–2105 Eighth St. E
Saskatoon
(306) 955-7500
Fax (306) 955-8144

**MacBradee's Brewing
  Co.**
Swift Current

Places to Enjoy Beer

Elephant & Castle
Midtown Plaza
Saskatoon
(306) 652-5535
*Authentic British pub and
restaurant.*

Retail Stores

All alcoholic beverages are sold in
government liquor stores.

Festivals

Indoor Rodeo
Delisle Arena
Delisle
(306) 493-8283

*Late May, 2 days. Rodeo
events, beer gardens, dance,
roast beef supper.*

**Coors Country Band
  Stand**
Dinsmore
(306) 846-4511
*Early August. Six Sask bands
compete. Beer, food, dance
floor.*

**Great Western Country
  Bandstand**
Grenfel
(306) 697-2815
*Top six Sask bands compete.
Dancing, concessions, beer
garden.*

Sommerfest
Humboldt
(306) 682-3444
*Late June, 3 days. German-
style festivities: parade, art
show, bierfest.*

Indian Head Rodeo
Indian Head
(306) 695-2687
*Early June, 2 days. Rodeo
with parade, dance, midway,
beer garden.*

Fair Days
Lanigan
(306) 365-3444
*Mid-June, 2 days. Sports,
horse show, beer garden,
fireworks, more.*

Summer Fair
Melville
(306) 728-5277
*Mid-June, 2 days. Horse-
racing, rodeo, midway,
dances, beer garden, more.*

Sports Day & Rodeo
Sturgis
(306) 548-2050
*Early July. Rodeo, midway,
sports, music, beer gardens.*

Frontier City Stampede
Swift Current
(306) 773-2944
*Late May, 4 days. Rodeo
events, cabaret, casino, beer
garden, arts and crafts.*

Yukon Territory

Yukon Tourism
P.O. Box 2703
Whitehorse
YT Y1A 2C6
(403) 667-5340
Fax (403) 667-2634
Information on the Yukon.

Places to Enjoy Beer

Eagle Plains Hotel
Bag Service 2735
Whitehorse
YT Y1A 3V5
(403) 979-4187

Sam 'N' Andy's
506 Main St.
Whitehorse
(403) 668-6994
Mexican bar and grill.

Yukon Inn
4220 Fourth Ave.
Whitehorse
YT Y1A 1K1
(403) 667-2527
Fax (403) 668-7643

Excerpts from *The French Paradox & Drinking for Health*

À *votre santé. Prost. Skoal. L'Chayim.* There is hardly a language in the world in which drinking is not linked with good fortune and long life. Despite the universality of its abuse, drinking symbolizes good health and longevity in the folklore and poetry of most nations.

A *60 Minutes* airing of the "French Paradox" suggested an answer to the riddle of how the French people could eat foods thought harmful to the heart and sustain low rates of heart disease. The answer suggested was the consumption of alcohol.

[There is] a profound and extensive body of research that attests that moderate drinking itself can contribute to good heart health, to a lessening of other diseases, and that drinking can and does contribute to general well-being. The real "drinking problem" is the myth of *demon rum* [America's] 200-year-old distorted way of looking at one of nature's blessings — potable alcohol.

There is no question that alcohol abuse is both universal and persistent. Yet there is very little meaningful research about moderate drinking. Drinking today is perceived and discussed only in negative terms.

Moderate drinkers know that their drinking habits are not harmful. What they lack are official sources of information on the specific benefits from a health viewpoint. The positive data are out there, but the coalition of an overcautious government and a highly vocal private advocacy [against drinking] make it difficult for doctors and other health authorities to endorse moderate drinking — or even to be positive about the practice.

Drinking must once again be valued in America for what it gives as well as what it takes.

— Gene Ford

Gene Ford, editor of The Moderation Reader, *campaigns on behalf of the moderate drinker against those in government and elsewhere who would see drinking alcohol rated alongside using illegal drugs.*

CENTRAL AND SOUTH AMERICA AND THE CARIBBEAN

Listings by Country

Antigua

Places to Enjoy Beer

Admiral's Inn
Nelson's Dockyard
English Harbour
Tel 0 1027
C17 setting.

English Bar
The Inn
English Harbour
Tel (809) 460-1014
Fax (809) 460-1603

Big Banana Holding Co.
Redcliffe Quay
St. John's
Tel 2 2621
Pizza joint with cheap beer.

Argentina

Chamber of Tourism
Tucuman 1610
Buenos Aires
Tel 40-5108
Tourist information.

Enatur
Santa Fe 883
Buenos Aires
Tel 312-2232
Central information office.
Tourist information.

Breweries

Cerveceria Bieckert
Antartida Agrentina 1851
Loberia Buenos Aires 1836

Cerveceria Quilmas
 Saicaq
12 de Oct y Gran Canaraia
Ramallo Buenos Aires 1878

Cerveceria Santa Fe
The Gral J de Peron 949
Buenos Aires 1038

Places to Enjoy Beer

Pizzeria Guerrin
Avda Corrientes 1372
Buenos Aires
Pizza and beer.

Cerveceria Modelo
Calles 4 and 5
La Plata
Good cerveza tirada (lager type beer).

Cafe del Consejo
Mitre
Salta
Cheap lager beer.

Un Rincon de Napoli
Rivadavia 175 Sur
San Juan
Pizzeria with good beer.

Aruba

Places to Enjoy Beer

Balashi Bar
85 Lloyd G. Smith Blvd.
Palm Beach
Tel 8 31234

Bunker Bar
64 Lloyd G. Smith Blvd.
Palm Beach
Tel 8 24150

Charlie's Bar
Veen Zeppenveldstraat 56
San Nicolas
Tel 45086

Brisas del Mar
Savaneta
47718

Bahamas

Brewery

Commonwealth Brewery
Southwest Rd.
Nassau
Kalik brand.

Places to Enjoy Beer

Harry's American Bar
Deadman's Reef

Brittania Pub
Kings Rd.
Bell Channel
Freeport
Tel (809) 373-5919

Prince of Wales
Ranfurly Circus
Freeport

Pusser's Co. Pub
Port Lucaya Marketplace
Freeport

Barbados

Banks Breweries
Wildey St. Michael
Tel (809) 429 2113

Places to Enjoy Beer

Ship Inn
St. Lawrence Gap
Christ Church
Tel (809) 435-6961
*Bar food, live music, darts,
nautical memorabilia.*

TGI Boomers
St. Lawrence Gap
Christ Church
Tel (809) 428-8439

Cricketers Pub
St. James

Belize

Belize Tourist Information Association
Box 62
99 Albert St.
Belize City
Tel 2-75717
Fax 2-78007
Tourist information.

Breweries

Belize Brewing Co.
1 King St.
P.O. Box 1066
Belize City

Places to Enjoy Beer

Lindbergh's Landing
162A Newtown Barracks
Belize City
Tel 02 30-890

Lumba Yaad Bar & Grill
Mile 1
Northern Hwy.
Belize City
Tel 2-44068
*Belizian BBQ; live music
weekends.*

Marin's Bar & Restaurant
Caye Caulker
Cayes

Jene's Restaurant & Bar
on the beach
Placencia

Belbrit Restaurant & Bar
30A Burns Ave.
San Ignacio
*Belizian and British food and
drink.*

Eva's Restaurant & Bar
22 Burns Ave.
San Ignacio
Tel 092 22-67

Red Rooster
2 Far West St.
San Ignacio
Tel 092 30-16

Sandals
Barrier Reef Dr.
San Pedro

Bermuda

Bermuda Department of Tourism
Global Ho
43 Church St.
P.O. Box HM 465
Hamilton HM BX
Tourist information: Tel U.S.
(800) 223-6106; Canada
(416) 923-9600; UK 071-
734 8813

Places to Enjoy Beer

Woody's
Boaz Island

The Docksider
123 Front St.
Hamilton

Hog Penny
5 Burnaby Hill
Hamilton

Ye Olde Cock & Feather
27 Front St.
Hamilton

Ram's Head Inn
91 Reid St.
Hamilton

Robin Hood Pub
Richmond Rd.
Pembroke
Hamilton

Rum Runners
60 Front St.
Hamilton

Black Horse Tavern
St. David's Rd.
St. David's

Clyde's Cafe & Bar
York St.
St. George's

Somers Pub on the Square
King's Square
St. George's

Wharf Tavern
14 Water St
St. George's

White Horse Tavern
Market Wharf
St. George's

Charing Cross Tavern
Somerset Village
Sandys

Loyalty Inn
Sandys

Somerset Country Squire
10 Mangrove Bay Rd.
Sandys
Three draught beers.

Henry VIII Pub
S Shore Rd.
Southampton

Bolivia

Instituto Boliviano de Tourismo
Ed Ballivian
Calle Mercado
Casilla 186
La Paz
Tel 367 463
Fax 374-630
Tourist information, city maps, calendar of events.

Breweries

Cerveceria Taquina
C Columbus 578
Casilla 494
Cochabamba
Tours available, restaurant at weekends.

Cerveceria Boliviana Nacional
Calla Chuquisaca 421
Casilla 421
La Paz 491

Places to Enjoy Beer

El Socavon
Av. 20 de Oct 2174
La Paz

La Cueva Bar
Calle Mexico
La Paz

Matheus
Calle Guachalla
La Paz
Jazz pub.

Bar el Tapekua
corner Calles Balliviant and
La Paz
Santa Cruz
Tel 343390

Tijuana Saloon
Velardi 230
Santa Cruz

Bonaire
Places to Enjoy Beer
Karel's Beach Bar
Waterfront

Zeezicht Bar
Kaya Corsow
Tel 8434

Brazil
Breweries
Cervejaria de Brasilia
Rod BR-060 s/n Km 12
CEP 77100 Anapolis GO
Tel (062)321 0655

Xingu Brewery
Cacador Sta Catarina
Xingu is a black lager beer.

Cervejaria Kaiser Minas
Av. R Noronha Guarany
2000
Icarai
CEP 35500 Divinopolis MG
Tel (037) 214 1355
Fax (037) 214 1311

Cervejaria Astra
R des Lauro Nogueira 1353
Papico
CEP 60155 Fortaleza CE
Tel (085) 234 1133
Fax (085) 234 1997

Cervejaria Serramalte
R Alexndre Bramatte 673
CEP 20550 Getulio Vargas
RS
Tel (054) 341 1100
Fax (054) 341 1162

Cervejaria Brahma de
Sao Paolo
Estr do Jaguare s/n Km 12
Pag Andrade
CEP 12300 Jacarei SP
Tel (0123) 51 4211
Fax (0123) 51 9766

Cervejaria Miranda
Correa
R Com A Amorim 26
Aparecida
CEP 69007 Manaus AM
Tel (092) 622 3274
Fax (092) 622 1795

Cervejaria Kaiser Sao
Paolo
R Joao Finazzi 55
Centro
CEP 13800 Mogi Mirim SP
Tel (0192) 62 3710
Fax (0192) 62 3935

Cervejaria Kaiser Rio
R A de Moraes Sarmento
100
Queimados DI
CEP 26300 Nova Iguacu RJ
Tel (021) 767 3745
Fax (021) 767 2654

Cervejaria Antarctica
Niger
R Mariana Junquiera 33
Centro
CEP 14100 Ribeirao Preto
SP
Tel (016) 634 5665
Fax (016) 625 0446

Cervejaria Princeza
R J Rodrigues 54 on 60A
Sao F Xavier
CEP 20960 Rio de Janeiro
RJ
Tel (021) 261 1202
Fax (021) 261 1175

Cervejaria Reunidas
Skol Caracu
R Alm Cochrane 146 an 7
CEP 20550 Rio de Janeiro
RJ
Tel (021) 234 2074

Cervejaria Monte Alegre
R A Barbieri Schincariol 10
Dist Ind.
CEP 18650 Sao Manuel SP
Tel (0149) 41 3733
Fax (0149) 41 2904

Places to Enjoy Beer

Blumenau Biergarten
Park
Blumenau
Tuesday to Sunday. Complex
with restaurant, beer garden,
shops, German bands.

Bar Luiz
Rua Carioca 39
Rio de Janeiro
Tel 626 9600
German style restaurant and
bar.

Biblo's Bar
Av. epitacio Pessoa 1484
Lagoa
Rio de Janeiro
Tel 521 2645

Lord Jim Pub
Rua Paul Redfern 63
Ipanema
Rio de Janeiro
Tel 259 3047
British pub restaurant. Open
Tuesday to Sunday.

Neal's
Rua Sorocaba 695
Botafogo
Rio de Janeiro
Tel 286 0433
American bar-restaurant.

Chariot
Caesar Park Hotel
Rua Augusta 1508
San Paolo
Tel 285 6622
English-style pub.

Supremo
Rua da Consolacao 3473
Consolacao
San Paolo
Tel 282 6142

Festivals

Oktoberfest
around town
Blumenau
October. Parades, costumes,
beer drinking contests, food
fair, more beer.

British Virgin Islands

Places to Enjoy Beer
BVI Tourist Board
Box 134
Road Town
Tortola
Tel (809) 494-3134
Tourist information.

The Last Resort
Bellamy Cay
Tel (809) 495 2520
Contact: Tony Snell, owner

Abe's by the Sea
Little Harbour
Jost van Dyke
Tel 5 9239
Local bar and restaurant. Pig
roast on Wednesday.

Drake's Channel Lounge
Peter Island Resort
Peter Island
Tel (800) 346-4551
Fax (809)494-2313
Contact: P.O. Box 211
Road Town
Tortola
BVI
Open daily.

Pusser's Ltd.
Main St.
Road Town
Tortola
Tel 4 3897
Courage on draft.

Bath & Turtle Pub
Yacht Harbor
Spanish Town
Virgin Gorda
Tel 5 5239

Cayman Islands

Breweries

Santiago's Brewpub
Grand Cayman

Places to Enjoy Beer

Hog Sty Bay Cafe & Pub
N Church St.
Grand Cayman
Tel 9 6163

Lobster Pot
N Church St.
Grand Cayman
Tel 9 2736
*English ales, darts. Good
seafood, steaks.*

Ten Sails Pub
West Bay Rd.
Grand Cayman
Tel 7 4444
*Island music, comedy
Wednesday to Sunday.*

Chile

**Sernatur — National
   Tourism Service**
Santiago
Tel 02-698 2151
Tourist information.

Breweries

**Compania Cervecerias
   Unidad**
Paseo Ahumada 131
Piso 2
Casilla 1977
Santiago

Places to Enjoy Beer

Pianissimo Pub
Alonso de Cordova 4347B
Las Condes
Tel 2080570

Der Munchner Hof
Diego de Velasquez 2105
Providencia
Tel 2332452
*German cuisine. Open daily
for lunch and dinner.*

Phone Box Pub
Avda Providencia 1670
Providencia
Tel 496627

Sotito's Bar
Lib Bernado O'Higgins
   1138
Punta Arenas
Tel 223565

Bavaria
San Martin 255
Rancagua
Tel 226362

Bar Nacional
Huerfanos 1151
Santiago
Tel 6965986
Chilean cuisine.

American Bar
Yungay 647
Curico
Talca
Tel 075 312706

Bar Ingles
Cochrane 851
Valparaiso
Tel 214629

Colombia

Breweries

Cerveceria Aguila
Calle 10 no 38–58
Aptdo 1797
Barranquilla Atlantico

Grupo Ardilla Lulle
Cerveceria Leona
Bogota

Bavaria
Calle 94 no 74–47
Aptdo Aereo 3539
Bogota D Especial

Cerveceria Union
Carrera 50A no 38–39
Hagui
Aptdo 627
Medellin

Places to Enjoy Beer

Lloyd's Pub
Carrera 14A
between Calles 54 and 55
Bogota
*English pub where journalists
gather.*

Taberna la Quemada
Old City
Cartagena

Costa Rica

Breweries

Cerveceria Costa Rica
Brewery owned by
Coca Cola

Cerveceria Tropical
Brewery owned by
Pepsi

Florida Ice & Farm Co.
Calle 12, Av. 416
Aptdo 10021
San Jose 1000

Places to Enjoy Beer

Johnny's
On the beach.
Puerto Viejo

Atlas Bar
Avda 3
Calle 4–6
San Jose
Indoor biergarten.

Promesas
Av. 2A, between Calles 7
and 9
San Jose

Taberna Chelles
Calle 9, between Av. Central
and Av. 2A
San Jose
Tel 22 80 60

Taberna Valverdes
Santa ELena

Tortuguero Lodge
Tortuguero

Cuba

**Cia Cerveceria Interna-
tional**
Havana

Cerveceria Cutral
Havana

Cerveceria Modelo
Havana

Curacao

Breweries

Antillaanse Brouwerij

Places to Enjoy Beer

De Taveerne
Landhuis Groot Davelaar
Silena
Willemstad
Tel 370669
*Restaurant, bar, and wine
cellar.*

The Pub
Salinjas
Willemstad
Tel 9 612190

Dominican Republic

**Sec de Estado de
Turismo**
Santo Domingo
Tel 682-8181
Tourist information.

Breweries

Cerveceria Bohemia
Av. JF Kennedy 16
Aptdo 2470
Santa Domingo

**Cerveceria Nacional
Dominicana**
Av. Independencia Km 6
Aptdo 1086
Santa Domingo

Places to Enjoy Beer

Bar Jai-Alai
Av. independencia 411
Santo Domingo
Tel (809) 685-2409

Raffles Pub
calle Hostos 350
Santo Domingo
Tel (809) 686 3069
American bar.

Ecuador

**Cetur — National
Tourist Office**
Reina Victoria 514 and
Roca
Quito
Tel 527-002
Tourist information.

Breweries

**Compania de Cervezas
Macionales**
Casilla 519
Guyaquil
Tel 253467
*Cervezas Pilsener, Club, Chop
de Barril.*

El Salvador

**Institute Salvadoreno de
Turismo**
Calle Ruben Dario 619
San Salvador 01115
Tel 022-8000
Contact: L. D. Benavides
Tourist information.

Places to Enjoy Beer

La Constancia
Final Av. Independencia no
526
Aptdo 101
San Salvador

Los Pitufos
Calle Concepcion
San Salvador

Falkland Islands

Places to Enjoy Beer

Globe Hotel
Crozier Pl. and Philomel St.
Stanley

Rose Hotel
Brisbane Rd.
Stanley

Victory Bar
Philomel St. and Fitzroy Rd.
Stanley

French Guiana

**Agence Regionale de
   Tourisme**
12 rue l'allouette
97300 Cayenne
Tel 30-0900
Tourist information.

Grenana

Breweries

Grenada Breweries
Grand Anse
P.O. Box 202
St. George's

Places to Enjoy Beer

**Fantazia 2001 Beach
   Bar**
Morne Rouge Bay
Tel (809) 444-4244

Spice Island Inn
Grand Anse Beach
St. George's
Tel (809) 444-4258

Guadeloupe

**Grandes Brasseries
   Antillaises**
ZI de Jarry
Baie Mahault
97122

Places to Enjoy Beer

Le Wahoo
Le Bas du Fort
97190 Gosier
Tel 90 84 44

Guatemala

**Institute Guatemalteco
   de Turismo**
7A Ave. 1–17
Zona 4
Centro Civico
Guatemala City
Tel (502-2) 311333
Fax (502-2) 318893
Tourist information.

Breweries

**Cerveceria
   Centroamericana**
3a Av. Fin El Zapote
Zona 2
Aptdo 65
Guatemala City

Places to Enjoy Beer

**La Bota Tejara (The
   Texas Boot)**
7A Av. Norte
Antigua

Bar Europa
11 Calle 5–16
Zona 1
Guatemala City
Tel 02 534-929

**El Meson de Don
   Quixote**
11 Calle 5–27
Zona 1
Guatemala City
Tel 02 21-741

Circus Bar
Calle los Arboles
Panajachel

Beer Puffs

1 cup beer	4 eggs
¼ lb butter	Salt to taste
1 cup sifted flour	

Put beer and butter in a pan, and bring to a boil. When the butter is melted, add the flour and salt all at once. Cook over a low heat, stirring until the mixture leaves the sides of the pan.

Remove from heat, and beat in one egg at a time until the dough is shiny.

Drop by teaspoonful on to a greased baking sheet. Bake for 10 minutes at 450° F, 225 C. Reduce heat to 350° F, 180 C, until browned and free from moisture.

Cool, split, and fill with a savory filling such as crabmeat, shrimp, or chicken in bechamel sauce.

— *Recipe from Alabama*

Music Center
12A Av.
Quetzaltenango

Taberna de Don Rodrigo
14 Av.
Quetzaltenango
Dark beer on tap.

Guyana

Banks Brewing Co.
Thirst Park
P.O. Box 10.914
Georgetown Demerara

Haiti

**Brasseries Nationales
d'Haiti**
Port au Prince

Honduras

Cerveceria Hondurena
Aptdo 86
San Pedro Sula

Places to Enjoy Beer

Tunkul Bar
near the park
Copan Ruinas
*Bar, restaurant, travel agency,
Spanish language school,
outfitters.*

Sopa de Cardan
3A Av., between Calles 2A
and 3A
San Pedro Sula
*Free frijole soup with fried
pork comes with beer.*

Wilmer's Bar
7A Av., between Calles 2A
and 3A
San Pedro Sula
Tel 57 9381
Free snacks with beer.

Hungry Fisherman
Av. Rep. de Chile
Tegucigalpa
Tel 32 6493

Kloster
Blvd. Morazan
Tegucigalpa
Tel 32 2255

Jamaica

Jamaica Tourist Board
2 St. Lucia Ave.
P.O. Box 360
Kingston 5
Tel (809) 929-9200
Fax (809) 929-9375
Tourist information.

Breweries

Desnoes & Geddes
Kingston
Dragon Stout.

Guinness Jamaica
Central Village Brewery
Box 620
St. Catherine

Places to Enjoy Beer

Indies Pub & Grill
8 Holborn Rd.
Kingston
Tel (809) 929-9655

Surrey Tavern
81 Knutsford Rd.
Kingston
Tel 926 3690

Revival Room Pub
62 Ward Ave.
Mandeville
Tel 962 3265

Cosmo's Bar
Norman Manley Blvd.
Negril
Tel (809) 947-4330

Mariners Inn
West End Rd.
Negril
Tel (809) 957-4348

Little Pub Restaurant
59 Main St.
Ocho Rios
Tel (809) 974-2324

The Ruins
Turtle River
Da Costa Dr.
Ocho Rios
Tel (809) 974-2442

Festivals

Oktoberfest
Kingston
Tel (809) 927 8202
Contact: Herman Tobisch
*Jamaican German Society.
October. Beer drinking
contests, Jamaican and
German food, music, etc.*

Martinique

Tourist Office
Blvd. Alfassa
97200 Fort-de-France
Tourist information.

Places to Enjoy Beer

Brasserie Lorraine
Union-Lamartin
Fort-de-France

Mexico

**Beer Manufacturers
  Association**
Oracio 1556
Chapultapec Morales
11570 Mexico City
Tel 5 5206283

Breweries

Cerveceria del Pacifico
G. Leyva y Melchor Ocampo
  s/n
Centro
82000 Mazatlan Sin
Tel 0678 2 7966
Fax 0678 2 3325
Cerveza Pacifico.

Cerveceria Modelo
Lago Alberto 156
Col Anahuac
11320 Mexico DF
Tel 05 545 6060
Fax 05 545 2773
*Corona, Negra Modelo,
Modelo Especial.*

Cerveceria Cuautemoc
Ave. Alfonso Reyes 2202 N
64442 Monterrey NL
Tel 083 752200
Fax 083 748037
Carta Blanca, Tecate.

Cerveceria Moctezuma
Ave. Alfonso Reyes 2202 N
64442 Monterrey NL
Tel 083 746871
Fax 083 748037
*XX Amber, XX Special Lager,
Superior, Sol.*

Places to Enjoy Beer

Carlos 'n Charlie's
Av. Rafael Melgar
Cozumel
Tel 987 20191

Papa's & Beer
Av. Ruiz
Ensenada

Bar la Opera
Cinco de Mayo 10
Mexico City
Tel 5 512-8959

Cantinas & Clubs
Plaza Garibaldi
Mexico City
*A wide assortment of places
surrounds the square.*

Montserrat

Places to Enjoy Beer

The Plantation
Wapping Rd.
Plymouth
Tel 1 2892

**Yacht Club Bar &
  Restaurant**
Wapping
Tel 1 2237

Nicaragua

Breweries

Industrial Cerveceria
Carretera Notre K-6
Aptdo 4652
Managua

**Comp Cerveceria de
  Nicaragua**
Carretera Norte Frente
Aptdo 72
Managua

Places to Enjoy Beer

Bar Tropicana
Airport Rd.
Bluefields
*Live reggae and costeno
music.*

Bar Chaplin
Km 5 Carretera Masaya
Managua
Tel 02 74375

Videoteca
Near Estatua Montoya.
Managua
Tel 02 27092
Cinema with bar.

Panama

Places to Enjoy Beer

Varela Hermanos
Lado de Coagro
Aptdo 1274
Panama City

Casa de Cerveza
Via Espana
Panama City

Pavo Real
Calle 51
Panama City
Tel 69 0504
British-style pub.

Paraguay

National Tourist Office
Palma 468
Asuncion
Tel 491-230
Tourist information.

Breweries

**Industrializadora
  Guarani Group**
Asuncion
Carlsberg.

Cerveceria Paraguay
Palma 11139
Cc126
Asuncion

Peru

**Foptar, Peruvian Tourist
  Office**
Andres Reyes 320
San Isidro
Lima
Tel 424438
Fax 701370
Tourist information.

Breweries

**Comp Cerveceria del
  Sur del Peru**
Variante de Uchumayo 1801
Aptdo 43
Arequipa

**Cerveceria Bachus &
  Johnson**
Jr Chiclayo 594
Aptdo 189
Lima

**Comp Nacional de
  Cerveza**
Av. Saenz Pena 471
Aptdo 256
Lima

Society Paramonga
Augusto Tamayo 160
Aptdo 2488
Lima

Places to Enjoy Beer

Brenchley Arms
174 Atahualpa
Miraflores
Lima
Tel 45 9680
English pub restaurant.

Haiti
160 Diagonal
Miraflores
Lima
Tel 47 5052

St. Barthelemy

Places to Enjoy Beer

Le Select
rue de la France
Gustavia
Tel 27 86 87

Santa Fe Bar Restaurant
Morne Lurin
Tel 27 61 04

St. Kitts

Breweries

St. Kitts Brewery
Basseterre

Places to Enjoy Beer

Fisherman's Wharf
Fortlands
Basseterre
Tel (809) 465-2754

Turtle Beach Bar
SE Peninsula
Basseterre
Tel (809) 469-9086

St. Lucia

Breweries

**Windward & Leeward
  Breweries**
Vieux Fort

Places to Enjoy Beer

Jimmie's
Vigie Cove Marina
Tel 2 5142

St. Maarten

Breweries

St Maarten Breweries

Places to Enjoy Beer

West Indian Tavern
8 Front St.
Philipsburg
Tel 22965

St. Vincent

Breweries

St. Vincent Brewery
Kingstown

Places to Enjoy Beer

The Attic
Kentucky Bldg.
Melville and Grenville Sts.
Kingstown
Tel 7 2588

Basil's Bar
Bay St.
Kingstown
Tel 7 2713

Surinam

Breweries

Surinaamse Brouwerij
Brouwerijweg
P.O. Box 1854
Paramaribo

Tobago

Places to Enjoy Beer

Blue Waters Inn
Batteau Bay
Speyside
Tel (809) 660-4341

Trinidad

Breweries

National Brewery Co.
Princess Mary Hwy.
P.O. Box 1131
Port-of-Spain St. George

Places to Enjoy Beer

Chaconia Inn
106 Saddle Rd.
Maraval
Tel (809) 628-8603

Mascamp Pub
French St. at Ariapata Ave.
Port-of-Spain
Tel (809) 623-3745

Uruguay

Ministerio de Turismo
Av. Agraciada 1409
Montevideo
Tourist information.

Breweries

Fab Nacional de Cerveza
Entre Rios 1060
Montevideo

**Cerveceria y Maltera
Paysandu**
Rbla Baltasar R Brum 2933
Cc 762
Montevideo

Comp Salus
Dr. Luis Alberto de Herrera
311
Montevideo

Places to Enjoy Beer

Chopperia Vieja Bavaria
Estados Unidos 422
Asuncion
*German fast food and good
beer.*

Venezuela

Turismo de Venezuela
37th floor
Torre Oeste
Parque Central
Caracas
Tel 507-8815
Tourist information.

Breweries

Cerveceria Nacional
Av. R Gallegos
Edif Zulia
Apt. Post 504
Caracas DF 1070

Cerveceria Polar
4ta Transversal Edif
Apt. Post 2331
Caracas DF 1071

Cerveceria Modelo
Km 10
Carretera via la Canada
Maracaibo Zulia 4033

EUROPE

European Listings

Listings by Country

European Beer Consumers Union. Members are CAMRA (UK), PINT (Netherlands), OBP (Belgium), SO (Sweden). Works for the preservation of European brewing traditions and consumer rights.

EFTA Brewing Industry Council, Scheibenpogenstr 15, A-4020 Linz, Austria. Tel 0732 43394.

The European Beer Almanac, by Roger Protz. Guide to a selection of European beers, bottled and draught, with tasting notes and recipes, Brewery addresses and details. Available from CAMRA, UK, and bookstores. Published by Lochar, in English.

Breweries & Maltsters in Europe, published by Hoppenstedt, Havelstr 9, Postfach 40 06, D-6100 Darmstadt, Germany. Tel 51 3 80 0, Fax 51 380 360. Over 2000 listings in 24 countries: addresses, personnel, range of products, etc. Trade associations, training, research institutions, press. In German, English, and French.

Brewing & Beverage Industry International, Schloss Mindelburg, Postfach 14 63, D-8948 Mindelheim, Germany. Tel 08261 999 0, Fax 98261 999 132. 2/year. Brewing news from around the world.

Listings by Country

Austria

Breweries

Brauerei Fohrenburg
Postfach 192
A-6700 Bludenz
Tel 05552 62081

Vorarlberger Brauerei Frastanz
Bahmhofstr 22
A-6820 Frastanz
Tel 05522 51701
Fax 05522 517014

Brauerei Hirt
Rt 83/E7
Friesach
A brewery since 1270. Beer garden, restaurant.

Brauerei Puntigamer
A-8020 Graz

Brauerei Reininghaus
A-8020 Graz

Steirische Braueindustrie
Reiningshausstr 1-7
Postfach 1028
A-8021 Graz
Tel 0316 5020
Fax 0316, 502200

Adambraeu
Adamgasse 23
Postfach 64
A-6010 Innsbruck
Tel 0512 52007
Fax 0512 5200736

Hubertus-Braeu Johan Kuehtreiber
Hubertusgasse 1
A-2136 Laa an der Thaya
Tel 02522 246
Fax 02522 4460

Brauerei Goesser
Goess
Leoben
Tel 03842 22621
Brewery in former monastery (founded 1020), with small beer museum.

S. Spitz & Co.
Fiedlerstr 10
Postfach 102
A-4040 Linz Donau
Tel 0732 231336
Fax 0732 238107

Josef Sigl Brauerei
A-5162 Obertrum

Osterreichische Brau
Alanovaplatz 5
Postfach 100
A-2320 Schwechat
Tel 01 701 40
Fax 01 707 26 77
Kaiser, Schwechater, Zipfer, Moeven, Schlossgold, Edelweiss Bier.

Anton & August Kriser
Gewerberstr 4
A-2601 Sollenau
Tel 02628 81130
Fax 02628 81139

Ottakringer Brauerei Harmer
Ottakringerstr 91
Postfach 97
A-1171 Vienna
Tel 01 49100
Fax 01 49100239

Vereinigte Kaerntner Brauereien
Brauhausgasse 6
A-9500 Villach
Tel 04242 27777
Fax 042442 2777754

Brauerei Eggenberg
Eggenberg 1
Postfach 44
A-4655 Vorchdorf
Tel 07614 345
Fax 07614 345 40
Urbock 23, Hopfenkoenig, McQueen's Nessie.

Braeu
Town center
A-6280 Zell am Ziller
Tel 05282 2313
Historic hotel with brewery, Braeustuebl restaurant. Brewers of Gauderbier for the festival in early May.

Places to Enjoy Beer

Gambrinuskeller
Faerbergasse 6-8
A-8020 Graz
Tel 0316 810181
Restaurant with eclectic menu and local beers.

Cafe Zappa
Rehengasse 5
A-6020 Innsbruck
Beer and light fare. Open evenings.

Stiegelbraeu
Wilhelm-Greilstr 25
Innsbruck

Treibhaus
Angerzellgasse 8
A-6020 Innsbruck
Tel 58 68 74

Student hangout with live
music. Open Monday to
Saturday, 4PM to 1AM;
Sunday 9AM to 2PM.

Batzenhaeusl
Zwergergasse 1A
A-9900 Lienz
Tel 633 70
*Beer garden with a view of the
Dolomites and hearty food.*

Zum Klosterhof
Landstr 30
A-4020 Linz
Tel 0732 773 3730
*Restaurant serving traditional
Austrian cuisine with
Salzburger Stiegl beer.*

Damboeck Haus
*Top of the cogwheel steam
railway, Puchberg am
Schneebrg. Operated by the
Austrian Touring Club,
serving mountain food and
draft beer.*

Augustiner Braeustueble
Augustinergasse 4-6
A-5010 Salzburg
Tel 0662 312 46
*Home of Salzburg's first
brewery. Barrels tapped before
your eyes. Open daily, 3 to
11PM. 3–11PM.*

Sternbraeu
Griegsgasse 23
A-5010 Salzburg
Tel 0662 842140
*Outdoor beer garden with
buffet, folk music Friday and
Sunday, indoor beer tavern.*

Stiegkeller
Festungsgasse 10
Salzburg
*Open air, open May to
September.*

Zum Fidelen Affen
Priesterhausgasse 8
Salzburg
Good draft beer.

Goesser Bierklinik
Steindlgasse 4
Vienna
Tel 0222 535 6897
*Restaurant serving local fare
and beer from the Goesser
Brewery in Styria. Open
Monday to Saturday.*

Goesser Brau
Elisabethstr 3
Vienna
Tel 0222587 4750
*Restaurant, game specialities,
Goesser beer.*

Krah Krah
Rabensteig 8
Vienna 1

Nachtasyl
Stumpergasse 53
Vienna 6
Owner is Czech.

Schweizerhaus
Strasse des 1 Mai 116
A-1020 Vienna
*Serves daily specials and beer
in a garden.*

Stiftsrestaurant
Zwettl Abbey
Zwettl
Tel 02822 531 8117
*Restaurant serving local fare
and beer from nearby brewery.*

Festivals
Gauderfest
A-6280 Zell am Ziller
*May, first weekend. Four
hundred-year-old celebration,
with music, song, and
specially brewed Gauderbier.*

Of Historic Interest
Beer Museum
Town Fortress
A-2136 Laa an der Thaya
Tel 02522 5010
*Open weekends, May to
September.*

Griechenbeisl Restaurant
Fleischmarkt 11
Vienna
*There has been a tavern at
this address for 500 years.*

Belgium
Belgian Tourist Office
Rue Marche aux Herbes/
   Grasmarkt 63
Brussels
Tel 02-504 03 86
Tourist information.

**De Objectieve
   Bierproevers**
Postbus 32
B-2600 Berchem 5
*The Objective Beer-Tasters.
Consumer organization like
CAMRA (UK), promoting
quality beers. Magazine Den
Bierproever, 4/year. Runs beer
festival in Antwerp, September,
second weekend.*

CAMRA
Brussels Branch
Boite no 5
rue des Atrebates
B-1040 Brussels
Contact: Stephen d'Arcy
*Regular meetings, informa-
tion on beer festivals, brewery
development, cafe details.*

CBB
Grand'Place 10
B-1000 Brussels
Tel 02 511 49 87
Fax 02 511 32 59
Confederation des Brasseries
de Belgique. Association of
Belgian Brewers.

Books and Magazines
A Selective Guide to
Brussels Bars, by
CAMRA
Brussels Branch. Local beer
guide, updated regularly.

Good Beer Guide to
Belgium & Holland, by
Tim Webb
Lists all the breweries and
many of the best bars.
Available from CAMRA, UK,
and bookstores. Published by
Alma Books, in English.

The Great Beers of
Belgium, by Michael
Jackson
Published by MM Communi-
cations. Photos, maps,
illustrations. In English.

Biere
Bureau du Depot
B-1040 Brussels 4
Magazine about beer.

Breweries
Brasserie d'Achouffe
Rue du Village 32
B-6666 Achouffe
Tel 061 28 81 47
Fax 061 28 82 64
Tours available. Small bar on
premises.

Brouwerij Alken-Maes
Stationstraat 2
B-3570 Alken
Tel 011 31 27 11
Fax 011 31 39 82

Brouwerij de Koninck
Mechelsesteenweg 291
B-2018 Antwerp 1
Tel 03 218 40 48
Fax 03 230 85 19

Brouwerij Bavik
Rijksweg 33
B-8531 Bavikhove
Tel 056 71 90 91
Fax 056 71 15 12

Brouwerij Bockor
Vanderghinste
Kwabrugstr 5
B-8510 Bellegem
Tel 056 21 65 71
Fax 056 22 76 83

Brouwerij Facon
Kwabrugstr 23/27
B-8510 Bellegem
Tel 056 22 07 69
Fax 056 25 93 47

Brasserie la Binchoise
Rue Faubourg St. Paul 38
B-7130 Binche
Tel 064 33 61 86

Brouwerij Martens
Reppelerweg 1
B-3950 Bocholt
Tel 089 47 29 80
Fax 089 47 27 00
Contact: Fons Martens
Kwik Pils, Bocholter Pils,
Martens Pils, Sezoens,
Tafelstout, Damburger.

Brouwerij Haacht
Provinciesteenweg 2
B-3190 Boortmeerbeek
Tel 016 60 15 01
Fax 016 60 83 84
Primus Pils, Gildenbier,
Blanche de Haecht, Tongerlo,
Adler.

Brouwerij St. Josef
Itterplein 19
B-3581 Bree
Tel 089 86 47 11
Fax 089 86 74 19

Brouwerij Moortgat
Breendonkdorp 58
B-2870 Breendonk-Puurs
Tel 03 886 71 21
Fax 03 886 46 22
Duvel, Bel Pils, Maredsous.

Brouwerij de Gouden
Boom
Langestraat 45
B-8000 Bruges
Tel 050 33 06 99
Fax 050 33 46 44
Brewery tours by appointment.
Museum. Brugs Tarwebier-
Blanche de Bruges, Biere
d'Abbaye de Steenbrugge,
Brugse Tripel.

Huisbrouwerij Straffe
Hendrik
Walplein 26
B-8000 Bruges
Tel 050 34 59 35
Fax 050 33 26 97
Contact: O. Blancquaert
Small brewery. Tours Monday
to Saturday, March to
September. Brugse Straffe
Hendrik.

**Brouwerij Belle-Vue et
  Zuun**
Rue Delaunoy 58–60
B-1080 Brussels
Tel 02 412 44 11
Fax 02 410 78 58
Noted for fruit beers.

Brasserie Cantillon
Rue Ghende 56–58
B-1070 Brussels
Tel 02 521 49 28
*Brewery tour included in
museum visit.*

Brasserie Speculum
Pl. Reine Astrid 24
B-1090 Brussels 9
Tel 02 424 04 78

Brouwerij Unies
Henegouwenkaai 33
B-1080 Brussels 8
Tel 02 522 71 00

Brouwerij Bosteels
Kerkstr 92
B-9255 Buggenhout
Tel 052 33 22 82
Fax 052 33 59 56
Contact: Antoine or Ivo
  Bosteels
Pauwel Kwak, Prosit, Bugg's.

Brasserie de Chimay
Rte. Charlemagne 8
B-6464 Chimay
Tel 60 21 03 11
Fax 60 21 34 22

Brasserie Demarche
Rte. de Rochefortrie 4
B-5590 Ciney
Tel 32 83 21 21 80
Fax 312 83 21 12 95
*Ciney Blonde, Brune, Speciale
10.*

Brouwerij Riva
Wontergemstr 42
B-8720 Dentergem
Tel 051 63 36 81
Fax 051 63 62 08
*Dentergems Wit Bier, Lucifer,
Vondel, Liefmans Kriek en
Frambozen, Gouden Carolus,
Toison d'Or, Staffe Hendrik.*

De Dolle Brouwers
Roeselarestraat 128
B-8600 Diksmuide
Tel 051 50 27 81
Open Sunday.

Brasserie de Blaugies
Rue de la Frontiere 435
B-7370 Dour (Blaugies)
Tel 065 65 03 60
Fax 965 65 03 60

Interbrew
Stationsstr 88
B-9900 Eeklo
Tel 091 77 36 85
Fax 091 77 06 63

**Brouwerij van
  Steenberge**
Lindenlaan 25
B-9940 Ertvelde
Tel 091 44 50 71
Contact: Paul van
  Steenberge
*Specialised in top-fermenta-
tion beers with re-fermentation
in the bottle. Augustijn,
Augustijn Grand Cru, Dubbel
& Trippel Bornem, Gulden
Draak, Piraat.*

Brouwerij Eupenoise
Pavestr 12/14
B-4700 Eupen
Tel 087 55 47 31

Brouwerij Neyt
Molenstr 7
B-9940 Evergem
Tel 091 53 04 59

Brasserie Voisin
Rue Aulnoit
B-7880 Flobecq
Tel 068 44 70 71

Abbaye de Scourmont
Rue de la Trappe 294
B-6464 Forges-les-Chimay
Tel 060 21 30 63
Fax 060 21 34 22
Trappiste de Chimay.

Brouwerij Contreras
Molenstr 115
B-9890 Gavere
Tel 091 84 27 06

**Brasserie Poncelet
  Maurice**
Rue Charleville 70–72
B-5575 Gedinne
Tel 061 58 85 54
Fax 061 58 90 72

Brasserie Gigi
Grand'rue 96
B-6769 Gerouville
Tel 063 57 75 15
Formerly Brasserie de l'Etoile.

Interbrew
Rte. de Wallonie 4
B-7011 Ghlin
Tel 065 35 72 11
Fax 065 35 72 22

Brouwerij vander Linden
Brouwerijstr 2
B-1500 Halle
Tel 02 356 50 59

Brouwerij de Gouden Arend
Kerkstr 24
B-9550 Herzele
Tel 053 62 23 02
Fax 053 62 87 80

Brouwerij van den Bossche
St. Lievensplein 16
B-9550 Herzele
Tel 054 50 04 11

De Kluis Brouwerij van Hoegaarden
Stoopkenstraat 46
B-3320 Hoegaarden
Tel 016 76 76 76
Fax 016 76 76 91

Brouwerij Sterkens
Meerdorp 20
B-2320 Hoogstraten-Meer
Tel 03 315 71 45
Fax 03 315 94 20

Brouwerij Strubbe
Markt 1
B-8630 Ichtegem
Tel 051 58 81 16

Brouwerij van Honsebrouck
Oostrozebekekestr 43
B-8770 Ingelmunster
Tel 051 30 34 14
Fax 051 31 38 39
Gueuze, Kriek, Framboise,
Peche & Cassis St.-Louis,
Bacchus, Brigand,
Kasteelbier, Flemish White.

Brouwerij Timmermans
Kerkstraat 11
B-1701 Itterbeek
Tel 02 569 03 58
Fax 02 569 01 98
Gueuze-Caveau; Gueuze,
Kriek, Framboise, Peche,

Cassis, Faro Lambics,
Bourgogne des Flandres.

Brasserie Piedboeuf
Rue de Vise 253
B-4500 Jupille sur Meuse

Interbrew
Rue des A. Houblonnierers 2
B-4020 Jupille/Meuse
Tel 041 45 82 11
Fax 041 45 86 08

Brouwerij Biertoren
Brouwerijstr 23
B-1820 Kampenhout
Tel 016 65 51 02
Fax 016 65 57 87
The Smedts family. Campus
brand.

Brouwerij de Keersmaeker
Lierput 1
B-1730 Kobbegem
Tel 02 452 63 24
Fax 02 452 43 10

Brouwerij Gebr Louwaerge
Markt 14
B-8610 Kortemark
Tel 051 56 60 67
Fax 051 57 05 10

Brouwerij Walrave
Lepelstr 36
B-9270 Laarne
Tel 091 69 01 34

Brasserie Friart
Rue d'Houdeng 220
B-7070 Le Roeulx
Tel 064 66 21 51
Fax 064 76 76 30

Brouwerij Frank Boon
Fonteinstr 65
B-1502 Lembeek
Tel 02 356 66 44
Fax 02 356 33 99

Interbrew
Vaartstr 94
B-3000 Leuven
Tel 016 24 71 11
Fax 016 24 74 07
Stella Artois.

Brouwerij Gouden Carolus
Guido Gezellelaan 49
B-2800 Mechelen
Tel 015 20 38 80

Interbrew
Eggestr 1
B-2800 Mechelen
Tel 015 41 69 91

Brouwerij Huyghe
Brusselsesteenweg 256
B-9090 Melle
Tel 091 52 15 01
Fax 091 52 29 31

Brouwerij de Block-Joostens
Nieuwbaan 92
B-1795 Merchtem
Tel 052 37 21 59

Interbrew
Langesteenweg 12
B-1785 Merchtem
Tel 052 37 11 11
Fax 052 37 29 62

Interbrew
Rue du Riquau 1
B-1435 Mont-St-Guibert
Tel 010 64 42 11
Fax 010 65 74 23
Leffe Blond, Vieus Temps,
Ginder Ale.

Brouwerij Slagmuylder
Denderhoutembaan 2
B-9400 Ninove
Tel 054 33 18 31

Brouwerij de Smedt
Ringlaan 18
B-1745 Opwijk
Tel 052 35 99 11
Fax 052 35 83 57

Brouwerij Clarysse
Krekelput 18
B-9700 Oudenaard
Tel 055 31 17 21
Fax 055 31 94 76

Brouwerij Omer Cnudde
Fabriekstr 8
B-9700 Oudenaard
Tel 055 31 18 34

Brouwerij Liefmans
Aalststraat 200
B-9700 Oudenaarde
Tel 055 31 13 92
Fax 055 31 94 86
Goudenband, Kriekbier,
Frambozenbier.

Brouwerij Roman
Hauwaert 61
B-9700 Oudenaarde
Tel 055 45 54 01
Fax 055 45 56 00
Romy Pils, Romy Luxe,
Rouman Oudenaards, Special
Roma, Dobbelen, Sloeber,
Abdij can Ename dubbel et
tripel.

Brasserie Dubuisson
Chausee de Mons 28
B-7904 Pipaix
Tel 069 66 20 85
Fax 069 66 17 27
Bush Beer, Beer de Noel,
Scaldis.

Brasserie du Bocq
Rue de la Brasserie 4
B-5530 Purnode-Yvoir
Tel 082 61 37 37
Fax 082 61 17 80
Blanche de Namur, Saison
Regal, St.-Benoit blonde et
brune, Triple Moine, Deugniet,
La Gauloise, Regal Christmas.

Brasserie Lefebvre
Rue du Croly 52
B-1430 Quenast
Tel 067 67 07 66
Fax 067 67 02 38

Abbaye Notre Dame St.
  Remy
B-5580 Rochefort
Tel 084 21 31 81

Brouwerij Rodenbach
Spanjestraat 133
B-8800 Roeselare
Tel 051 22 34 00
Fax 051 22 92 48
Rodenbach Grand Cru,
Alexander Rodenbach.

Brouwerij Brabrux
Isabellastr 52
B-1703 Schepdaal
Tel 02 569 55 92

Brouwerij de Vene
Isabellastr 52
B-1703 Schepdaal
Tel 02 569 09 02

Brasserie de Silly
Ville Basse A 141
B-7830 Silly
Tel 068 55 16 95
Fax 068 56 84 36
Saison de Silly, Double
Enghien, Titje Blanche.

Brouwerij Louis
  Girardin
Lindenbergstr 10/12
B-1730 Sint Ulricks Kapelle
Tel 02 452 64 19

Brouwerij Palm
Steenhuffeldorp 3
B-1840 Steenhuffel
Tel 052 30 94 81
Fax 052 30 41 67
Palm-Ale, Aerts 1900, Bock
Premium Pils.

Brasserie Dupont
Rue Basse 5
B-7904 Tourpes
Tel 069 66 22 01
Fax 069 66 19 86

Brouwerij Verhaeghe
Beukenhofstr 96
B-8570 Vichte
Tel 056 77 70 32
Fax 056 77 70 32

Brasserie d'Orval
Abbaye Notre-Dame
Orval 218
B-6823 Villiers-devant-
  Orval
Tel 061 31 12 61
Fax 061 31 29 27
Trappiste d'Orval.

Brouwerij Lindemans
Lenniksebaan 1479
B-1602 Vlezenbeek
Tel 02 569 03 90
Fax 02 569 05 10
Contact: R. Lindemans, T.
  Dillen
Kriek, Gueuze, Framboise,
Pecheresse, Cassis Faro.

Brouwerij Alken-Maes
Waarloosveld 10
B-2550 Waarloos-Kontich
Tel 015 30 90 11
Fax 015 31 41 91
Grimbergen Dubbel, Tripel,
Blond, Optimo Bruno; Mort
Subite Gueuze, Kriek,
Framboise, Peche, Cassis.

Brouwerij de Troch
Langestr 20
B-1741 Wambeek
Tel 02 582 10 27

Brouwerij Sint
  Bernardus
Trappistenweg 23
B-8978 Watou
Tel 057 38 80 21

Brouwerij van Eecke
Douwieweg 2
B-8978 Watou
Tel 057 38 80 30
Fax 057 42 39 70

Abdij der Trapisten
  Westmalle
Antwerpsesteenweg 496
B-2390 Westmalle
Tel 03 312 05 35
Fax 03 311 77 35
Abbey brewery.

Abdij St. Sixtus
Donkerstraat 12
B-8640 Westvleteren
Tel 057 40 03 76
Abbey brewery.

Brouwerij van Roy
Nieuwstr 2
B-9290 Wieze
Tel 053 21 52 01
Fax 053 77 58 40

Brouwerij G. Crombe
Hospitaalstr 10
B-9620 Zottegem
Tel 091 60 02 40

Brouwerij Callewaert
Lichterveldestr 45
B-8750 Zwevezele
Tel 051 61 10 87

Places to Enjoy Beer

Bierland
28 Korte Nieuwstraat
Antwerp

Kulminator
Vleminckveld 32–34
Antwerp

Drie Fonteinen
Herman Teirlinckplein 3
B-1650 Beersel
Tel 02 33 10652

't Traptje
Wollenstraat 38
Bruges
Around 40 brews.

La Becasse
11 rue Tabora
B-1000 Brussels
Tel 02 511 00 06
Gueuze Becasse on tap.

Chaloupe d'Or
24–25 Grand'Place
B-1000 Brussels
Pub and bistro.

Le Cirio
18 rue de la Bourse
B-1000 Brussels
Over 50 beers.

Au Corbeau
18 rue St.-Michel
B-1000 Brussels
Tel 02 219 52 46

Good selection of beer on tap
and bottled.

Flastaff
17–23 rue Henri Maus
B-1000 Brussels
Tel 02 511 87 89
Pub and bistro. Around 50
beers on tap and bottled.

La Fleur en Papier Dore
5 rue des Alexiens
B-1000 Brussels
Tel 02 511 16 59
Pub dating from 1846.

In 't Spinnekopke
Bloemenhofplaats 1
B-1000 Brussels
Tel 02 5118695

Le Jugement Dernier
165 chaussee de Haecht
B-1030 Brussels
Pub with 265 beers, snacks.

Moeder Lambic
68 rue de Savoie
B-1060 Brussels
Tel 02 538 09 38
Pub with over 1000 beers,
domestic and imports.

Moeder Lambic 2
441 chaussee de Boondael
B-1050 Brussels
Tel 02 538 09 38
Fifty-five taps plus bottles.

Mort-Subite
7 rue Montagne-aux-
  Herbes-Potageres
B-1000 Brussels
Pub and bistro.

Le Pere Faro
442 chaussee d'Alsemberg
B-1060 Brussels
Pub-cafe with around 100
beers, outdoor beer garden.

Roi d'Espagne
1 Grand'Place
B-1000 Brussels

De Ultieme Hallucinatie
316 rue Royale
B-1030 Brussels
Tel 02 217 06 14
*Pub, bistro, and restaurant
with around 60 beers.*

De Hopduvel
Rokerelsstr 10
B-9000 Ghent
Tel 091 253729

**Waterhuis aan de
Bierkant**
Groentenmarkt 9
B-9000 Ghent
*Pub with over 100 domestic
beers, outdoor patio.*

In de Rare Vos
Marktplaats 22
B-1750 Schepdaal
Tel 02 5692086

Retail Stores

Biers Artisinals
Waverse Steenweg 174
B-1050 Brussels
Tel 02 412 17 88
Contact: Nasser Ektaferi,
 owner
Store with huge beer selection.

Biers Artisinals
Waterloo Steenweg 25
B-1060 Brussels
Tel 02 538 63 69
Store with huge beer selection.

Drinks Wets
Steenweg op Halle 209
B-1640 Sint-Genesius-Rode
Tel 02 380 32 27
Huge beer selection.

Festivals

PINT Nieuws
*From PINT (Netherlands).
Calendar of beer festivals and
events in the Netherlands,
Belgium, and the UK.*

Harvest Festival
Stienenshof
Aalst
Tel 053 77 09 57
*Late July, 3 days. Traditional
harvesting, plus tasting the
harvest beer. Folk music
performances.*

OBP Beer Festival
Postbus 32
B-2600 Berchem 5
*September, second weekend, in
Antwerp. Run by De Objectieve
Bierproevers. Twenty-four-
hour festival with special
Belgian beers.*

Of Historic Interest

**Oud Beersel 1882
 Museum**
250 Laarheidstraat
B-1650 Beersel
Tel 02 380 3396
*At Vandervelden Brewery.
Brewing artifacts. Brewery
tour included in museum visit.
Open first Sunday.*

**Brugs Brouwerij-
 Mouterij Museum**
10 Verbrand Nieuweland
B-8000 Bruges
Tel 050 330699
*In an old malt-house. History
of old Bruges breweries. Open
Thursday to Sunday, June to
September.*

**Confedn of Belgian
 Brewers Museum**
10 Grand'Place
B-1000 Brussels
Tel 02 511 49 87
Fax 02 511 3259
*In the Brewers' Guildhouse.
Laid out like a C18 brewery.
Small sampling bar. Open
Monday to Friday; Saturday
April to October.*

**Musee Bruxellois de la
 Gueuze**
Rue Gheude 56
Brussels
Tel 02 520 2891
*Living museum, with
Cantillon Brewery. Displays of
brewing history. Open Monday
to Friday; guided tours on
Saturday (make reservations),
includes sample.*

Stadhuis
B-3000 Leuven
Town Hall
*Small brewing museum, open
daily.*

Nationaal Hopmuseum
71 Gasthuisstraat
Poperinge
*Museum of hops and hop
cultivation. Entrance includes
sample of local brew. Open
daily July and August,
Sunday and holidays May to
September.*

**Musee Europeen des
 Brasserie**
2A Fontaine St. Pierre
Romedenne
Tel 082 677275
*In the old Bouty Brewery.
Brewing equipment, memora-
bilia. Cafe. Open daily.*

Bulgaria

Breweries

Bulel
147 Rakovski St.
1000 Sofia
Tel 87 90 08
Fax 359 52

Bulgarska Pivo Corp.
Kvartal Gorublyane
P.O. Box 389
1738 Sofia
Tel 52 743 81

Places to Enjoy Beer

Bar Valeo
buk Gorki 21
Plovdiv

Hisar Kapiya
Kiril Nektariev
Plovdiv
A kiosk selling beer and spirits, surrounded by gardens.

Paldin Restaurant
Tseretelev 3
Plovdiv
Tel 032 23 17 20

Bulgarska Gozba
Bul Vitosa 34
Sofia
Tel 02 87 91 62

Union Jack Pub
Sveta Sofia 5
Sofia

Sozopol Tavern
Cervenoarmejska 46
Sozopol

Cafe Boyarka
ul D Blagoev 41
Tsarevets

Black Hole
Shipka 23
Varna

Rostock
bul VI Varnenchik 20
Varna
Serves hearty meals in a beer-hall atmosphere.

Zlatno Pile
Slivnitsa 7
Varna
Good draft beer.

Suhindol
G. Mamarchev 14
Veliko Tarnovo
Good draft beer.

Canary Islands

Sical Brewery
Aptdo 274
E-35050 Las Palmas
Tel 928 31300

Cyprus

Cyprus Tourism Organization
18 Theodotou St.
P.O. Box 4535
Nicosia
Tel 02-443374
Fax 02-366744
Tourist information, postal enquiries only. Walk-in inquiries: Laiki Yitonia, E of Eleftheria Square, (02) 444264. Also in other cities.

Breweries

Cyprus Carlsberg Brewery
Limassol

Keo Brewing Co.
1 F. Roosevelt Ave.
P.O. Box 209
Limassol
Tel 5 362 053
Fax 5 373 429
Tours, tastings.

Photos Photiades Brewery
Iii Makarios Ave., #101
P.O. Box 2391
Nicosia

Platanis Co.
P.O. Box 2391
Nicosia 137
Tel 02 422011

Places to Enjoy Beer

Antonaki's Tavern
18 Germanou Patron St.
Nicosia

Mikis Tavern
International Fair Hwy.
Nicosia
Tel 535925

Mandra Tavern
4 Dionysiou St.
Paphos
Tel 06 234129

Czech Republic and Slovak Republic

American Hospitality Center
Male namesti 14
Prague
Open 10 to 6, 10 to 8 in summer. Basic tourist information, and friendly English speakers.

CEDOK Intertravel
Overseas Department
Na prikope 18
CS-111 35 Prague 1
Tel 21 27 111
Tourist information.

Koospol
Leninova 178
CS-160 67 Prague 6
*Export agency for beer, malt,
and other food products. Also
at Sputnikova 12, CS-826 27
Bratislava.*

Books

**Prague Pub Guide, by
Sarah Shaw**
Published by Pragolem
Guides.
*Shaw also has a weekly
column on pubs in the Prague
Post, an English weekly
newspaper.*

Breweries

Pivovar Podluzan
Zamecka nam 5
CS-690 57 Breclav
Tel 0627 20329
Fax 0627 21942

Pivovary Brno
Hlinky 12
CS-657 12 Brno
Tel 05 339126

Pivovary A. Sodovkarny
Hlinky 12
CS-657 12 Brno
Tel 05 336811
Fax 05 338686

Budweiser Budvar
Karoliny Svetle 2
CS-370 54 Ceske
  Budejovice
Contact: Josef Tolar,
  brewmaster

Jihokeske Pivovary
Karoliny Svetle 4
CS-370 54 Ceske
  Budejovice
Tel 038 24027
Fax 038 28823

**Chrudimsla Sladovnicka
  Spolecnost**
Gorkeho 580
CS-537 01 Chrudim

Pivovar Decin
Sofijska 2
CS-405 51 Decin
Tel 0412 26001

**Pivovary Hradec
  Kralove**
Csl Armady 363
CS-500 62 Hradec Kralove
Tel 049 24051
Fax 049 22496

Pivovar Klaster
Klaster
CS-294 14 Hradistea and
  Jizerou
Tel 0329 2727

Pivovary Krusovice
CS-270 53 Krusovice
Tel 0313 95131
Fax 0313 95112

Pivovary Liberec
Vlatislavice nN
CS-463 11 Liberec

Pivovar Litomerica
Lidicka 15
CS-412 66 Litomerica
Tel 0416 5151

Pivivar Louny
Cerncice
CS-440 85 Louny 1

Pivovar Sluzby
Husova 64
CS-440 39 Louny
Tel 0395 3522
Fax 0395 3522

Pivovar Most
CS-424 35 Most-Sedlec

Pivovar Radegast
p Dobra 4
CS-739 51 Nosovice
Tel 0658 22851
Fax 0658 89 393

Pivovar Ostravar
Hornopolni 57
CS-728 25 Ostrava
Tel 069 234624
Fax 069 231978

Gambrinus Brewery
U Prazdroje
CS-304 97 Plzen

**Pilsner-Urquell
  Brewerypalaca**
U Prazdroje 7
CS-304 97 Plzen
Tel 019 34031
Fax 019 227283
*Open only to group tours, but
the Beer Hall is open.*

Pivovary Bohemia
Korunni 106
CS-101 00 Prague 10

Brewery Branik
Udolni 212
CS-147 00 Prague 4
Tel 02 46 18 41
Fax 02 46 98 42

Pragovar Brewery
U Pruhonu 13
CS-170 04 Prague 7
Tel 02 80 89 48
Fax 02 80 11 68

Pivovary A. Sladovny Praha
Lipova 15
CS-120 44 Prague 2
Tel 02 29 66 41
Fax 02 23 55 28 5
Herold.

Staropramen Brewery
Nadrazni 84
CS-150 54 Prague 5
Tel 02 53 85 41
Fax 02 53 83 33
Prazske Pivovary.

U Fleku
Kremencova 9
Prague 1
Tel 29 32 46
Contact: Cedok, 02 231
0255
Pub and brewery, founded 1499. Open daily 8AM to 11 PM. Last pub in Prague still brewing its own beer. Food available. Special brewery tour departs 24 Wenceslas Square on Friday morning, lasts 1–{1/2} hours.

Moravskoslezske Pivovary
Komenskeho 35
CS-750 51 Prerov

Pivovar Prostejov
Vrahovicka 57
CS-796 24 Prostejov
Tel 0508 237224174
Fax 0508 24174

Ustecke Pivovary
Drazdanska 80
CS-401 73 Usti nad Labern

Pivovar Velke Popovice
Hlavni 1
CS-251 69 Velke Popovice
Tel 02 99 27 09
Fax 02 99 27 03

Pivovar Zatec
Zizkovo nam 81
CS-438 33 Zatec
Tel 0397 4471

Pivovary A Sodovkarny
Hradni 2
CS-669 28 Znojmo
Tel 0624 6551
Fax 0625 3041

Places to Enjoy Beer

Spalicek
12 Zelny trh
Brno
Tel 05 23692
Beer hall with food. Terrace overlooks the Cabbage Market.

Spalicek
Zelny trh
Brno

Pivnice Stopkova
Ceska ul 5
Brno
Tel 05 233

Pivnice U tri knizat
Minoritska ul
Brno

Masne Kramy
Krajinska ulice 23
CS-370 54 Ceske
  Budejovice
Tel 38 37957
Beer hall.

U Trojice
next door to Budvar Brewery
Ceske Budejovice

Krystal Restaurace
Zizkova ul
Jihlava

Plzenska Pivnice
Husova ul 20
Jihlava

Zlata Husa
Palackeho
Jindrichuv Hradec
The Golden Goose.

Bar Lotka
Legionarska ul
Olomouc
Bar in an old airplane.

U Cerneho Vola
Lorestanska 2
Prague 1
Tel 53 86 37

Cerny Pivovar Plzenska
Karlovo nam 15
Prague
Tel 27 32 09

U Dvou Kocek
pl Stare Mesto
Uhelny Trh 10
Prague
Tel 26 77 29

U Medvidku (The Bear's Den)
Na Perstyne 7
Prague
Tel 23 58 904

U Kotvy
Spalena ul 11
Prague
Tel 29 57 28

U sv Tomase (St Thomas')
Letenska 12
Prague 1
Tel 53 00 64
Serves Branik dark beer. Open daily 11AM to 3PM, 4PM to midnight.

U zlateho tygra (Golden Tiger)
Husova 17
Prague 1
Tel 26 52 19
Serves Pilsner Urquell. Open Monday to Saturday, 3 to 11PM.

Bily Konicek
Town Square
Trebon
Tel 0333 2248
Little White Horse Restaurant, dating from 1544, serving local beer.

Festivals

PIVEX
Fairgrounds
Brno
Tel 00425 314 4922
Fax 00425 314 1111
Contact: PP 491
Vystaviste 1
660 91 Brno
Late May, 5 days. Brewery and maltings trade show (machinery, materials, beer and brewery products), with exhibitors from the former Czechoslovakia and other European countries. Open to the public.

Beer Party
Hotel International
Koulova 15
CS-160 45 Prague 6
Tel 311 82 01
Daily, May 15 to November 30. Brass band for dancing, singing or listening, folklore program, complete dinner, unlimited consumption of Pilsner Urquell.

Of Historic Interest

Pivovarske Museum
Veleslavinova ul 6
CS-304 97 Plzen
Tel 019 33989
Brewery museum in a late Gothic malthouse. Open Tuesday PM, Wednesday to Sunday.

Slovak Republic

Places to Enjoy Beer

Pivovarska Restauracia
Krizna 26
Bratislava
Also known simply as Stain.

Smichovsky Dvor
Heydukova
Bratislava

Stara Sladovna
Cintorinska ul 32
Bratislava
Old malthouse, seats 1600. Velkopopovicky and Budvar on tap.

Pivaren U Eda, Biela ulica, Bratislava.

Pivaren Wolkerova
Biela 5
Bratislava

U Maka
Bocna
Kosice
Draft beer, Hungarian food.

Jelen
Nam SNP 22
Kremnica
Beer hall with good local food.

Restauracia Pod Agatmi
nr Zupne Namestie
Nitra
Open-air barbecue and beer joint.

Thurzo
Stefanikova and ul pri Synagogue
Nitra

Central
Piestany
Self-service buffet with draft beer.

Plzenska Pivnica
Zlata Fatima Arcade
Trencin

Denmark

Breweries

Bryggeriforeningen
Frederiksbergggade 11
DK-1459 Copenhagen K
Tel 33 12 62 41
Fax 33 14 25 13

Ceres Bryggerierne
Ceres Alle 1
DK-8100 Aarhus C
Tel 86 12 58 55
Fax 86 19 92 71

Thor Bryggerierne
P.O. Box 548
DK-8100 Aarhus C
Tel 86 12 58 55
Fax 86 13 65 06

Bryggeriet Vestfyen
Faaborgvej 4
DK-5610 Assens
Tel 64 71 10 41
Fax same

Bryggeriet Apollo
Vesterbrogade 3
DK-1620 Copenhagen V
Tel 33 12 33 13
The first house brewery in
Denmark.

Carlsberg Brewery
Elephant Gate
140 Ny Carlsbergvej
Copenhagen
Tel 33 27 13 14
Guided tours Monday to
Friday, 9 and 11AM,
2:30PM, free samples.
Brewery museum.

Tuborg Brewery
54 Strandvejen
Hellerup
Copenhagen
Tel 33 27 22 12
Tours Monday to Friday,
10AM, 12:30 and 2:30 PM.
Free samples.

Wibroes Bryggeri
Elsinore
Brews Carlsberg, Tuborg,
Neptun Krone, Pokal, NAB,
and Dansk LA.

Faxe Bryggeri
DK-4640 Fakse
Tel 53 71 37 00
Fax 53 71 47 64
Tours Monday to Friday.

Fredericia Bryggeri
Fredericia
Brews Carlsberg and Tuborg
for W Denmark.

Bryggeriet S C Fuglsang
Bryggerivej 2
DK-6100 Haderslav
Tel 74 52 33 02
Fax 74 53 38 59

Carlsberg International
Strandvejen 50
DK-2900 Hellerup
Tel 45 31 29 81 22
Fax 45 31 29 35 07

Bryggeri Albani
Tvaergade 19
DK-5100 Odense C
Tel 66 13 23 01
Fax 65 91 68 00
Giraf.

Harboe's Bryggeri
Spegerborgvej 34
DK-4230 Skaelskor
Tel 53 59 40 40
Fax 53 59 40 86

Places to Enjoy Beer

Bent J
Norre Alle 66
Arhus
Tel 86 120492
Bar with live jazz most nights.

Casablanca
Rosengade 12
Arhus

Axel Dans Bar
Axeltorv 2
DK-1069 Copenhagen V
Tel 33 13 03 78

Britannia
Lovestrade 4
Copenhagen
Tel 33 14 89 69

Cafe & Olhalle
Romersgade 22
Copenhagen
Tel 33 93 25 75

McGrath's Irish Pub
Osterbrogade 112
Copenhagen
Tel 35 26 62 56

Queens Pub
Vester Volkgade 25
Copenhagen
Tel 33 12 59 02

Shamrock Inn
Vesterbrogade 2 E
Scala
Copenhagen
Tel 33 14 06 02
Irish pub. Open daily.

Spunk Bodega
Istedgade 17
Copenhagen
Tel 31 31 57 45

On-Off
Ny Vestergade 19
Odense

Of Historic Interest

Carlsberg Museum
Valby Langgade 1
Copenhagen
Tel 31 21 01 12
A century of Danish brewing.
Open Monday to Friday, free.

Glasmuseet
Ebeltoft
Glass museum.

Funen Village
Sejerskovvej 20
Odense
Open-air living history
museum that occasionally
brews beer, which it then gives
to visitors. Summer.

Estonia

Tourist Information
30 Toome St.
Tallinn
Tel 66-479

Breweries

Industrial Plant Varma
Pikk 59
EE-3300 Kuressaare
Tel 01445 55844
Fax 01445 56409

Valtu kolhoos
Valtu
EE-3500 Rapla
Tel 01448 62693

Estonian Union of Land Industries
Gonsiori 29
EE-0104 Tallinn
Tel 0142 422004
Fax 0142 442325

Tartu Brewery
Tahtvere 56-62
EE-2400 Tartu
Tel 01434 34330
Fax 01434 31193

August
Mustla
Tarvastu
EE-2922 Viljandi
Tel 01443 41146

Karksi Collective Farm
Karksi
Polli
EE-2944 Viljandi
Tel 01443 31210

Karme
Karski
EE-2944 Viljandi
Tel 01443 31533

Places to Enjoy Beer

Veski Cafe
Parna 19
Kuressaare
Pub in old windmill, serves Saaremaa beer.

Kannike
108 Vabaduse Puiestee
Talinn
Tel 447888
Beer, light snacks, and sauna.

Lucky Luke's
20 Mere Puiestee
Talinn

Sky Bar
3 Vabaduse Valjak
Talinn
Tel 451510

Baar Regatt
Merivalja tee 1
Pirita
Tallinn

Eeslitall Keldribaar
Dunkri 4
Tallinn

Humal
Kuutri 12
Tartu
Beer cellar.

Finland

Finnish Tourist Board
P.O. Box 625
Toolonkatu 11
SF-00101 Helsinki
Tel 0 403 011
Fax 4030 1333
Tourist information, calendar of events.

Breweries

Hartwall Brewery
P.O. Box 31
SF-00391 Helsinki
Tel 0 540 21
Fax 0 540 2453
Home of Lapin Culta, meaning the gold of Lapland.

Sinebrychoff Brewery
Mallaskatu 1
P.O. Box 24
SF-00121 Helsinki
Tel 0 162 11
Fax 0 162 1464
Usually known as Koff beer.

Olvi Brewery
Tehtaankatu 13
P.O. Box 16
SF-74101 Iisalmi
Tel 77 158 51
Fax 18 521 552

Joutsan Sahti
Yhdystie 3
SF-19651 Joutsa
Tel 47 23379

Toppilan Mallasjuomatehdas
Timperintie
SF-87500 Kajaani
Tel 86 385 06
Non-alcoholic beer.

Mallasjuoma
Kolankatu 17
P.O. Box 44
SF-15151 Lahti
Tel 18 862 11
Fax 18 521 552

Hartwall Brewery
Oravaisenkatu 6
P.O. Box 33
SF-95401 Tornio
Tel 698 41751

Brostromin Panimo
Kustaala
SF-65250 Vaasa
Tel 61 212228

Cidermakers

Suomen Marjat
Yrittajankatu 6
SF-67100 Kokkola
Tel 68 311 011
Fax 68 311 016

Places to Enjoy Beer

Angleterre
Fredrikinkatu 47
Helsinki

Kaarle XII
Kasarmikatu 40
Helsinki

O'Malley's
Helsinki
Irish pub.

Vanham Kellari
Mannerheiminti 3
Helsinki

Henry's Pub
Kauppakatu 18
Kuopio

Jumpru
Kauppurienkatu 6
Oulu

Hunter's Inn
Itensaisyydenkatu 3
Tampere
*Hard rock downstairs,
vegetarian pizza upstairs.*

Salhojankadun
Itensaisyydenkatu
Tampere
Draft Guinness.

France

Organizations

ABF
25 blvd. Malesherbes
F-75008 Paris
Tel 01 42 66 29 27
Fax 42 66 52 79
*Association des Brasseurs de
France: association of French
brewers.*

CSMF
22 rue Lavoisier
F-75008 Paris
Tel 01 42 66 28 74
*Chambre syndicale de la
Malterie Francaise.*

**Institut Francais des
Boissons**
Vandoeuvre
Technical research.

Biere, le Magazine
33 av. de Wagram
F-75017 Paris
Tel 47 66 51 81

Editions Coprur
34 rue du Wacken
F-67000 Strasbourg
Tel 88 35 91 11
Fax 88 35 25 70
Books on beer.

Breweries

Interbrew France,
14 av. Pierre Brosolette
F-59426 Armentieres
Tel 20 48 30 30

**Brasserie Nouvelle de
Lutece**
15 rue Moulin-Bateau
F-94387 Bonneuil-sur-
Marne
Tel 43 77 00 78

Kanterbrau
204 Rond Point du Pont de
Sevres
F-92516 Boulogne-
Billancourt
Tel 46 94 73 73

**Brasserie l'Abbaye de
Crespin**
Crespin
Tel 27 45 42 10

**Grande Brasserie
Enfants de Gayant**
63 faubourg de Paris BP 89
F-59502 Douai CEDEX
Tel 27 93 26 22
Fax 27 87 55 49
*Saaz Old Lager, Goldenberg,
Bieres du Demon, du Desert,
abbaye de St.-Landelin.*

Haag Metzger
Hochfelden
Tel 88 71 73 73

Brasserie Meteor
6 rue du General Lebocq
F-67270 Hochfelden
Tel 88 91 52 41
*Tours available. Meteor,
Ackerland.*

Brasserie Duyck
Rte. Nationale
BP 6
F-59144 Jenlain
Tel 27 49 70 03
Fax 27 49 74 81
*Biere Jenlain, biere de
Printemps.*

Brasseries Heineken
Av. Francois Chardigny
F-13011 Marseilles
Tel 91 18 85 18

Brasserie Amos
Metz
Tel 87 66 71 11

Brasseries Heineken
Zl la Pilaterie rue du
 Houblon
F-59370 Mons-en-Baroeul
Tel 20 33 67 00

Brasserie des Deux
 Rivieres
1 place de la Madeleine
Morlaix Brittany
Tel 98 63 41 92
Corleff Ale.

Higy Fernand
Mulhouse
Tel 89 46 34 44

Brasseries Kronenbourg
Blvd. de l'Europe
F-67210 Obernai
Tel 88 27 44 88

La Micro Brasserie
106 rue de Richelieu
F-75002 Paris
Tel 96 55 31
Brewpub.

Lyons
Pierrelaye
Tel 34 13 54 50

Brasserie de la Rance
Quevert
Tel 96 39 27 84

Brasserie Jeanne d'Arc
38 rue Anatole France
F-59790 Ronchin
Tel 20 53 62 85

Grande Brasserie
 Moderne
3 quai d'Anvers
BP 409
F-59057 Roubaix
Tel 20 26 92 26
Fax 20 36 75 05
Terken Blonde, Brune,

Septante 5, Christmas,
Orland, Noordheim, Breug.

Brasseries Heineken
19 rue des Deux-Gares
F-92565 Rueil-Malmaison
Tel 47 13 36 50
Fax 47 14 36 84

Brasserie St. Omer
9 rue Edouard Devaux
F-62600 St. Omer
Tel 21 98 76 00
Fax 21 98 76 30
St.-Omer, Semeuse, Facon.

Brasserie de St Sylvestre
1 rue de la Chapelle
F-59114 St.-Sylvestre
 Cappel
Tel 28 40 15 49
3 Monts.

Brasserie de Saverne
60 rue de Dettwiler
F-67700 Saverne
Tel 88 71 74 74
Fax 88 91 85 04
Campus.

Grande Brasserie
 d'Adelshoffen
87 rte. de Bischwiller
F-67302 Schiltigheim
 CEDEX
Tel 88 83 90 20
Fax 88 62 30 25
Adelscott, Rheingold,
Tradition, Alsator.

Brasserie Fischer
7 rte. de Bischwiller
F-67300 Schiltigheim
Tel 88 33 82 99

Francaise de Brasserie
4–10 rue St.-Charles
BP 43
F-67301 Schiltigheim
 CEDEX
Tel 88 62 90 80
Heineken's Schiltigheim
Brewery. Tours available
Monday to Friday in French,
English, German: contact
Visitors Department.

Gde Brasserie Patrie
 Schutzenberger
F-67300 Schiltigheim
Tel 88 33 14 67

Brasseries Kronenbourg
68 rte. d'Oberhausbergen
BP 13
F-67200 Strasbourg
Tel 88 27 41 59
Fax 88 27 42 06
Tours available. Kronenbourg,
Kronenbourg Light, 1664,
1664 Brune, Obernai, Tourtel,
Silver, Force 4, Krony.

Cider

Route du Cidre
Cambremer Normandy
Contact: Calvados Tourisme
pl. du Canada
Caen
Tel:31 86 53 30
A signposted route through the
Pays d'Auge, highlighting the
cider farms.

Musee du Cidre
Melleray-la-Vallee
Tel 43 04 71 48
Cider museum. Tastings of
ciders, apple juices, and
liqueurs. Open Easter to
November 1.

Les Celliers Associes
Pleudihen-sur-Rance
Tel 96 83 20 02
Cider production.

Places to Enjoy Beer

Des Amis
35 rue Haute
Honfleur
Normandy

Le Pubstore
44 rue de la Halle
Lille

Albion Public House
12 rue St.-Catherine
Lyon

Le Stendhal
92 rue Jean-de-Bernady
Marseille

Scarlett O'Hara
22 rue Droite
*Nice. Irish pub, good
Guinness.*

L'Abbaye
1 place de la Bastille
Paris
Tel 72 16 39

L'Academie de la Biere
88 bis blvd. Port Royal
F-75005 Paris
Tel 43 54 66 65

Bar Belge
75 ave. de St.-Ouen
F-75017 Paris
Tel 46 27 41 01

Brasserie Lipp
151 blvd. St.-Germain
Paris
Tel 45 48 53 91
*Restaurant, traditional fare
and good beer.*

Gambrinus
56 rue des Lombards
F-75001 Paris
Tel 42 21 10 30

Au General LaFayette
52 rue LaFayette
Paris
Tel 70 59 08

La Gueuze
19 rue Soufflot
Paris
Tel 54 63 00P
Pub with Belgian specialties.

Hall's Beer Tavern
68 rue St.-Denis
F-75001 Paris
Tel 42 36 92 72
*Pub restaurant. British,
German, and Czech beers.*

La Mazet
61 rue St.-Andre des Arts
Paris
Tel 54 68 81

L'Oiseau de Feu
12 place de la Bastille
Paris
Tel 19 07 52

Le Sous-Bock
45 rue St.-Honore
F-75001 Paris
Tel 40 26 46 61

La Taverne de Rybens
12 rue St.-Denis
F-75001 Paris
Tel 08 14 59

Tavern St.-Germain
17 rue de l'Ancienne-
   Comedie
F-75006 Paris
Tel 22 88 98
*Pub restaurant. Twenty taps,
170 bottles.*

La Taverne de Nesle
32 rue Dauphine
F-75006 Paris
Large beer selection.

Tight Johnny
55 rue Montmartre
F-75002 Paris

Au Trappiste
4 rue St.-Denis
F-75001 Paris
Tel 42 33 08 50

Bierstub
Place de la patinoire
niveau 1
F-92092 Paris la Defense
Tel 47 23 71 03
*Restaurant serving the cuisine
of Alsace.*

Ceili
rue Aristide-Briand 4
Quimper
Brittany

Les Deux Cournouailles
rue Aristide-Briand 2
Quimper
Brittany

Barantici
rue St.-Michel
Rennes
Brittany

Big Ben Pub
95 rue du Gros-Horloge
Rouen
Normandy
Tel 35 84 44 50

La Boite a Bieres
33 rue Cauchoise
Rouen
Normandy
Tel 35 07 76 47

La Taverne St.-Armand
11 rue St.-Armand
Rouen
Normandy
Tel 35 88 51 34

L'Academie de la Biere
17 rue Adolphe Seyboth
Strasbourg

Festivals

Beer Festival
F-67300 Schiltigheim
Tel 88 83 90 00
Early August, 4 days.

Eurobiere
6 place de Bordeaux
F-67000 Strasbourg
Tel 88 36 67 31
Early April, odd years. Trade
exhibition, open to the public.
European brewers and
beverage service companies.

Instruction and Training Courses

ENSAIA Massy
1 av. des Olympiades
F-91305 Massy
Tel 69 20 05 23
L'Ecole Nationale Superieure
d'Agronomie et des Industries
Alimentaires de Massy.

ENSAIA Nancy
2 av. de la Foret de Haye
BP 172
F-54505 Vandoeuvres les
Nancy CEDEX
Tel 83 59 59 59
L'Ecole Nationale Superieure
d'Agronomie et des Industries
Alimentaires de Nancy.

ENSAIA Villeneuve d'Ascq
369 rue Jules Guesde
F-59651 Villeneuve d'Ascq
Tel 20 05 45 00
L'Ecole Nationale Superieure
d'Agronomie et des Industries
Alimentaires de Villeneuve
d'Ascq.

Of Historic Interest

Pasteur's House
Arbois
Tel 84 66 11 72
Home of Louis Pasteur.

Musee de la Biere
14 av. Pierre Brossolette
F-59426 Armentieres
Tel 20 48 30 30

Chateau d'Etoges
4 rue Richebourg
F-51270 Etoges
Tel 26 59 30 08
Former coaching inn of the
kings of France. Not your
usual pub.

Musee Industriel & Commercial
F-59000 Lille

Musee de la Polyculture
Grande Rue
F-54200 Lucey
Tel 83 63 85 21

Musee de la Biere
510 av. de la Republique
F-52100 St. Dizier

Musee Francais de la Brasserie
62 rue Charles Courtois
F-54210 St.-Nicholas de-
Port
Tel 83 46 95 52

Musee Europeen de la Biere
Rue de la Citadelle
F-55700 Stenay
Tel 29 80 68 78
Fax 29 80 42 42

Musee Vosgien de la Brasserie
F-88270 Ville sur Illon
Tel 29 36 53 18

Georgia

Intourist
7 Rustaveli Prospekt
Tbilisi 380004
Tel 99-7089
Fax 99 78 28
Tourist information.

Germany

National Tourist Board
Beethovenstr 69
D-6000 Frankfurt am Main
Tel 069 75720
Fax 069-751 903
Tourist information.

Arnegger Brau
Hoher Wall 5-7
D-4600 Dortmund 1
Tel 0231 18 22 239
Fax 0231 18 22 232
Association of 40 small
private breweries: non-
alcoholic beer.

Hopfenforschungsinstitut
Huell
Hop research institute.

Verband deutscher Hopfenpflanzer
Kellerstr 1
Postfach 229
D-8069 Wolnzach
Tel 08442 3511
Fax 08442 4270
German hop-growers' association. Magazine Hopfen, *in German and English. Information on hop culture.*

Books and Magazines

Brauindustrie
Schloss Mindelburg
D-8948 Mindelheim
Tel 08261 999 0
Fax 08261 999 225
Industry magazine with technical and marketing information. 12/year.

Beer Drinker's Guide to Munich, by Larry Hawthorne
D-8000 Munich
Freizeit Publishers. Available in U.S. from the Beer Enthusiast catalogue.

Brauwelt
Verlag Hans Carl
Postfach 9110
D-8500 Nuremburg 11

Breweries

Alpirsbacher Klosterbraeu
Postfach 1220
D-7297 Alpirsbach
Tel 074 44 67 0
Fax 074 44 15 10

Andechs Brewpub
Andechs Monastery
Ammersee

Max Wagner
D-85653 Ampferbach
House beers (contract-brewed), good food.

Brauerei Aying
Zornedingerstr 1
D-85653 Aying
Tel 08095 880
Fax 08095 8850

Brauerei Koestrizer
Bad Koestritz
Producers of Schwarzbier.

Faessla
Obere Koenigstr 21
D-8600 Bamberg
Brewpub with good food.

Griefenklau
Laurenziplatz 20
D-8600 Bamberg
Tel 53219

Kaiserdom Privatbrauerei
Breitaeckerstr 9
D-8600 Bamberg 14
Tel 0951 60450
Fax 951 60 45 60

Spezial
Obere Koenigstr 10
D-8600 Bamberg
Tel 24304
Brewpub. Rauchbier.

Privatbrauerei Gebr Maisel
Hindenburgstr 9
Postfach 10 07 30
D-8580 Bayreuth
Tel 0921 401 0
Fax 0921 40 1206
With brewery museum.

Peter Schopen Brauerei
Gischer Weg 7
D-5012 Bedburg
Tel 02272 20 08 9
Fax 02272 8 23 80
Schopen Pils, Severins Koelsch.

Brauerei K Silbernagel
Hauptstr 78
Postfach 1160
D-6729 Belheim
Tel 72 72 70 10
Fax 72 72 70 11 77
Lord Pils, Silber Pils, Hefenweizen, Weizenperle.

Berliner Kindl Brauerei
Werbellinstr 50
Postfach 44 02 53
D-1000 Berlin 44
Tel 30 6 89 92 0
Fax 30 68 99 22 12

Landbierbrauerei
Brauereistr 2—5
Postfach 1164
D-7616 Biberach/Baden
Black Forest country beer.

Bitburger Brauerei
Roemermauer 3
Postfach 1164
D-5520 Bitburg/Eifel
Tel 65 61 140
Fax 65 61 14289

Boennsch Hausbrauerei
Sternbruecke 4
D-5300 Bonn
Brewpub serving Boennsch (local version of Koelsch).

Schlossbrauerei Braunfels
Gebr-Waehlstr 21
D-6333 Braunfels
Tel 064 42 50 55
Fax 064 42 42 15

Gebr Schoemaker
Ingolstadterstr 4
D-2800 Bremen 1
Tel 0421 38 91 0
Fax 0421 39 44 59

Hofmark Brauerei
Postfach 1333
D-8490 Cham-Loifling
Tel 9971 3301
Fax 9971 32233

Gebr Paeffen
Friesenstr
D-5000 Cologne
Brewpub with food, beer garden.

Crailsheimer Engel-Braeu
Hallerstr 29
D-7180 Crailsheim
Tel 07951 21075
Fax 07951 21556

Fuerstlich Fuerstenbergische Brau
Postplatz 1–4
D-7710 Donaueschingen
Tel 0771 86 0

Dortmunder Actien-Brauerei, DAB
Steigerstr 20
Postfach 10 50 12
D-4145 Dortmund
Tel 02 31 84 00 0
Fax 02 31 8 40 05 30

Dortmunder Union Brauerei, DUB
Rheinischestr 2
D-4600 Dortmund 1

Hoevel's
Hoher Wall
D-4600 Dortmund
Brewpub. Bitterbier.

Kronen Brauerei
Kronenburgallee 1
Pf 10 50 46
D-4600 Dortmund 1
Tel 0231 54 13 0
Fax 0231 54 13 390

Wenker's
Marktplatz
D-4600 Dortmund
Brewpub owned by Kronen Brewery. Urtrueb.

Koenig Brauerei
Postfach 66 01 40
D-4100 Duisburg 12
Tel 0203 455 3486
Fax 0203 455 2593

Ferdinand Schumaker
Oststr
D-4000 Dusseldorf
Brewpub.

Im Fuechsen
Ratingerstr
Altstadt
D-4000 Dusseldorf
Brewpub.

Zum Schluessel
Bolkerstr
Altstadt
D-4000 Dusseldorf
Brewpub.

Zum Uerige
Bergerstr
Altstadt
D-4000 Dusseldorf
Brewpub.

Privatbrauerei Erdinger Weissbraeu
Lange Zeile 1–3
D-8058 Erding
Tel 081 22 4090
Fax 081 22 409 315
Weissbier, Dunkel, Pikantus Weizenbock.

Brauerei Neder
D-8550 Forchheim
Brewpub.

Zu den Zwolf Aposteln
D-6000 Frankfurt am Main
Brewpub restaurant.

Henninger-Braeu
Hainerweg 37–53
D-6000 Frankfurt-am-Main
Tel 069 6 06 30
Fax 069 60 63 640

Bayerische Staatsbrauerei
Weihenstephan
Postfach 11 55
D-85311 Freising
Tel 081 61 30 21 24
Fax 081 61 1 21 01

Postbrauerei M Renkl
Postgasse 3
D-8316 Frontenhausen
Tel 08732 12 12
Fax 08732 29 05

Schlossbrauerei Kaltenberg
Schlossstr 8
D-8085 Geltendorf

Griefswalder Brauerei
Grimmerstr 84–85
D-2200 Griefswald
Tel 37 51 67

Eders Familienbrauerei
Postfach 1220
Aschaffenburgstr 3–5
D-8754 Grossostheim
Tel 06026 509 0
Fax 060 26 90 EDER
Eders Pils, Export; Alt-Ostheimer (non-alcoholic).

Bavaria-St. Pauli
 Brauerei
Hopfenstr 15
Postfach 30 02 10
D-2000 Hamburg 364
Tel 040 311 03 0
Fax 040 31 103500

Groeninger Braukeller
Ost-Weststr 47
D-2000 Hamburg
Tel 33 13 81
*Brewery with pub serving food
after 1PM.*

Holsten Brauerei
Holstenstr 224
Postfach 50 07 49
D-2000 Hamburg 50
Tel 40 38101 0
Fax 40 38101 904

Gilde Brauerei
Postfach 3807
D-3000 Hanover 1
Tel 0511 80051

Brauerei Herrenhausen
Herrenhaeuserstr 83–97
Pf 21 01 40
D-3000 Hanover 21
Tel 0511 79 07 0
Fax 0511 790 72 59

Brauerei Felsenkeller
 Herford
Postfach 13 51
D-4900 Herford

Scherdelhof
 Privatbrauerei
Unterkotzauer Weg 14
Postfach 1604
D-8670 Hof
Tel 09281 896 0
Fax 09281 896 31
Premium and Weizenbier.

Schlossbrauerei
 Unterkotzau
Hirschbergerstr 6
D-8670 Hof
Fax 09281 6 11 87

Karlsberg Brauerei
Karlsbergstr 62
Postfach 1351
D-6650 Homburg Saar

Herrenbraeu
Buegerlisches Brauhaus
Manchingerstr 95
D-8070 Ingolstadt

Privatbrauerei Diebels
Postfach 1161
D-4174 Issum 1
Tel 02835 30 0
Fax 02835 301 45

Friesiches Braeuhaus zu
 Jever
Elisabethhufer 17
Postfach 260
D-2942 Jever
Tel 040 31 10 33 95
Fax 040 31 10 35 00

Aktien-Brauerei
 Kaufbeuren
Hoelzlestr 12
Postfach 1134
D-8950 Kaufbeuren
Tel 08341 4304 0
Fax 08341 43 04 50

Rosenbrauerei
Afraberg 5
D-8950 Kaufbeuren
Tel 08341 43 06 0
Fax 08341 43 06 55

Privatbrauerei G.
 Schneider & Sohn
Emil-Ottstr 1–5
Postfach 1644
D-8420 Kelheim/Donau
Tel 09441 705 0
Fax 09441 705 190
Weissbier.

Allgaeur Brauhaus
Beethovenstr 7
D-8960 Kempten/Allgaeu
Tel 0831 2 05 00
Fax 0831 2 05 0114

Koenigsbacher Brauerei
Neustadt 5
Postfach 1120
D-5400 Koblenz an Rhein
Tel 06831 84245
Fax 06731 891289

Adlerbrauerei
 Goeggingen
Kirchweg 2
D-7482 Krauchenweis-
 Goegg
Tel 075 76 867
Fax 075 86 78 99
Goegginger-Export, Pils.

Krombacher Brauerei
Hagenerstr 261
Postfach 760
D-5910 Kreuztal-Krombach
Tel 027 32 880 0
Fax 027 32 88 02 54

Erste Kulmbacher
 Actienbrauerei
EKU Str. 1
D-95326 Kulmbach
Tel 09221 82272
Fax 09221 82281
EKU beers.

**Kulmbacher
  Moenschshofbraeu**
Hoferstr 20
Postfach 1560
D-8650 Kulmbach
Tel 09221 80 50
Fax 09221 805 79

Reichelbraeu
Postfach 1860
D-8650 Kulmbach/Bayern
Tel 09221 705 0
Fax 09221 70 53 17

**Exportbierbrauerei
  Sternberg**
Lutzshena
D-7143 Leipzig
Tel 59 41 66

Brauerei Stumpf
Postfach 320
D-8770 Lohr am Main
Tel 09352 90 67

**Privatbrauerei Ernst
  Barre**
Berlinerstr 122–124
Postfach 1159
D-4990 Luebbecke 1
Tel 057 41 27 01 0
*Barre-Braeu, Barre's Light,
Altstadt Alt.*

Kronen-Brauerei
Heilgengeiststr
Lueneburg
*Has C15 beerhall serving beer
and food.*

Eichbaum Brauerei
Kaefertalerstr 170
D-6800 Mannheim 1
Tel 0621 39 03 290
Fax 0621 3 90 32 11
Eichbaum Ureich Pils.

Hoesl-Braeu
Bahnhofstr 1
D-8596 Mitterteich

Franken Braeu
Postfach 1250
D-8621 Mitwitz
Tel 09266 721
Fax 09266 6341

Hannen Brauerei
Senefelderstr 25
D-4050 Moenchengladbach
  1
Tel 02161 667 0
Hannen Alt, Tuborg

Arcobraeu
Graefliches Brauhaus
D-8351 Moos bei Plattling
Tel 09938 18 0
Fax 09938 1878
*Urfass, Pilsener, wheat beers,
light white beer, Coronation
Doppelbock.*

Brauerei Pinkus Mueller
Kreuzstr 4–10
D-4400 Muenster

Hacker-Pschorr Braeu
Hochstr 75
D-8000 Munich 90
Tel 089 51 06 8 00
Fax 089 51 06 289

Loewenbraeu
Nymphenburgerstr 4
D-80013 Munich 2
Tel 089 52 00 0
Fax 089 52 00 651

**Paulaner-Salvator-
  Thomasbraeu**
Hochstr 75
D-81541 Munich 95
Tel 089 4 80 050
Fax 089 4 80 05 438

**Spaten-Franziskaner-
  Braeu**
Marsstr 46–48
D-80018 Munich 2
Tel 089 51 22 0
Fax 089 51 22 403

Staatliches Hofbrauhaus
Hofbrauallee 1
Postfach 82 08 49
D-81808 Munich 82
Tel 089 921 050
Fax 089 906 426

Brauerei Stegmaier
Lammstr 1
Postfach 20
D-7075 Mutlangen
Tel 07171 7888
Fax 07171 7837

Postbrauerei
Hauptstr 25
D-8964 Nesselwang
Tel 08361 309 60
Fax 08361 309 74

Kaiser Braeu
Postfach 1
D-8574 Neuhaus/Pegnitz
Tel 091 56 88 0
Fax 091 56 88 50

Geussenbraeu
Ketschenbacherstr 25
D-8632 Neustadt/Coburg

Patrizierbraeu
D-8500 Nuremburg
Tel 0911 28 22 82

Tucherbraeu
Schillerplatz 10
D-8500 Nuremburg 10
Tel 0911 36 06 0
Fax 0911 360 62 53

Ankerbraeu
D-8703 Ochsenfurt
Tel 09331 615
Fax 09331 2 01 02

Kauzenbraeu
Uffenheimstr 17
D-8703 Ochsenfurt
Tel 09331 606
Fax 09331 58 32
*Independent brewery since
1809.*

Paderborner Brauerei
Halberstaedterstr 45
D-4790 Paderborn
Tel 05251 707 0
Fax 05251 707 105

Pfungstaedter Brauerei
Eberstaedterstr 89
D-6102 Pfungstadt
Tel 061 57 8020
Fax 06157 86191

Parkbrauerei
Zweilbrueckerstr 3–5
D-6780 Pirmasens
Tel 06331 80 50
Fax 06331 805 220

**Plochinger
  Waldhornbrauerei**
Neckarstr 25–33
D-7310 Plochingen

Werner Braeu
Hauptstr 13–15
D-8721 Poppenhausen
Tel 09725 670
Fax 09725 67 99

Brauerei Bischofshof
Heitzerstr 2
D-8400 Regensburg
Tel 0941 20 01 0
Fax 0941 2 89 28

Fuerstliches Brauerei
Galgenbergstr 14
Postfach 98
D-8400 Regensburg 1
Tel 0941 786 130
*Brewery of the Duke of Thurn
and Taxis. Free tours and
samples, advance reservations
necessary.*

Riegeler Brauerei
Postfach 20
D-7839 Riegel
Tel 07642 67181
Fax 07642 67 151

Engel Brauerei
Engelgasse 2
D-7070 Schwaebisch-
  Gmund
Tel 071 71 6 10 58
Fax 071 71 3 73 66

Brauhaus Schweinfurt
Klingenbrunnstr 22–26
Pf 4020
D-8720 Schweinfurt
Tel 09721 536 0
Fax 09721 5 36 33

Calwer-Eck-Braeu
Calwerstr 31
D-7000 Stuttgart 1
*Brewpub with good homemade
food.*

Dinkelacker Brauerei
Tuebingerstr 46
Postfach 10 11 52
D-70178 Stuttgart 1
Tel 711 64 81 233
Fax 711 64 81 200

Tue 8
Tuebingerstr 8
D-7000 Stuttgart 1
Brewpub with food.

Kieselbraeu
Postfach 1449
D-8220 Traunstein
Tel 0861 6 00 11
Fax 0861 42 65

Gasthaus Winkler
Velburg-Lengenfeld
Tel 09182 326
*Brewpub, restaurant, and
hotel Kipfer Spezial, Pils,
Helles, Export.*

Warsteiner Brauerei
Domring 4–10
Postfach 1366
D-59564 Warstein
Tel 29 02 88 0
Fax 29 02 88 299

**Exportbierbrauerei
  Wernesgrun**
Bergstr 4
D-9709 Wernesgrun
Tel 4-16

**Privatbrauerei Gebr
  Euler**
Postfach 1244
D-6330 Wetzlar
Tel 06441 47055
Fax 06441 47029

**Erzquell Brauerei
  Bielstein**
Bilesteinerstr 108
Postfach 2120
D-5276 Wiehl-Bielstein
Tel 02262 820
Fax 02262 8 21 06

**Praesidenten Pils
  Brauerei**
Kreuznacherstr 4
Postfach 1
D-6531 Windesheim
Tel 06706 14 45
Fax 06707 17 39

Brauerei Bischoff
An den Hopgengaerten 6
D-6742 Winnweiler
Tel 063 02 60 10
Fax 063 02 6 01 20
*Traditional family-owned
brewery.*

**Privatbrauerei
Wickueler**
Postfach 10 01 04
D-5600 Wuppertal 1
Tel 0202 8 90 32 11
Fax 0202 8 90 32 75

Hirsch Brauerei Honer
Friedrichstr 34
D-7204 Wurmlingen
Tel 07461 5062
Fax 07461 6025

Places to Enjoy Beer

Greiffenklau
Laurenziplatz 20
Bamberg

Mahr
Obere Stephansberg 36
Bamberg
*Serves beer from Brauerei
Mahr.*

**Schlenkerla
Dominikanerstr**
D-8600 Bamberg

Spezial
Sternwartstr
Bamberg

Wilde Rose
Obere Stephansberg 49
Bamberg

**Alt Koepenicker
Bierstube**
Alt Koepenicke 32
Berlin
Tel 657 2453

Cafe Mephisto
Wilhelm-Pieck 22
Berlin
*Mexican restaurant with
locally brewed beer on tap.*

Golgota
Dudenstr 48–64
Berlin
*Leftist beer garden. Open
daily, 4PM to 6AM.*

Grossbeerenverkehr
Grossbeerenstr 90
Berlin
Tel 251 3064

Ku'dorf
Joachimstalerstr 15
Berlin
Tel 883 66 66
*Below street level are around
22 Kneipen (bars) serving a
wide selection of beers.*

Tegernseer Toennchen
Mommsenstr 34
Berlin
Tel 323 38 27
*Bavarian restaurant, large
selection of beers and Wurst.
Open daily.*

Weissbierstube
Berlin Museum
Berlin

Brauhaus Sion
Untere Taschenmacher
D-5000 Cologne
Restaurant tavern.

Frueh am Dom
Am Hof
D-5000 Cologne
Pub restaurant.

Malzmuehle
An der Malzmuehle
D-5000 Cologne
Tavern with food.

Museum
Zuelpicher Platz 9
D-5000 Cologne
Serves Koelsch, the local brew.

Papa Joe's Biersalon
Alter Markt 52
D-5000 Cologne
Tel 21 67 59
*Pub with saloon piano from
8PM. Newsletter lists
entertainment schedule,
anecdotes, recipes.*

Am Thor
Str. der Befreiung und Pl.
   der Einheit
Dresden
Good beer, good food.

Restaurant Braugold
Anger
Erfurt

Irish Pub
Kleine Rittergasse 11–13
D-6000 Frankfurt am Main
Tel 61 59 86
*Live music, lots of Brits,
Guinness on tap.*

Wagner
Schweizerstr 71
D-6000 Frankfurt am Main
*With biergarten. Brews
Aepfelwein (apple wine), a
local specialty.*

zum Schlappen
Loewenstr 2
Freiburg im Breisgau

Burgkeller
Naschmarkt 1
Leipzig

Schmidt's Gasthaus
Dr. Julius-Leberstr 9
Luebeck
International menu, good beer
selection.

Augustine
Neuhauserstr 16
D-8000 Munich
Tel 55 19 92 57
With beer garden. Open daily.

Augustine
Arnulfstr 52
D-8000 Munich
Tel 59 43 93
Open daily.

Chinesischer Turm
Englischer Garten
D-8000 Munich
Tel 39 50 28
German beer-garden next to
the Chinese pagoda in the
English Garden.

Forschungsbrauerei
Unterhachingerstr 76
D-8000 Munich
Tel 670 11 69
Research Brewery.

Franziskaner-Keller
Perusastr 5
D-8000 Munich
Tel 231 81 20
Open daily from 8AM.

Hacker-Keller
Theresienhoehe 4
D-8000 Munich
Tel 50 70 04
Open daily. Live music and
dancing after 7PM.

Hirschgarten
Hirschgartenallee 1
D-8000 Munich
Tel 17 25 91
Largest beer garden in
Munich.

Hofbraeuhaus
Am Platzl 9
D-8000 Munich
Tel 22 16 76
Literally court brewhouse.
Historic but touristy beer hall.
Open daily.

Hofbraeukeller
Innere Wienerstr 19
D-8000 Munich
Tel 448 73 76
With beer garden. Open daily.

Loewenbraeukeller
Nymphenburgerstr 2
D-8000 Munich
Tel 52 60 21
Open daily from 9:30AM.

Mathaeser Bierstadt
Bayerstr
D-8000 Munich
Beer hall.

Paulaner Beer Hall
5 Kapuzinerplatz
D-8000 Munich
Tel 89 55 03 31

Schorr Keller
Theresienhoehe 7
D-8000 Munich
Tel 50 10 88
Brews from the Hacker-
Pschorr Brewery. Open daily
from 8AM.

Rattlesnake Saloon
Schneegloeckchenstr 91
D-8000 Munich

Kaiserburg
Obere Kraemergasse 20
D-8500 Nuremburg
Tel 22 12 16
Occasional live jazz and blues.

Retail Stores

Groesste Biermarkt der
Welt
Pfungstaedterstr 1000
Darmstadt-Eberstadt
Contact: Bruno Maruhn
The largest beer store in the
world. Over 900 beers.

Bierland
Elsenerstr
D-4790 Paderborn
Store with around 200 beers.

Festivals

Oktoberfest
Theresienwiese
D-8000 Munich
September, 2nd-to-last
Saturday, to October, 1st
Sunday, around 16 days.
Begun in 1810, and still
going strong. This is the
original, after which all others
are named.

Kiliani Festival
Wuerzburg
July

Instruction and Training
Courses

Brewing Studies
Technische Universitaet
Weihenstephan
Education facility for brewers
and research center.

Of Historic Interest

Brauerei Museum
Markischestr 85
D-4600 Dortmund
*Part of the Kronen Beer
Works. Open Tuesday to
Sunday, free, no samples.*

**Frankfurter Brauerei-
Turm**
Hainer Weg 60–64
D-6000 Frankfurt am Main
70
Tel 069 606 3445

Brauereimuseum
Heilgengeiststr 39–41
Lueneburg
Tel 410 21
*Was a working brewery for
500 years. Stein collection
next door.*

**German Museum of
Brewing**
St.-Jakobs-Platz 1
D-8000 Munich 2
Tel 2 33 23 70

**Schwaebisches
Brauereimuseum**
D-7000 Stuttgart
*History of beer and current
brewing techniques. No
samples. Open Tuesday to
Sunday, free.*

Gibraltar

Places to Enjoy Beer

The Angry Friar
287 Main St.
Tel 71570
Pub with 6 draught beers.

Splendid Bar
George's Lane

Copacabana
242 Main St.
Tel 77596
*English, German, and
Spanish beers.*

Saccone & Speed
35 Devils Tower Rd.
Tel 74600
Beer sales.

Greece

**National Tourist Organi-
zation (EOT)**
2 Amerikis St.
Athens
Tel 01-322 3111
Fax 01-322 2841
Tourist information.

Breweries

**Amstel Beer Athenian
Brewery**
102 Kifisou Ave.
G-102 41 Aigaleo
Tel 01 561 3605
Fax 01 562 4731

**Lowenbrau Hellas
Brewery**
131 Iera Odos Av.
G-105 33 Aigaleo
Tel 01 346 9071
Fax 01 346 9131

Karolas
59 Panepistimiou Str.
G-105 64 Athens
Tel 01 346 4861

**Henninger Hellas
Kaubos Brewery**
Kantza Atikis
Tel 01 665 8424

Places to Enjoy Beer

Cafe-Bar Dhodhoni
Solonos 64
Athens

Oggi Music Pub
17 Filellinon
Athens

Taverna St.
Crete
Street with many small bars.

Soumbousakis
Nikiforou Foka 98
Rethimno

Zythos
Katouni 5
Thessaloniki

Greenland

*Part of the Danish kingdom, but not a
member of the EEC.*

Greenland Travel
Box 330
DK-3900 Nuuk
Tel 2 44 55
Fax 2 33 69
Travel information, tours.

Breweries

Nuuk Imeq
DK-3900 Nuuk
Marketers of Carlsberg.

Places to Enjoy Beer

Hotel Arctic
Narsarsuaq
Tel 35253

Nanoq
Qaqortoq

Skipperkroen
Qaqortoq

Hungary

Tourinform
Suto utca 2
Budapest
Tel 179-800
Tourist information.

Magyar Sorgyartok Szovetsege
Maglodi ut 17
H-1106 Budapest
Tel 157 13 18
Fax 127 08 37
Contact: Klara Kende, manager
Association of Hungarian Brewers.

Breweries

Borsodi Sorgyar
Rakoczi ut 81
Pf 6
H-3547 Bocs
Tel 46 329 139
Contact: Otto Bachl, general director

Brau Hungaria
Tokory utca 4
H-1392 Budapest

Classic Europa
Vigado ter 2
Pf 329
H-1052 Budapest

Kobanyai Sorgyar
Maglodi ut 17
Pf 43
H-1487 Budapest 10
Tel 1 147 28 54
Contact: Istvan Nemeth, general director

HBH Kolostor Sorozo
Kossuth utca 14
Keszthely
Tel 86 48408
Brewery and restaurant.

serving local fare. Closed Jan to Easter.

Komaromi Sorgyar
Tuzolto ut 2
Pf 13
H-2922 Komaron
Tel 34 340 478
Contact: Andras Szentirmay, director

Elso Magyar Szovetkezeti Sorgyar
Pf 43
H-5435 Martfu
Tel 56 350 568
Contact: Frigyes Nagy, Director

Kanizsa Sorgyar
Csengery ut 111
H-8800 Nagykanizsa 2
Tel 93 310 167
Contact: Zoltan Furak, general director

Pannonia Sorgyar
Alkotomany ut 94
H-7601 Pecs
Tel 72 314 742
Contact: Istvan Timar, general director

Soproni Sorgyar
Vandor S ut 1
Pf 74
H-9407 Sopron
Tel 99 312 158
Contact: Arpad Nemeth, director

Places to Enjoy Beer

Aranymokus Kertvendeglo
Istenhegyi ut 25
Budapest XII
Tel 361 1556 728
The Golden Squirrel. Restaurant whose menu goes

well with beer. Open Tuesday to Sunday, Reservations advised.

Fregatt
Molnar utca 26
Budapest V
British-style pub. Live music on weekends.

Kaltenberg Brewery & Restaurant
Kinizsi utca 30–36
Budapest IX
Tel 361 1189 792
Choice of filtered (HBH) or unfiltered (Aszok) draft beer. Mostly German food with some Hungarian specialities.

Kehli Tavern
Mokus utca 22
Budapest III
Tel 361 1886 938
Hearty fare and local beer. Open Monday to Saturday.

Oreber Sorozo
Kos Karoly setany 14
Budapest
Tel 1 1222 680
Beer out of doors under a huge tent. Live Dixieland music, cheap food.

Svejk
Fo ter 6
Budapest III
Tel 361 1223 278
Czech restaurant serving draft Pilsner.

Tabani Kakas Vendeglo
Attila ut 27
Budapest
Tel 1 175 7165

Sorpince a Flaskahoz
Miklos utca 4
Debrecen
Tel 52 14 582
Neighborhood pub with good food.

HBH Bajor Sorhaz
Bajcsy Zsilinszky ut 19
Eger
Tel 36 16312
Restaurant serving Munich Hofbrauhaus beer.

Gosser Sorozo
Kossuth Lajos ut 35
Keszthely
Tel 82 22 65
Beer garden with mainly Austrian clientele. Hungarian food. Live German beer hall music in summer.

Tettye Vendeglo
Tettye ter 4
Pecs
Tel 72 10-438

Varkerulet
Varkerulet 83
Sopron
Tel 99 12-327

Fekete Hollo
Rev ut 15
Visegrad
Tel 26 28-158
Good place for local food or just a beer. Or two.

Festivals

Foodapest
International Fair Center
H-1441 Budapest
Tel 361 263-6074
Fax 361 263-6435
Contact: HungExpo Agro Studio
Late November, 5 days. Even-

numbered years. Food and drink trade show, open to public on last day.

Krakofood
Cracow Expo Center
Cracow
Tel 361 263-6077
Fax 361 263-6435
Contact: HungExpo
P.O.B. 44
H-1441 Budapest
Early June, 11 days. Odd-numbered years. Food and drink trade show, open to public last 2 days.

Iceland

Iceland Tourist Board
Laekjargata 3
Gimli
IS-101 Reykjavik
Tel 01-27 488
Fax 01-624749
Tourist information.

Breweries

Sana
Nordurgotu 57
IS-602 Akureyki
Tel 96 21444

Viking Brugg
Furuvollum 18
IS-600 Akureyri
Fax 6 27845

Gosan
Kollunarklettsveg 4
IS-105 Reykjavik
Tel 01 678990
Fax 01 674758

Olgerdin Egill Skallgrimsson
Grjothalsi 7–11
IS-110 Reykjavik
Tel 01 672000
Fax 01 814235

Places to Enjoy Beer

Skansinn Pub & Restaurant
Hotel Gestfjafinn
Heidarvegur
Heimaey

Edda Hotel
Reykholt
Tel 93 51260

Bjorhollin
Gerduberg
Breidholt
Reykjavik

Cafe Hresso
Austurstraeti and Laekjartorg
Reykjavik

Gaukur a Stong
Tryggvagata 22
Reykjavik
Home of vodka-spiked beer.

Festivals

Pjodhatio
Herjolfsdalur
Heimaey
Early August. Commemorates the Constitution granted on 1 July 1874. Bonfire, music, singing, dancing, drinking.

Ireland.

Breweries

Beamish & Crawford
S Main St.
Cork
Tel 021 276841
Fax 021 272210
Beamish Stout.

Murphy Brewery
Lady's Well Brewery
58 Leitrim St.
Cork
Tel 021 503371
Fax 021 503926
Murphy Stout, Heineken,
Amstel.

Arthur Guinness
  Son & Co.
St. James Gate
Dublin 8
Tel 01 536 700
Fax 01 544253
Brewing museum, visitor
center in former hop store.
Tours available. Guinness,
Harp. Smithwicks.

Tennants
Blackwater Rd.
Glasnevin
Dublin 11
Tel 01 300977
Fax 01 300746

Irish Ale Breweries
St. Francis Abbey Brewery
Kilkenny
Tel 056 21014
Fax 056 62101

Places to Enjoy Beer

McCarthy's
Baltimore
Co. Cork

Carlingford Arms
Newry St.
Carlingford
Co. Louth
Tel 042 734 18

Connie Doolan's Pub
Cobh
Contact: Jay Mulligan
Mr. Mulligan, of Boston,
U.S.A., won this pub in a
Guinness contest.

An Bodhran
42 Oliver Plunkett St.
Cork
Tel 021 274 544

An Phoenix
3 Union Quay
Cork
Tel 021 964 275

Schooner's
Main St.
Donegal
Tel 073 216 71

O'Connor's
Main St.
lower village
Doolin
Co. Clare

Carbery's
N Strand
Drogheda
Co. Meath

Brozenhead
Bridge St.
Dublin

Brussels Pub
Harry St.
Dublin

Club Conradh
Harcourt St.
Dublin

Flannery's
Fleet St.
Dublin

Hughes
19 Chancery St.
Dublin
Tel 01 872 6540
Good pub for traditional
music sessions.

John F. Keating Pub
Mervis and Mary Sts.
Dublin

MacDaid's
Harry St.
Dublin

Mulligan's
8 Poolbeg St.
Dublin
Tel 01 677 5582

Neary's
1 Chatham St.
Dublin
Tel 01 677 8596

O'Donoghue's
15 Merrion Row
Dublin
Tel 01 676 2807
Famous for its impromptu
Irish music sessions.

O'Dwyer's Pub
Lower Mount St.
Dublin
Tel 01 676 2887

Munphy's Pub
W George's St.
Dun Laoghaire

Brandon's
70 O'Connell St.
Ennis
Co. Clare
Tel 065 28133

Oak Tavern
Ferrycarrig
Co. Wexford
Tel 053 24922

An Pucan
11 Forster St.
Galway

Munroe's Tavern
Galway

The Blackwater
Farrell St.
Kells
Co. Meath
Tel 046 408 36

Cleere's Pub
28 Parliament St.
Kilkenny
Tel 056 625 73

Yer Man's
Plunkett St.
Killarney
Co. Kerry
Tel 064 326 88

Locke Bar
George's Quay
Limerick
Tel 061 413 753
Contact: Richard Costello
Open from 9AM.

Leinster Arms
Main St.
Maynooth
Co. Kildare
Tel 01 628 6323

Caffrey's
Munt St.
Mullingar
Westmeath

Jug o' Punch
Main St.
Roscommon
Tel 0904 252 24
*Outdoor beer garden in
summer.*

Cahalane Bar
20 Bridge St.
Skiboreen
West Cork
Tel 028 211 61

McLynn's
Market St.
Sligo

Thatch Pub
Sligo
300 years old.

Jerpoint Inn
Market St.
Thomastown
Kilkenny
Tel 056 24234

Val O'Shea's
Bridge St.
Tralee
Co. Kerry
Tel 066 215 59

Jeoff's Pub
9 John St.
Waterford
Tel 051 747 87

Matt Molloy's Pub
Bridge St.
Westport
Co. Mayo
*Owned by the flutist of The
Chieftains.*

Thomas Moore Tavern
Cornmarket
Wexford
Tel 053 243 48

Of Historic Interest

Guinness Museum
Old Hop Store
Crane St.
Dublin
*Brewing equipment, coopers'
tools, history of brewing in
Ireland, beer advertising,
samples of Guinness.*

Literary Pub Crawl
Dublin
Tel 01 540288
*Guided tour of the pubs where
Beckett, Joyce, and Brendan
Behan drank.*

Italy

Il Mondo della Birra
Via Cagliero 21
I-20125 Milan
Tel 02 688 2228
Fax 02 6072185
Magazine: The World of Beer.

Breweries

Birra Forst
Vinschgauerstr 8
Postfach 29
I-39022 Algund

Wuehrer
Viale Bornana 62
I-24123 Brescia
Tel 0303 81381

Industrie Poretti
Ceccano
Splugen
Tuborg

Mecati Francesco & Co.
Via Oriani 78
I-48016 Cervia/Mil
    Marittima (RA)
Tel 0544 972114
Fax 0544 972288

Birra Forst
Via Venosta 8
I-39022 Forst/Lagundo (BZ)
Tel 0473 260111
Fax 0473 48365

Turatello Itali
Via Zambrini 1
I-40026 Imola (BO)
Tel 0542 640468
Fax 0542 640747

Barbieri F. Lli
Via Gattamelata 136
I-35128 Padua
Tel 049 8070017
Fax 049 774833

Birra Peroni Industriale
Zona Industriale la Stada 56
I-35100 Padua
Tel 049 773802
Fax 049 775273

Life
Via Aie 28
I-12040 Sommariva Perno
 (CN)
Tel 0172 46221
Fax 0172 46214

Birra Moretti
Viale Venezia 9
I-33100 Udine
Tel 0432 203441

Industrie Poretti
Varese
Splugen
Tuborg

Places to Enjoy Beer

Senzanome
Via Senzanome 42
Bologna

Fiddler's Elbow
Piazza Santa Maria Novella
 7R
Florence
Tel 215 056

Grand Hotel Pub
Via Ascanio Sforza 75
Milan
Tel 895 11 586

Bar Magenta
Via Caarducci 13
Milan

Druid's Den
Via San Martino ai Monte
 28
Rome
Tel 488 0258
*Irish pub. Occasional music
sessions.*

Enoteca Cavour
Via Cavour 313
Rome
Good selection of bottles.

Fiddler's Elbow
Via dell'Olmata 43
Rome
Irish bar.

Four Green Fields
Via Constantino Morin 42
Rome
Tel 06 359 5091

La Scala
Piazza della Scala
Rome
Pub food, cheap beer.

The Black Cat
Via Pacchiotti 61
Turin

La Divina Commedia
Via San Donato 47
Turin

Doctor Sax
Mura di Lungo Po Cadorna
 4
Turin

Bar Ducale
San Marco 2354
calle dell'Ostreghe
Venice
Tel 521 0002

Osteria de Libero
Via Risorte 8
Venice

Birreria Spofford
Via Rosetti
Venice

Festivals

Fiera della Birra
Largo Fiera della Pesca
I-60100 Ancona
Tel 071 58971
Fax 071 5897213
*Mid-July. Beer and pub
exhibition. The first was in
1992.*

Kazakhstan

Intourist
49 Kommunistichesky
 Prospekt
Alma-Ata
Tel 33-0002
Tourist information.

Latvia

Lattur
29–31 Bruninieku Str.
LV-1001 Riga
Tel 0132 274952
Fax 0132 272589
Tourist information,

Tourist Information
Riga Hotel
2 Aspazia Blvd.
Riga
Tel 0132 216090

Breweries

Cesis State Brewery
11 Lencu Str.
LV-4100 Cesis
Tel 013 34 22423

Latgales Alus State Plant
22 Dzirnavu Str.
LV-5400 Daugavpilis
Tel 013 54 35835

Liepaja State Beer Plant
4–6 Kronu Str.
LV-3400 Liepaja
Tel 013 34 2883

Aldaris State Food Trade Enterprise
44 Tvaika Str.
LV-1005 Riga
Tel 0132 391652

Riga State Brewery
2 Bruninieku Str.
LV-1001 Riga
Tel 0132 273217

Varpa Riga State Brewery
231 Maskavas Str.
LV-1019 Riga
Tel 0132 241222

Places to Enjoy Beer

Ala
Vecpilsetas iela
Riga

Fredis
Audeja iela
Riga

Jever Bistro
Sharnu Iela
Riga
Tel 227078
German restaurant and beer garden.

Pie Kristapa
25–29 Jaun Iela
Old Town
Riga
Tel 224368
Serves brown ale from Lacplecis Collective Farm.

Liechtenstein

Tourist Office
FL-9490 Vaduz
Tel 075 214 43
Tourist information.

Lithuania

Tourist Information
Hotel Lietuva
20 Ukmerge St.
Vilnius
Tel 35-6074

Breweries

Ragutis
2 Kauna Kiemro St.
LT-3000 Kaunas

Klaipeda Svturys
Kuliu Vartai 7
LT-5799 Klaipeda
Tel 13904

Panavezys Kapnapilis
Taikos alejal
LT-5319 Panavezys
Tel 61645

Siauliai Gubernija
Dvaro 179
LT-5419 Siauliai
Tel 40250

Utenos Gerimai
12 Pramonis St.
LT-4910 Utena

Vilnius Tairas
Dainavos 11–2
LT-2649 Vilnius
Tel 627526

Galerija Langas
8 Asarnos
Vilnius
Tel 221505
Bar with jazz.

Places to Enjoy Beer

Senasis Rusys (Old Cellar)
16 Sv Ignoto Gatve
Vilnius
Tel 450777

Stikliai
7 Gaono Gatve
Vilnius
Tel 222109
Restaurant and bar with beer and beer cuisine. Open 11AM to 9PM.

Zirmunai
67 Zirmuna
Vilnius
Tel 779939
Open 11PM to 3AM.

Luxembourg

Office National de Tourisme
P.O. Box 1001
L-1010 Luxembourg
Tel 40 08 08
Fax 40 47 48
Calendar of events, plus usual tourist information.

Breweries

Brasserie Nationale
2 blvd. J. F. Kennedy
L-4930 Bascharage
Tel 50 90 11 21
Tours and tasting by appointment.

Brasserie de Diekirch
BP 148
L-9214 Diekirch
Tel 00352 802131

La Ferme au Chene
115 rue Comte d'Ursel
Durbuy
Tel 086 211067
*Tiny brewery with video on
brewing process.*

**Brasserie Mousel et
 Clausen**
BP 371
L-2013 Lucembourg-
 Clausen

Brasserie de Wiltz
BP 22
L-9501 Wiltz
Tel 00352 958015

Places to Enjoy Beer

Scott's
near the bridge
Grund
Engligh pub.

Interview
rue Aldringen 21
Luxembourg

Pygmalion
rue de la Tour Jacob 19
Luxembourg
Irish bar.

Um Piquet
rue de la Poste 30
Luxembourg

Festivals

Beer Festival
Diekirch
July, 3rd Sunday.

Malta

**National Tourism
 Organization**
280 Republic St.
Valetta
Tel 224444
Fax 220401
Tourist information.

Breweries

Simonds Farsons
The Brewery
Mriehel BKR14
Tel 44 0331
*Possibly the only ale brewery
in the Mediterranean. Mild,
Bitter, Pale Ale, Sweet Stout.*

Lowenbrau Malta
Triq I-Lljun
Qormi QRM11
Tel 485 221

Monaco

Direction de Tourisme
2A blvd. des Moulins
MC-93308 Monte Carlo
Tel 93 30 87 01
Tourist information.

Netherlands

VVV Tourist Office
Stationsplein 10
Postbus 3901
NL-1001 AS Amsterdam
Tel 020-6266444
*Tourist information, calendar
of events.*

PINT
Postbus 3757
NL-1001 AN Amsterdam
Tel 010 212262
Contact: Frank Boogaard,
 chairman
*Promotion information about
Traditional Beer. A nation-
wide, volunteer, beer-lovers
organization, dedicated to
supporting the Netherlands
beer culture. Runs beer
festivals. PINT Nieuws has
news, events calendar, reviews,
overviews of industry. 6/year.*

Produktschap voor Bier
Herengracht 282
NL-1016 BX Amsterdam
Tel 020 623 10 79
Fax 929 622 60 74

Aqua Tours
Postbus 406
NL-2000 AK Haarlem
Tel 023 422078
*Beer cruises, with visits to
museums, breweries, etc. in
Flanders.*

**Allantie van Bier
 Tapperijen**
Ruynemanstr 62
NL-5012 JH Tilburg

**PINT Reggio Midden
 Brabant**
Postbus 1222
NL-5004 BE Tilburg
Tel 013 701750
Regional branch.

**European Brewery
 Convention**
P.O. Box 510
NL-2830 BB Zoeterwoude
Tel 71 456047
Fax 71 410013
Symposia, exhibitions.

Books and Magazines

**Bier Jaarboek, by Peter
 Crombecq**
*Available from OBP. Tasting
notes on all Dutch beers.*

**Good Beer Guide to
   Belgium & Holland,** by
   Tim Webb
*Lists all the breweries and
many of the best bars.
Available from CAMRA, UK,
and bookstores. Published by
Alma Books, in English.*

PINT Nieuws
Postbus 3757
NL-1001 AN Amsterdam
*Magazine of PINT. News,
reviews, ads, calendar of beer
events. 6/year.*

Breweries

**Amsterdams Brouwhuis
   Maximilaan**
Kloveniersburgwal 6–8
NL-1012 CT Amsterdam
Tel 020 6242778
*Brewery in a restaurant,
where the cook uses beer in
cooking.*

**De Drie Ringen
   Brouwerij**
Kleine Spui 18
NL-3811 BE Amsterdam
Tel 033 620300
With brewery cafe.

Heineken Brewery
Stadhouderskade 78
NL-1072 AE Amsterdam
Tel 020 5239239
*Guided tours at 9:30 and
11AM.*

't Ij Brouwerij
Funenkade 7
NL-1018 AL Amsterdam
Tel 010 228325

Arcener Stoombrouerij
Kruiswej 46
NL-5944 EN Arcen
Tel 04703 2459
*Visit to the brewery may be
combined with a visit to its
bar, De Proeverij.*

**Oranjeboom
   Bierbrouwerij**
Ceresstr 13
Postbus 3212
NL-4800 MA Breda
Tel 076 252424
Tours by appointment.

Budelse Brouwerij
Nieuwstr 9
Postbus 2026
NL-6020 AA Budel
Tel 04958 91369
*Tours by appointment.
Capucijn.*

Heineken Brewery
Rietveldenweg 37
NL-5222 AP Den Bosch
Tel 071 457155
Enquire in advance for tours.

Grolsche Bierbrouwerij
Brouwerijstr 1
Postbus 55
NL-7500 AB Entschede
Tel 053 833333
Enquire in advance for tours.

Gulpener Bierbrouwerij
Rijksweg 16
Postbus 51
NL-6720 AB Gulpen
Tel 04450 1956
Tours by appointment.

Brouwerij 't Kuipertje
Appeldijk 18
NL-4161 BH Heukelum
Tel 03451 11839
Fax 04188 1602

Brouerij Raaf
Rijksweg 232
NL-6582 AB Heumen
Tel 080 581177
*Brewery tour included in
museum visit.*

Bavaria Brouwerij
Burg van der Heuvelstr 35
Pbus 1
NL-5737 BN Lieshout
Tel 04922 8111
Enquire in advance for tours.

Brouwerij De Ridder
Oerverwal 3–9
Postbus 3072
NL-6202 NB Maastricht
Tel 043 216057
Tours by appointment.

**Lindeboom
   Bierbrouwerij**
Engelmanstraat 54
Postbus 4416
NL-6086 ZG Neer
Tel 04759 2900
Fax 04759 2750

**De Kroon's
   Bierbrouwerij**
Koestr 20
Postbus 138
NL-5600 ZJ Oirschot
Tel 04977 72002
Tours by appointment.

**Herberg Brouwerij de
   Peizer Hopbel**
Hoofdstr 3
NL-9320 AA Peize
Tel 05908 3607
*Brewery and restaurant, beer
used in cooking too.*

Alfa Brouwerij
Thull 15–19
NL-6365 AC Schinnen
Tel 04493 2888
Tours by appointment.

Bierbrouwerij De Schaapskooi
Eindhovensweg 3
Postbus 394
NL-5000 AJ Tilburg
Tel 013 358147
Tours by appointment.

Leeuw Bierbrouwerij
Prinses Beatrixsingel 2
NL-6301 VL Valkenburg
Tel 04406 13434
Enquire in advance for tours.

Bierbrouwerij De Leeuw
Prinses Beatrixsingel 2
Pbus 815
NL-6300 AV Valkenburg a/d
Geul
Tel 04406 13434
Tours by appointment.

Interbrew Nederland
Brouwerijplein 84
Postbus 14
NL-5550 AA Valkenswaard
Tel 04902 87911
Tours by appointment.

Brand Bierbrouwerij
Brouwerijstr 2–10
NL-6320 AA Wijlre
Tel 04450 8282
Tours by appointment.

Heineken Brewery
Burgemeester Smeetwseg 1
NL-2382 PH Zoeterwoude
Tel 071 456111
Enquire for tours in advance.

Places to Enjoy Beer

De Beiaard
Spui 30
Amsterdam
Specialty beer cafe.

Het Laaste Ordeel
Raadhuisstr
Amsterdam
Wide range of tap and bottled beers.

De Man van Drank
Piet Heinkade 23
Amsterdam
Tel 020 627 46 13

De Beiaard
Oude Markt 22
Enschede
Specialty beer cafe.

't Hoogeland
Eibergsestr 157
Haaksbergen

De Bier Art
Smeepoortstr 42
Harderwijk
Specialty beer cafe.

De Beiaard
Langestr 25
Hengelo
Specialty beer cafe.

Braai-Tapperij
Restaurant de Mug
Vlasmarkt 54–56
NL-4331 PG Middelburg
Tel 01180 14851

't Pumpke
Molenstr 65
Nijmegen
Tel 229255

Cambrinus
Blaak 4
NL-3011 TA Rotterdam
Tel 010 4146702
Excellent beer selection, cooking with beer. Open daily.

Retail Stores

1001 Bieren
Huidenstraat
Amsterdam
Enormous selection, specializing in Belgian beers.

Festivals

PINT Nieuws
Calendar of beer festivals and events in the Netherlands, Belgium, and the UK.

Noordelijk Bierfestival
Huize Mass
Vismarkt 52
NL-9701 BL Groningen
Tel 050 420267
Contact: Postbus 1480
Mid-April, 2 days. Around 25 small breweries from the Netherlands, Belgium, and northern Germany.

Of Historic Interest

Biermuseum de Boom
Houttil 1
NL-1811 JL Alkmaar
Tel 072 113801
In an old brewery. Displays on brewing, malting, cooperage. Cafe.

Bierreclamemuseum
Haagweg 375
NL-4813 XC Breda
Tel 076 220975
Open Sunday, 11AM to 8PM.

Brouwerijmuseum Raaf
Rijksweg 232
NL-6582 AB Heumen
Tel 080 581177
Old brewery equipment. Brewery tour included in museum visit. Open daily. Cafe.

Museumbrouwerij De Roos
Vrijthof 20
NL-5081 CB Hilvarenbeek
Tel 04255 1315
Contact: Harrie de Leijer, Jan van Pelt

Norway

Nortra
Nortravel Marketing
Pb 499
Sentrum
N-0105 Oslo 1
Tel 02 42 70 44
Tourist information.

Breweries

Hansa Bryggeri
Postboks 300
N-5001 Bergen
Tel 05 997700

P. Aass
Postboks 1107
N-3001 Drammen
Tel 03 832580

Ringnes Tou Bryggeri
Postboks 68
N-4033 Forus
Tel 04 576000

Christianssands Bryggeri
N-4616 Kristiansand S
Tel 042 22965

Moss Aktibryggeri
Postboks 186
N-1501 Moss
Tel 09 252540

Oslo Mikrobryggeri
Bogstadvn 6
Oslo
Tel 02 56 97 76
Brewpub.

Ringnes
Postboks 7152
Homansbyen
N-0307 Oslo
Tel 02 309500
Fax 02 309770

Grans Bryggeri
Kamfjordgata 56
N-3200 Sandefjord
Tel 034 63087

Borg Bryggerier
Postboks 7
N-1701 Sarpsborg
Tel 09 152222

Macks Olbryggeri
Storgaten 5
N-9005 Tromso
Tel 083 84800
Northernmost brewery in the country. Traditionally, the beer is served with seagull's eggs (whether in or on the side we're not sure . . .).

Tromi Fabrikker
Tempevegen 35
N-7031 Trondheim
Tel 07 941090

Places to Enjoy Beer

Bryggen Tracteursted
Bryggestredet
Bergen
Three hundred-year-old building, now a pub with outdoor seating.

Dickens
Ole Bulls Plass 8–10
Bergen
Draft beer and food.

Hulen
Olav Ryesvei 47
Bergen

Theatercafeen
Chr Michelsensgate 10
Bergen

Bar Beint
Drammensveien 20
Oslo

Lorry
Parkveien 12
Oslo
Over 80 beers.

Rockall
Rosenkrantzgt 20
Oslo

The Scotsman
Karl Johansgate 17
Oslo
Scottish-style bar with food, live C&W music.

Cafe Garagen
Strandkaien
Stavanger

Cafe Sting
Valberggate 3
Stavanger

Britannia Engelsk Pub
Stortorvet
Tromso
English-run pub with darts, pooltable.

Olhallen
Storgaten 4
Tromso
The northernmost pub in the world.

Pub Adrian
Kongensgate 15
Trondheim

Of Historic Interest

Horten Bilmuseum
Sollistrandsvn 12B
Horten
Tel 033 42 601
*Car museum housed in an old
brewery.*

Bokkerbua
Kvinesdal
Tel 043 50455
*Old cooper's shop, where
young people learn
barrelmaking in summer.
Barrels for sale.*

Poland

ORBIS
ul Bracka 16
PL-00 028 Warsaw
Tel 262-02-71
Fax 814761
*National tourist enterprise.
Offices in many countries. All
tour arrangements.*

**Tourist Information
  Center**
Pl Zamkowy 1/13
PL-00 262 Warsaw
Tel 635-18-81
*Tourist information, maps,
brochures.*

Breweries

Browar w Barczewie
PL-11 010 Barczewo

Browar w Bialymstoku
ul Dojlidy Fabryozne 28
PL-15 565 Bialystok

Browar w Biskupou
ul Warszawska 28
PL-11 300 Biskupiec

Browar w Boguszowie
ul Browarna 8
PL-58 370 Boguszow

Browar w Bojanowie
ul Zwirki i Wigury 16
PL-63 940 Bojanowo

Browar w Brzegu
ul Lokietka 45
PL-49 304 Brzeg

**Browar w Brzesku-
  Okocimiu**
ul Browarana 14
PL-32 801 Brzesko-Okocin

**Browar w Bydgoszczy
  nr 1**
ul Ustronie 7
PL-85 161 Bydgoszcz

**Browar w Bydgoszczy
  nr 2**
ul Zbozowy Rynsk 9
PL-85 116 Bydgoszcz

Browar Bytom
ul Wrocklawska 10
PL-41 902 Bytom

Browar w Chelmie
ul Piwna 1
PL-20 100 Chelm

Browar w Chojnowie
ul Swierczewskiego 32
PL-59 520 Chojnow

Browar w Ciechanowie
ul Kilinskiego 8
PL-06 400 Ciechanow

Browar w Bielsku-Bialej
ul Cieszynska 78
PL-43 400 Cieszyn

Browar w Czarnkowie
ul Browarna 1
PL-64 700 Czarnkow

Browar w Czestochowie
ul Armii Ludowej 18–22
PL-42 201 Czestochowa

Browar w Elblagu
ul Dzierzynskiego 71
PL-82 300 Elblag

Browar w Gdansku
ul Kilinskiego 1–5
PL-80 452 Gdansk

Browar w Glubczycach
ul I Armii W P 16
PL-48 101 Glubczynce

**Browar w Grodzisku
  Wlkp.**
ul Kolejowa 10
PL-64 340 Grodzisk Wlkp.

Browar w Grudziadzu
ul Gen Sikorskiego 35
PL-98 300 Grudziadz

Browar w Grybowie
ul Siolkowa
PL-33 330 Grybow

**Browar w Janowie
  Lubelskim**
ul Bielska 73
PL-23 300 Janow Lubelski

Browar w Jatutowie
PL-22 400 Jatutow

Browar w Jedrzejowie
ul Kowalskiego 1
PL-28 300 Jedrzejow

Browar ul Koszalinie
ul Spoldzielcza 8
PL-75 950 Koszalin

Browar w Krakowie
ul Lubicz 17
PL-31 503 Krakow

Browar w Krotoszynie
ul Slodowa 15
PL-64 700 Krotoszyn

Browar w Lancucie
ul Cetnarskiego 35
PL-37 100 Lancut

Browar w Legnicy
ul Lenina 6
PL-59 200 Legnica

Browar w Lezajsku
ul II Armii W P 5
PL-37 300 Lezajsk

Browar w Lodzi nr 1
ul Polnocna 35
PL-91 425 Lodz

Browar w Lodzi nr 2
ul Orla 25
PL-90 318 Lodz

Browar w Lodzi nr 3
ul Sedziowska 15
PL-91 321 Lodz

Browar w Lomzy
ul Poznanska 8
PL-18 400 Lomza

Browar w Lublinie nr 1
ul Kunickiego 106
PL-20 409 Lublin

Browar w Lublinie nr 2
ul Dabroskiego 15
PL-20 950 Lublin

**Browar w Lwowku
Slaskim**
ul Traugutta 7
PL-59 600 Lwowek Slaski

Browar w Miloslawiu
ul Wrzesinska 24
PL-62 320 Miloslaw

Browar w Namyslowie
ul Olesnicka 4
PL-46 100 Namyslow

Browar w Nowej Soli
ul Armii Czerwonej 31
PL-67 100 Nowa Sol

Browar w Psztynie
ul Aleja Armii W P 20
PL-10 225 Olsztyn

**Browar w Ostrowie
Wlkp.**
ul Raszkowska 68
PL-63 400 Ostrow Wlkp.

**Browar w Polczynie-
Zdroju**
ul Zymierskiego 10
PL-78 320 Polczyn-Zdroj

Browar w Poznaniu
ul Polwarczna
PL-61 302 Poznan

Browar w Raciborzu
ul Zamkowa 2
PL-47 400 Raciborz

Browar w Radkowie
ul Piastowska 24
PL-57 420 Radkow

Browar w Radomiu
ul Limanowskiego 71
PL-26 600 Radom

Browar w Rybniku
ul Zamkowa 3
PL-44 201 Rybnik

**Browar w
Siemianowicach**
ul Browarna 1
PL-41 100 Siemianowice
Slaskie

Browar w Sierpcu
ul Switokrzyska 54
PL-09 200 Sierpc

Browar w Slupsku
ul Kilinskiego 26
PL-76 200 Slupsk

Browar w Sobotce-Gorce
ul Piastowska 24
PL-55 050 Sobotka-Gorka

Browar w Suwalkach
ul Swierczweskiego 65
PL-16 400 Suwalki

Browar w Swiebodzicach
ul Browarna 1
PL-58 100 Swiebodzice

Browar w Zaczerniu
ul Chmielewskiego 16
PL-70 028 Szczecin

Browar w Ketrzynie
ul Mickiewicza 5
PL-12 100 Szczytno

Browar w Tychach nr 1
ul Mikolowska 5
PL-43 100 Tychy

Browar w Tychach nr 2
ul Browarna 7
PL-43 100 Tychy

Browar w Warce
ul Gosniwska 27A
PL-05 660 Warka

**Zaklady Piwowarskie
Warka**
ul Gosniewska 27A
PL-05-660 Warka
Tlx 67365

Agros
Postfach 41
PL-00950 Warsaw
Tel 022 30100

Browar Warszawski
ul Grzybowska 50
PL-00 958 Warsaw

Browar w Witnicy
ul Marii Konopnickiej 1
PL-66 460 Witnica

**Browar we Wrocklawiu
nr 1**
ul Jednosci Narodowej 204–
210
PL-50 302 Wroclaw

**Browar we Wrocklawiu
nr 2**
ul Hubska 44
PL-55 502 Wroclaw

Browar w Zabrzu
ul Wolnosci 327
PL-41 600 Zabrze

Browar w Zaczerniu
PL-36 062 Zaczernie

Browar w Zakrzewie
ul Chmielna 1
PL-51 212 Zakrzow

Browar w Zarach
ul Zamkowa 1
PL-68 200 Zary

Browar w Zdunskiej Woli
ul PKWN 12
PL-98 220 Zdunska Wola

Browar w Ziebicach
ul Browarna 1
PL-57 220 Ziebice

Browar w Zielonej Gorze
ul Kozuchowska 8
PL-65 364 Zielona-Gora

Browar w Zninie
ul Mickiewicza 27
PL-88 400 Znin

Browar w Zwierzyncu
ul Browarna 14
PL-22 470 Zwierzyniec

**Zaklady Piwowarskie
Browar**
ul Browarna 88
PL-34-300 Zywiec

Browar w Zywcu
ul Browarna 88
PL-34 300 Zywiec

Places to Enjoy Beer

Flisak
ul Chebnicka 10–11
Gdansk

The Scottish Bar
ul Piwna
Gdansk
Waiters in kilts.

Restauracja Staropolska
ul Nadrzeczna 14
Kazimierz Dolny
Tel 081 102-36

Maxime's
ul Florianska 32
Krakow

Pod Strezelnica
ul Krolowej Jadwig 184
Krakow

Strawberry Club
ul Tomasz 1
Krakow

Czarna Oberza
Rabianska 9
Torun

Piwiarnia
28 Rynek
Torun

Guinness Bar
ul Koszykowa 1
Warsaw
Guinness, Becks on tap.

Gwiazdeczka
ul Piwna 40
Warsaw

Heineken Pub
ul Pulawska 101
Warsaw
Tel 022 44 03 17
Bar and pizzeria.

The Irish Pub
ul Koszykowa 1
Warsaw

U Hopfera
Krakowskie Przedmiescie
53
Warsaw
Tel 022 635-7352

Portugal

**Institut de Promocoa
Turistica**
Rua A Herculano 51
3D
Aptdo 21066
P-1127 Lisbon Codex
Tel 01-68 11 74
*Tourist information, calendar
of events.*

**Min do Comercio e
Turismo**
Av. da Republica 79
9 fl.
P-1000 Lisbon
Tourist information.

**Assoc. da Indistria
Cervejeira**
Largo de Santos no. 9
3o
P-1000 Lisbon
Tel 01 397 8467
Fax 01 602996
Brewers' association.

**Assoc. dos Technicos de
Cerveja**
Av. Almirante Reis 115
P-1197 Lisbon Codex
Tel 01 355 8841
Fax 01 538405
*Technical association of
brewers and maltsters.*

Breweries

**Empresa de Cervejas da
Madeira**
Rua Alferes Veiga Festana
no. 22
P-9000 Funchal Madeira
Tel 091 230101
Fax 091 226439

Central de Cervejas
Av. Almirante Reis 115
P-1197 Lisbon Codex
Tel 01 3558841
Fax 01 538405
Tours available.

**Cervejas Joao de Melo
Abreu**
P-9502 Ponta Delgada
Azores
Tel 096 23222
Fax 096 26126

Cergal
Cervejas de Portugal
Quinta da Agua da Fonte do
Cedro ZZ
P-2745 Queluz
Tel 01 4312985
ZZ, Venda Seca, Belas.

Unicer-Uniao Cervejeira
P.O. Box 44
Leca do Balio
P-4466 S Mamede de
Infesta Codex
Tel 02 9022300
Fax 02 9022500
Tours available.

Places to Enjoy Beer

Jo Jo's
Rua sao Goncalo de Lagos
Albufeira
*British soccer and other sports
on satellite.*

Sir Harry's Bar
Largo Eng Duarte Pacheco
37–38
Albufeira
*English breakfasts, draft
English beer.*

Bar Diligencia
Rua Nova 30
Coimbra

Bar Neptune
rav J. Mola
Ericeira

Kingburger Bar
Rua do Prior 40
Faro

Lords Tavern
Rua Ant Crisogono Santos
56
Lagos
British-style pub.

Vee Jay's Bar
Trav 1 de Main
Lagos
Cheap beer, dartboard.

**Many small bars and
clubs**
Bairro Alto and Avda 24 de
Julho
Lisbon
*A maze of streets where bars
open and close with bewilder-
ing rapidity.*

Cargo
Avda 24 de Julho 88
Lisbon

Cervejaria da Trinidade
Rue Nova da Trinidade 20C
P-1200 Lisbon
Tel 01 342 3506
*Most famous beerhall in
Lisbon.*

Grog
Trav de Boa Hora 12
Lisbon
*An unpretentious place where
the price of beer is not
inflated.*

Labois de Vinho
Rua do Norte 52
Lisbon
Small blues bar.

Cafe Targus
Rua do Diario de Noticias
40B
Lisbon

Esta-Se Benn
Rua de Fonte Taurina 70
Porto

Arco Bar
Rua Almirante Candido dos
Reis 67
Tavira

Festivals

Beer Festivals
The towns of Silves, Castelo Branco, and others run beer festivals in the summer, but there is no fixed schedule.

Beer Festival
the Castle
Silves
June. Annual event. Many local brews.

Romania

Breweries

Bere Azuga
Str. Independentei 18
Azuga
Tel 26751

Vulturul
Str. Transilvaniei 311
Buzau
Tel 12934

Malt Bere
Str. Mesteacanului 18
Galati
Tel 26091

Bere Miercurea Ciuc
Str. Harghita 100
Miercurea Ciuc Harghita
Tel 15192

Zimca
Str. Ciocirliei nr 1
Piatra Neamt
Tel 14816

Pitber
Str. N Balcescu
Pitesti Arges

Silva
Reghin Mures
Tel 21037

Arcina
Str. Oltului nr 73
Rosiori de Vede Teleorman
Tel 62534

Bere Sadu
Str. Fabricii nr 158
Sadu Sibiu
Tel 109

Amylon
Str. Abatorilui nr 12
Sibiu
Tel 32732

Trei Stejari
Str. Fabricii 2
Sibiu Harghita
Tel 30591

Bergo
Tirgu Jiu Gorj
Tel 16281

Bere Delta Tulcea
Str. Prislav nr 176
Tulcea
Tel 13436

Places to Enjoy Beer

Restaurantul Ciresica
B-dul Kogalniceanu 45
Bucharest
Restaurant with beer garden.

Gambrinus
B-dul Kogalniceanu
Bucharest

Romana
B-dul Magheru 12
Bucharest

Restaurant Berber
B-dul Emenescu
Eforie Nord
Folkloric dance show.

Transylvania Bar & Restaurant
Str. Teatrului
Oradea

The Bulevard
B-dul 30 Decembrie 34
TImisoara
Restaurant with outdoor beer patio.

Cocosul de Aur
Str. Sinaia 1
Tiargu Mures
Tel 954 1-59-58
Once home of the local brewer, now a restaurant with beer garden.

Restaurant Union
Str. 23 August and Str. Isaccea, Tulcea

Sarpeltu Rosu
bu Dacia and Str. Icoanei
Bucharest

Gradina de Vara Boema
34 Str. Iuliu Maniu
Cluj
Beer garden.

Russia

Intourist
Y13 Mokhovaya St16 Marx Prospekt
Moscow 103009
Tel 203 69 62
Fax 292 23 86
Tourist information.

Cristall
Novy Arbat 15
121906 Moscow
Tel 00952 919810
Fax 0095 291 936
Beer agency.

Sojuzplodoimport
32–34 Smolenskaya-
Sennaya Ploschad
121200 Moscow
Tel 095 2244 2258
Fax 095 244 3636

Breweries

AES Co.
76 Leninsky Prospekt
117311 Moscow
Tel 095 131 51 04
Fax 095 200 32 71

Moscow City Brewery
23 Lev Tolstoy St.
119021 Moscow

Moskovskoye Brewery
Moscow

Ostankinskoye Brewery
Moscow

Zhigulevskoye Brewery
Moscow
*Probably the most popular
beer in Russia.*

Places to Enjoy Beer

German Beer House
Sadko Arcade
Moscow
Tel 095 940-4066

Loewenbraeu Beer Hall
3 ul Gorkogo
Moscow
Tel 203 14 49

Peter's Place
72 Zemlyanoy Zal
Moscow
Tel 095 298-3248

Rosie O'Grady's
Moscow

Shamrock Bar
Novy Arbat 19
Moscow
Tel 095 291-7641

Tren-Mos Bar
Ostozhenka ul 1/9
Moscow
Tel 095 202-5722
*Name stands for Trenton (NJ)/
Moscow.*

Tren-Mos
21 Komsomolsky Prospekt
Moscow
Tel 095 245-1266

John Bull Pub
79 Nevsky Prospekt
St Petersburg
Tel 164 9877
John Bull bitter on draft.

Sadko
Grand Hotel Europe
1/7 ul Mikhailovskaya
St. Petersburg
Tel 812 210-3667

Slovak Republic

See *Czech and Slovak Republics*

Spain

Breweries

Damm
Fabricas de Cerveza
Rosselo 515
E-08025 Barcelona
Tel 433 0101
Fax 347 4959
*Estralla Damm, Voll Damm,
Damm Bier Sin, Xibeca.*

San Miguel
Fabricas de Cerveza
Pol Ind El Segne
E-25080 Lerida
Tel 19 34 73 200 600
Fax 19 34 73 21 17 78

El Aguila
Fabricas de Cerveza
Vara de Rey 7
E-28045 Madrid

San Miguel
Fabricas de Cerveza
Carbonero y Sol 1-1A
E-28006 Madrid

La Cruz del Campo
Avda de la Innovacion
Edif Arena 3
E-41007 Seville
Tel 5 448 08 00
Visitor center.

Places to Enjoy Beer

Tapas Bars
All over
*Bars serving beer, wine, and
tapas, or appetizers, in vast
variety. Find them everywhere.
Handy places to eat around
7PM, since dining in Spain
doesn't start until 10PM.*

La Soccarena
Calle de la Mercie 21
Barcelona
*Bar serving Asturian cider
and food.*

**Bar-Restaurant
    Bizkaia II**
C. Jardines 2
Bilbao
*Open 1 to 4PM and 7 to
11PM.*

Lancelot
Cuesta del Marques
Caceres

L'Arcada
Rambla de Llibertat 38
Girona

Bodega Castaneda
Corner Calles Elvira and
  Almireceros
Granada

Cafe Cerveceria la Jara
C. Floridablanca 34
Madrid
Open 6PM to 3AM.

Cerveceria Allemana
Pl. Santa Ana 6
Madrid
Tel 429 70 33
Open noon to 2AM.

Cerveceria Ratskeller's
Corner C. Luchana and C.
  Palafox
Madrid
*The House of Beer. Open noon
to 3AM.*

La Dolores
Plaza de Jesus 4
Madrid
*Reputedly the best draft beer
in Madrid.*

El Corrillo
Plaza el Corrillo
Salamanca

Bar Ourense
Calle del Franco
Santiago

La Gitanilla
Calle Ximenez de Enciso
Seville

La Abadia
Calle de la Silleria
Toledo

Pub-Bolera
Calle de la Sinagoga
Toledo
Beer, and bowling.

Sweden

Swedish Tourist Board
Box 7473
S-103 92 Stockholm
Tourist information.

Svenska Olframjandet
Box 16244
S-103 25 Stockholm
Tel 08 669 36 30
*Swedish beer consumers'
association. Works with
CAMRA (UK) and PINT
(Netherlands).*

Breweries

Pripps Bryggerier
Bryggeriv 10
S-161 86 Bromma
Tel 08 757 70 00
Fax 08 28 98 61

Falken Bryggeri
Box 165
S-311 22 Falkenberg
Tel 0346 570 00
Fax 0346 171 55

Appeltofftska Bryggeri
Bryggareg 7
S-302 43 Halmstad
Tel 035 10 01 00
Fax 035 11 20 66

Guttsta Bryggeri
Malmav 17
S-730 30 Kolsva
Tel 0221 509 10
Fax 0221 517 68

Sofiero Bryggeri
Kristianstadsv 19
S-312 32 Laholm
Tel 0430 138 40
Fax 0430 142 95

Banco Bryggeri
Box 103
S-360 53 Skruv
Tel 0478 203 00
Fax 0478 200 32

Abro Bryggeri
Box 23
S-598 21 Vimmerby
Tel 0492 165 00
Fax 0492 136 90

Places to Enjoy Beer

Brasserie Lipp
Avenym 8
Gothenberg

C. Van
Linnegatan 23
Gothenberg

Gamle Port
Ostra Larmgatan 14
Gothenburg
Serves British beer.

Charles Dickens Pub
Sodergatan 43
Helsingborg
Cheapest beer in town.

Le Coeur
Sodergatan 7
Malmo

Dubliners
Birgerjarlspassagen
Stockholm
*Irish-run. Live music at
weekends.*

Engelen
Komhamnstorg 59B
Stockholm
Tel 01 07 22
Pub with live rock, jazz, blues.

Fenix
Gotgatan 40
Sodermalm
Stockholm
Good beer selection.

Halfway Inn
Wollmar Yxkullsgatan
Stockholm
English-style pub.

Kaos
Stora Nygatan 21A
Stockholm
Tel 20 58 86

Kristina
Vasterlanggatan 68
Gamla Stan
Stockholm

Tranan
Karlsbergsvagen
Stockholm
Old workers' beer hall.

Tudor Arms
Grev Turegatan
Stockholm
Authentic English pub. John Bull bitter.

Festivals

Midsommar.
June, 3rd weekend. Country-wide celebrations with maypoles, smorgasbords, beer, aquavit. Consult local tourist offices for details.

Switzerland

National Tourist Office
Bellariastr 38
CH-8027 Zurich
Tel 01 202 3737

Verband Schweiz Brauereien
Postfach
CH-4001 Basel
Tel 061 261 07 57
Fax 061 261 07 52
Contact: Dr H. Muench
Association of brewery workers.

Association of Swiss Brewmasters
c/o Brauerei Adler
CH-8762 Schwanden
Tel 058 81 11 08
Fax 058 81 12 97

Association of Swiss Landlords
Gotthardstr 61
CH-8027 Zurich
Tel 01 201 2611
Publishers of Schweizer Bierbuch, *160-page book on Swiss beer, breweries, and brewing. In German.*

Swiss Brewers' Association
Bahnhofplatz 9
CH-8023 Zurich
Tel 01 221 2628
Fax 01 211-6206

Books and Magazines

***Schweizer Bierbuch*, by Karl Thoene**
Pub by FSW
Gotthardstr 61
CH-8027 Zurich
Tel 01 201 2611 ext. 220
Swiss Beer-book. History and description of Swiss beers. Full-color photos.

Brauerei- und Getraenke-Rundschau
Bahnhofplatz 9
Postfach
CH-8023 Zurich
Tel 01 201 42 44
Fax 01 201 42 49
Magazine of Swiss Brewers' Association. News, technical information, ads. 12/year.

Breweries

Locher Brauerei
CH-9050 Appenzell
Tel 071 87 13 18
Fax 071 87 39 18

Country Inn & Brewery Frohsinn
Romanshornerstr 15
CH-9320 Arbon
Tel 071 46 10 46
Smallest brewery in Switzerland. Old Thurgovian house with 10 guest rooms. Adjoining tavern serves food, including brewer's brunch on Sunday.

Baar Brauerei
CH-6340 Baar
Tel 042 31 12 08
Fax 042 32 26 83

H. Mueller Brauerei
Dynamostr 8
CH-5401 Baden
Tel 056 22 80 22
Fax 056 22 55 94

**Brauerei/Restaurant
  Fischerstube**
Rheingasse 45
CH-4058 Basel
Tel 061 692 94 95
Restaurant 061 692 66 35
*Microbrewery can be seen at
the back of the restaurant.
Label Ueli-Bier.*

Warteck Brauerei
Postfach
CH-4002 Basel
Tel 061 695 77 11
Fax 061 695 74 40

Felsenau Brauerei
Strandweg 34
CH-3004 Bern
Tel 031 23 22 06
Fax 031 24 35 14

**Calanda Haldengut
  Brauerei**
Kasernenstr 36
CH-7007 Chur
Tel 081 26 01 11
Fax 081 26 01 49

Rosengarten Brauerei
CH-8840 Einsiedeln
Tel 055 53 21 42

**Aktienbrauerei
  Frauenfeld**
CH-8500 Frauenfeld
Tel 054 22 10 44
Fax 054 21 65 25

Brasserie Cardinal
Passage Cardinal
CH-1700 Fribourg
Tel 037 82 11 51
Fax 037 24 30 34
*Brewery with beer museum.
Typical tavern serving the
house brews in the annex.
Tours available for 15 or more
by appointment; free samples.*

Stadtbuehl Brauerei
Gebr E. and M. Krucker
CH-9202 Gossau
Tel 071 85 35 15

Lupo Brauerei
CH-6280 Hochdorf
Tel 041 88 17 22
Fax 041 88 33 93

Ziegelhof Brauerei
CH-4410 Liestal
Tel 061 921 30 66
Fax 061 921 53 75
Non-alcoholic beer.

Eichhof Brauerei
Postfach
CH-6002 Lucerne
Tel 041 49 11 11
Fax 041 49 12 06
Brewery and museum.

Rugenbraeu
CH-3800 Matten-Interlaken
Tel 036 22 10 12
Fax 036 23 32 60

Sonnenbraeu
CH-9445 Rebstein
Tel 071 77 12 02
Fax 071 77 35 02

Brasserie Cardinal
CH-4310 Rheinfelden
Tel 061 831 51 22
Fax 061 831 47 49

**Brauerei
  Feldschloesschen**
CH-4310 Rheinfelden
Tel 061 835 01 11
*1876 red and yellow brick
building. Tours available,
museum, gift shop. Brewery
has its own Tudor-style train
station.*

Brasserie du Boxer
rte. d'Eschallens 32
CH-1032 Romanel-sur-
  Lausanne
Tel 021 36 12 73
Fax 021 36 36 01

Loewengarten Brauerei
CH-9400 Rorschach
Tel 071 41 14 41
Fax 071 45 19 40

**Schuetzengarten
  Brauerei**
St. Jakobsstr
CH-9004 St. Gallen
Tel 071 24 75 24
Fax 071 25 82 28
*Brewery and museum.
Billwiller First Class
Premium.*

Falken Brauerei
Postfach
CH-8201 Schaffhausen
Tel 053 25 33 15
Fax 053 24 51 61

Karbacher Brauerei
CH-5012 Schoenenwerd
Tel 064 41 12 95
Fax 064 41 22 34

Adler Brauerei
CH-8762 Schwander
Tel 058 81 11 08
Fax 058 81 12 97

Brasserie Valaisanne
rte. de Riddes 42
CH-1951 Sion
Tel 027 33 11 33
Fax 026 31 48 58

Brauerei zum Gurten
CH-3084 Wabern
Tel 031 960 40 00
Fax 031 960 44 10

Brauerei Waedi-Brau-Huus
Florhofstr 13
CH-8820 Waedenswil
Tel 01 780 15 66
Fax 01 780 72 52
Demonstration brewery. Organically grown hops and barley. Tours available.

Weinfelden Brauerei
Lanter and Baerlocher
CH-8570 Weinfelden
Tel 072 22 30 66

Calanda Haldengut Brauerei
Haldenstr 69
CH-8401 Winterthur
Tel 052 264 41 41
Fax 052 264 44 44
Brewery and museum.

Brauerei A. Egger
CH-3076 Worb
Tel 031 839 03 57
Fax 031 839 03 25

Brauerei Huerlimann
P.O. Box 654
Brandschenkestr 150
CH-8027 Zurich
Tel 01 288 26 26
Brewery with museum of beer steins, inn signs, etc. Catalog available. Stable of Belgian horses. Brewery tours by appointment, free samples.

Loewenbraeu
Postfach
CH-8027 Zurich
Tel 01 288 20 20
Fax 01 288 22 88

National Experimental Brewery
Engimattstr 11
CH-8059 Zurich
Tel 01 201 42 44
Fax 01 201 42 49
Public access by appointment. Large collection of beer ads, steins, cans, coasters.

Places to Enjoy Beer

Brasserie Gambrinus
Falknerstr 35
CH-4001 Basel
Tel 272 21 12
Open daily.

Fischerstube
Rheingasse 4
Basel
Good beer and fresh fish.

Giger Bar
Chur

Peter's Pub
Engelberg

Segnes-Bar
Flims

Le Bourbon Street
19 rue Neuve du-Molard
CH-1204 Geneva
Tel 310 29 68
Restaurant with U.S. beef and beer, New Orleans ambience.

Brittania Pub
Place de Cornavin
Geneva

Le Planteur
rue du Molard
Geneva

St. George Pub
Geneva

Henry's Bar
Gstaad

Nelson Pub
Leysin

Bar del Pozzo
Piazza Sant'Antonio
Locarno

Tony's Bar zur Gerbern
Lucerne

Shakespeare Pub
7 rue des Terreaux
Neuchatel
Bar, with disco Tuesday, Friday, Saturday.

Schwyzerhofstubli
St. Moritz

The Bridge Pub
Villars

Sina's Pub
Wengen

Papperla Pub
Kirchenstr
Zermatt
Beer and pizza.

Londoner Pub
Kirchenstr 7
Zug
Open daily, evenings.

Bierhalle Kropf
In Gassen 16
CH-8001 Zurich
Tel 01 221 1805
A Zurich institution since 1444, serving Cardinal beer.

Bierhalle Wolf
Limmatquai 132
CH-8025 Zurich
Tel 01 251 0130
*Beerhall with musical
entertainment.*

Castel Pub
Spiegelgasse 1
Zurich

Konigstuhl
Zurich

Oliver Twist
Rindermarkt 4
Zurich

Rheinfelderbierhalle
Limmatquai
Zurich

Zeughauskeller
In Gassen 17
CH-8001 Zurich
Tel 01 211 2690
*Built in 1487, this beerhall
serves Huerlimann beer.*

Turkey

Tourist Information Office
Beyoglu Mesrutiyet Cad 57/6
Istanbul
Tel 01-145 68 75
Fax 01-143 65 64
Tourist information.

Tekel Genel Mudurlugu
Basin ve Halkle Iliskiler
  Mudurlugu
Unkanpani Istanbul
Tel 1 5323231
Fax 1 5347914
*Turkish Monopoly Press and
PR Directorate. Contact them
for tours of state breweries.*

Breweries

Ankara Bira Fabrikasi Mudurlugu
Ankara
Tel 4 2124 680 90
Brewery, state owned.

Efes Pilsen Bira Fabrikasi
Eski Kemalpasa Yolu
Issikent-Izmir
Tel 51 791900

Tuborg Bira Fabrikasi
Eski Kemalpasa Yolu
Issikent-Izmir
Tel 51 791730

Istanbul Bira Fabrikasi Mudurlugu
Istanbul
Tel 1 2320 900 03
Brewery, state owned.

Turk Tuborg Bira ve Malt
Izmir

Yozgat Bira Fabrikasi Mudurlugu
Yozgat
Tel 473 21500 02
Brewery, state owned.

Places to Enjoy Beer

Jazz Bar
Tunali Hilmi Cad 4/1
Kavaklidere
Ankara

Oz Canli Balik
Quayside
Ayvalik

Cicek Birahanesi
Bergama

Yuksel Birahanesi
Bergama

Piknik Bar
Dr. Alim Bey Cad
Bodrum

Tino Bar
Ataturk Cad
Bursa

Cartoon Bar
Macka Bronz sok 4–2
Nisantas
Istanbul

Cheers
Nispetiye Cad 27
Levent
Etiler
Istanbul

Ziya Bar
Muallim Naci Cad
Istanbul
*In summer, there's a garden
and outdoor bar.*

Barlar Sok (Pub Lane)
Kusadasi
*Alley with a bunch of English
and Irish-style pubs.*

Bebop
Cephane Sok 20
Kusadasi

Palm Tree
Hasi Mustafa Sok 97
Marmaris
Garden pub with music.

Ukraine

Breweries

Kiev Obolon Brewery
Bogatyrskaya St.
Kiev 22

UNITED KINGDOM

National Organizations

Importers of Beer

Cider

Courses of Instruction

Pub Chains

Books

Newspapers and Magazines

Festivals

UK Listings by Area

National Organizations and Festivals

Allied Brewery Traders Association
85 Tettenhall Rd.
Wolverhampton
Staffs WV3 9NE
Tel 1902 22303
Fax 1902 712066

Beer Hunts in Europe
31 Temple Hill
Whitwick
Leics LE67 5BD
Tel 1530 815353
Fax 1530 815255
Tours of European breweries, pubs, etc.

The Beer Lovers Club
9 Windsor Rd.
Finchley
London N3 3SN
Newsletter 6/year.

The Brewers Guild
8 Ely Pl.
London EC1N 6SD
Tel 171 405 4565

The Brewers Society
42 Portman Square
London W1H 0BB
Tel 171 486 4831
National body for brewers and licensed retailers.

Brewery History Society
Manor Side E
Mill Ln.
Byfleet
Weybridge
Surrey KT14 7RS
To promote and encourage interest in the history of breweries. Archive, book shop with new and used books, magazine Brewery History *4/ year, meetings around the country, more.*

Brewing Research Foundation International
Nutfield
Surrey RH1 4HY
Research organization. Database BREW-INFO. Many publications. Educational.

British Guild of Beer Writers
c/o 55 Elmete Hill
Leeds
Yorks LS8 2NT
Tel 1532 65895
Fax same
Contact: Barrie Pepper, Chairman
Professional association of writers. Membership queries: Peter Colson, Secretary, 30 Topps Field Parade, London N8 8PT.

British Beermat Collectors Society

30 Carters Orchard
Quedgeley
Gloucester
Gloucs GL2 6WB
Contact: John Sheehan
International membership association. Beermat
Magazine 12/year. International Exchange Meetings annually in August, other activities.

CAMRA — Campaign for Real Ale

34 Alma Rd.
St. Albans
Herts AL1 3BW
Tel 1727 867201
Fax 1727 867670
Consumers' association that promotes real beer and its enjoyment. Many local branches. Runs beer festivals, publishes books and guides, lobbies the authorities to help save traditional pubs and breweries. Over the years, CAMRA has had great success in waking Britain up to its brewing heritage. Now, almost every pub knows about "Real Ale," even if they don't actually have any.

IFBB

Weymouth Ave.
Dorchester
Dorset DT1 1QT
Independent Family Brewers of Britain.

Institute of Brewing

33 Clarges St.
London W1Y 8EE
Tel 171 499 8144
Fax 171 499 1156
Education, training, and
certification of brewers in the UK, Africa, Australia, and New Zealand. Conventions, research, library. Journal 6/ year, technical papers; Ferment 6/year, papers, news. Regional sections.

MCBLRA

Link Ho
The Rumbow
Halesowen
W Midlands B63 3HT
Tel 121 501 3761
Fax 121 585 6053
Midland Counties Brewers' and Licensed Retailers' Association.

Small Independent Brewers' Association

2 Balfour Rd.
London N5 2HB
Tel 171 359 8323
Fax 171 354 3962
Newsletter SIBA News.

SPBW

1 Montreal Rd.
Ilford
Essex IG2 4SH
Contact: Membership
  Secretary
Society for the Preservation of Beers from the Wood. Branches around the UK. Magazine Pint in Hand 4/ year.

Worshipful Company of Brewers

Brewers Hall
Aldermanbury Square
London EC2V 7HR
Tel 171 606 1301
Established in C12. Now mainly a charitable body.

Importers of Beer

Allied Breweries

107 Station St.
Burton upon Trent
Staffs DE14 1BZ
Tel 1283 45320
Fax 1283 39092
Lowenbrau Special Export, Lowenweisse (Germany).

Alvini Co.

Units 2–3
199 Eade Rd.
London N4 1DN
Tel 181 880 2525
Fax 181 880 2708
Von Wunster (Italy).

Anheuser Busch European Trade

6 Devonshire Square
Cutlers Gardens
London EC2M 4LP
Tel 171 522 911
Fax 171 522 9110
Budweiser, Michelob (USA).

Bavarian Lager Co.

12 The Sidings
Station Rd.
Whalley
Blackburn
Lancs BB6 9SE
Tel 1254 822672
Fax 1254 824857
Ingobrau (Germany).

B B Supply Center

91A Whitechapel High St.
London E1 7RA
Tel 171 247 1252
Fax 171 377 6454
Brooklyn Lager (USA); Budweiser Budvar, Gambrinus (Czech).

The Beer Cellar
10 Thame Pk.
Wenman Rd.
Thame
Oxon OX9 3XA
Tel 1844 260111
Fax 1844 260264
Nessi (Austria), Timmerman,
Du Bocque, Chimay, Orval,
Duvel, Rochefort, Silly
(Belgium); St. Landelin,
Demon (France); Rauchenfels,
Arcobrau, Mooser, Coronator
(Germany); Budels (Neth).

Beers International
Bridge Ho.
Summer Hill
Gouldhurst
Kent TN17 1JT
Tel 1580 211388
Fax 1580 212082
Budels, Krombacher (Hun-
gary); Liefmanns, Lucifer,
Strafe Hendrik (Belgium).

Berliner Kindl Beer
Importers
31 Cross Lances Rd.
Hounslow
Middx TW3
Tel 181 577 2997
Fax 181 572 6219
Berliner Kindl (Germany).

Birritalia
29 Romilly St.
London W1V 6HP
Tel 171 734 6112
Fax 171 434 1214
Nastro Azzurro, Perroni
(Italy).

British Beer Co.
17 Remington St.
London N1
Tel 171 253 0225

Bucktrout & Co.
P.O. Box 27
High St.
St. Peter Port
Guernsey
Tel 1481 722444
Fax 1481 728436
Corona (Mexico); Grolsch
(Neth).

C & D Wines
76 Kenwood Rd.
Beckenham
Kent BR3 2QZ
Tel 181 650 9095
Fax 181 663 6256
Damm, Xibeca (Spain).

Carlsberg Brewery
Bridge St.
Northampton
Northants NN1 1PZ
Tel 1604 234333
Fax 1604 234444
Dansk, Elephant Beer
(Denmark).

Cave Direct
20 Danson Mead
Welling
Kent DA15 1RU
Tel 181 303 2261
Fax 181 303 0180
Riva Pils, Liefmans, Strafe
Hendrik, Gouden Carolus,
Witcap, Moin-ette, Lucifer,
Vordel (Belgium).

Classic Ales
4 Ascot Rd.
Bedfont
Feltham
Middx TW14 8QH
Tel 1784 248475
Fax 1784 244109
Anchor Steam (USA); Efes
Pilsner (Turkey); Ringnes
(Norway).

James Clay & Sons
7 Thorpe Garage Tri
Sowerby Bridge
Halifax
W Yorks HX6 3DL
Tel 1422 822659
Fax 1422 822659

Courage Group
Ashbury Ho.
1 Bridge St.
Staines
Middx TW18 4TP
Tel 1784 466199
Fax 1784 468131
Kronenbourg (France); Tiger
(Singapore); Victoria
(Australia).

C V Sales & Marketing
S Sefton Business Center
Canal St.
Bootle
Lancs L20 8AH
Tel 151 933 0511
Fax 151 933 0091
Alsatia, Cristalor, Gold
Triumph, Orpal, Pilsor, Scotch
Triumph (France).

Cyprus Wines
195 Blackstock Rd.
London N5 2LL
Tel 171 354 4722
Fax 171 354 5027
KEO (Cyprus).

Deinhard & Co.
95 Southwark St.
London SE1 0JF
Tel 171 261 1111
Fax 171 261 9569
Paulaner-Salvator-
Thomasbrau (Germany).

Dortmunder Union Brewery
Wheel Inn
Welton le Marsh
Spilsby
Lincs PE23 5TA
Tel 1754 85481
Fax 1754 85481
Dortmunder Union (Germany).

The Drinks Agency
Pickles Ho.
460 Hackney Rd.
London E2 9EJ
Tel 171 613 5166
Fax 171 613 3224
Andes (Venezuela).

Dunn & Moor
556 London Rd.
Glasgow
Scotland G40 1EB
Tel 141 554 4771
Fax 141 556 5541
Gilde (Germany).

Ehrmanns Wine Shippers
29 Corsica St.
London N5 1JT
Tel 171 359 7466
Fax 171 636 7289
Fischer (France); La Cruz del Campo (Spain); Lammsbrau (Germany); West End (Australia).

Enotria Wines
4 Chandos Pk. Estate
Chandos Rd.
London NW10 6NF
Tel 181 961 4411
Fax 181 461 8773
Birra Moretti (Italy).

Faxe UK
Pudding Mews
The Market Place
Hexham
Northumberland NE46 3SW
Tel 1434 605463

Fax 1434 608605
Faxe (Denmark).

Food Brands Group
10 Calico Ho.
Plantation Wharf
Battersea
London SW11 3TN
Tel 171 978 5300
Fax 171 924 2732
'33 Export Dry, Pelforth Blonde (France).

German Lager Importers
Kobi Ho.
Alpine Way
London Industrial Pk.
Beckton
London E6 4LA
Tel 171 511 3116
Fax 171 511 7600
Dortmunder Kronen (Germany).

Greenalls Group
Wilderspool Ho.
Greenalls Ave.
Warrington
Cheshire WA4 6RH
Tel 1925 51234
Fax 1925 413137
Durtmunder Union (Germany); Martins Pils (Belgium).

Global Beer Distributors Co.
Old Hasland Rd.
Chesterfield
Derbs S41 0RW
Tel 1246 233777
Fax 1246 220857
Chilli Beer, Chiller, McMahon Irish, Pig's Eye Pils (USA).

Goujon & Fils
1 Monza St.
Wapping Wall
London E1 9SP
Tel 171 488 4971
Fax 171 481 3238

Baumgartner (Austria); Hinano (Tahiti); Schutzenberger (France).

Grandmartin
St. Andrews Ho.
14 Queen St.
Uppingham
Leics LE15 9QR
Tel 1572 823262
Fax 1572 821578
Cheb (Czech); Okocim (Poland).

Griersons
430 High Rd.
Willesden
London NW10 2HA
Tel 181 459 8011
Fax 181 459 4473
Dortmun-der Union, Germania (Germany).

Grolsch UK
Savoy Chambers
London St.
Andover
Hants SP0 2PA
Tel 1264 355777
Fax 1264 333097
Grolsch (Netherlands).

Holsten Distributors
Merchant Ho.
Station Rd.
Dorking
Surrey RH14 1UP
Tel 1306 875111
Fax 1306 876675
Holsten (Germany).

IBD International
1379 High Rd.
London N20 9LP
Tel 181 446 0046
Fax 181 446 0077
Topvar (Czech).

Irish Bonding Group
3 Marshalls Rd.
Belfast
N Ireland BT5 6SL
Tel 1232 790909
Fax 1232 797547
*Becks, Satzenbrau, Steiger
(Germany); Red Stripe
(Japan).*

J H Jaffe & Co.
P.O. Box 41
15 St. David's Pl.
St. Helier
Jersey CI
Tel 1534 25241
Fax 1534 37616
Red Stripe (Japan).

**Jenks Group (Interna-
tional Wines & Spirits)**
Castle Ho.
71–75 Desborough Rd.
High Wycombe
Bucks HP11 2HS
Tel 1494 442446
Fax 1494 424019
*Breug, Noordheim, Upstaal
(France); Boags Export Lager
(Austria); Herforder Pils
(Germany); Pleven (Bul-
garia).*

K I Ales
336A Kings Rd.
London SW3
Tel 171 352 8085
Fax 171 352 1604
Cobra (India).

Labatt Brewing UK
140 High St.
Esher
Surrey KT10 9QJ
Tel 1372 462131
Fax 1372 469986
Labatts (Canada).

Landmark Cash & Carry
32–40 Headstone Dr.
Harrow
Middx HA3 5QT
Tel 181 863 5511
Fax 181 863 0603
Scandia (Denmark).

C Le Masurier
P.O. Box 85
60 Stopford Rd.
St. Helier
Jersey CI
Tel 1534 30451
Fax 1534 30053
*Breda (Netherlands);
Budweiser (USA).*

**London Drinks
Distributors**
67A High St.
Saffron Walden
Essex CB10 1AA
Tel 1799 525455
Fax 1799 528265
*Erdinger Weissbier, Konig
(Germany).*

Maison Courette
144–152 Bermondsey St.
London SE1 3TQ
Tel 171 403 9191
Fax 171 403 9245
*Brahma (Brazil); Castle, Lion
(S Africa); DB Export, Kiwi
(NZ); Dos Equis, Sol
(Mexico); El Aguila (Spain);
Kulta (Finland); Schutz
(France); Miller Genuine
Draft (USA).*

Marble Head Trading
280 West-bourne Park Rd.
London W11 1EH
Tel 171 625 7777
Fax 171 243 3344
*Micky's (USA); Sapporo
(Japan); Primo, Simpatico
(Mexico).*

James E. McCabe
Carn Industrial Estate
Craigavon
Co. Armagh N Ireland
Tel 1762 3331020534 3045
Fax 1762 335916
Heineken (Netherlands).

**Mexican Beer Import
Co.**
Mexico Ho.
Old Mill Park
Kirkintilloch
Glasgow G66 1SS
Tel 141 777 6464
Fax 141 777 6600
*Bohemia (Mexico); Space Beer
(Germany).*

Molson UK
Manfield Ho.
376–379 Strand
London WC2R 0LA
Tel 171 836 0687
Fax 171 497 9529
Molson (Canada).

Nectar Imports
Unit 1E
Quarry Estate
Mere
Wilts BA12 6LA
Tel 1747 860440
Fax 1747 860221
*Amstel, Gulpner, Heineken
(Netherlands); Becks
(Germany); Brigand, Brugge,
Bush Bier, Chimay, Delerium
Tremmens, Dentegems,
Gouden Carolus, Grimbergen,
Judas, Le Trappe, Liefmans,
Lucifer, Hoegaarden, Orval,
Rochfort, St. Sixtus, Westmalle
(Belgium).*

Phipps Johnson Wine Co.
York Ho.
244 Amersham Rd.
Hazle-mere
Bucks HP15 7QN
Tel 1494 450696
Fax 1494 450687
Bavarian Lion (Germany).

Pilsner Urquell
3–9 Fanshaw St.
London N1
Tel 171 739 4355

**Premier Worldwide
Beers**
42 Beddington Ln.
Croydon
Surrey CR0 4TB
Tel 181 684 7682
Fax 181 689 3661
*Adelshoffen, Biere Amoureuse
(France); Aegean (Greece);
Eichbaum (Germany); Bir
Bintang (Indonesia); Amarit
(Thailand); Canadian Gold
(Canada); Chimay (Belgium);
Coopers (Australia); Europa
(Poland); Shanghai (China);
Zhiguli (Ukraine); many
more.*

Reihill-McKeown
38 Annesborough Rd.
Craigavon
Co. Armagh BT67 9JD
Tel 1762 344651
Fax 1762 341267
*Colt 45 (USA); Kaltenberg
Pils (Germany); Stella Artois
(Belgium).*

St. Stephen's Wines
15 Bridge Ho.
Bridge St.
Sunderland
SR1 1TE
Tel 191 514 0514
Fax 191 514 0510
Albani, Odense (Denmark).

San Miguel UK
174 Three Bridges Rd.
Crawley
W Sussex RH10 1LE
Tel 1293 543855
Fax 1293 543672
San Miguel (Spain).

Scottish & Newcastle
Abbey Brewery
Holyrood Rd.
Edinburgh EH8 8YS
Tel 131 558 1110
Fax 131 556 4005
*Becks (Germany); Jupiter
(France); Pilsner Urquell
(Czech).*

Alfred Shepherd
The Brewery St. Peter Port
Guernsey
CI
Tel 1481 724128
Fax 1481 710658
*Bitburger (Germany); Breug
(France); Labatts (Canada);
Rolling Rock (USA); Stella
Artois (Belgium).*

**Specialist Beer &
Wine Co.**
9 Brough Pk. TE
Fosse Way
Byker
Newcastle upon Tyne
Tyne and Wear NE6 2YS
Tel 191 224 11991
Fax 191 224 1886
*Cruze (Belgium);
Fuerstenberg (Germany).*

Swift Wines
West End Approach
Morley
Leeds LS27 0NB
Tel 1532 381111
Fax 1532 380855
Giraf (Denmark).

Temple Wines
472 Church Ln.
Kingsbury
London NW9
Tel 181 363 2092
Fax 181 363 2092
*Badan Export, Barron Pils
(Germany); Super Drix
(Belgium).*

United Wine Merchants
10 Boucher Rd.
Belfast
N Ireland BT12 6HR
Tel 1232 231231
Fax 1232 333557
Sol (Mexico).

Vaux Group
The Brewery
Sunderland
SR1 3AN
Tel 191 567 6277
Fax 191 514 2488
*Franzikaner Wheat Beer,
Spaten Premium (Germany).*

Vitkovich Bros.
Little Mostar
Virgil St.
London SE1 7EF
Tel 171 261 1770
Fax 171 633 9123
Grand Pivo (Yugoslavia).

Baron von Ritter
194 Ellerton Rd.
Surbiton
Surrey KT6 7UD
Tel 181 390 2376
Fax 181 390 8653
*Hannover, Lindener
(Germany).*

Warsteiner UK
P.O. Box 40
Saffron Walden
Essex CB10 1TH
Tel 1799 513950
Fax 1799 528265
Warsteiner (Germany).

Whitbread Beer Co.
Whitbread Ho.
Park St. W
Luton
Beds LU1 3BG
Tel 1582 391166
Fax 1582 397397
Bon Castel (France); Cascade
(Tasmania); Corona Extra
(Mexico); Damm (Spain);
Heineken Export (Holland);
Hoegaarden (Belgium); Kalik
(Bahamas); Toohey's Export
(Australia).

Wing Yip (London)
395 Edgware Rd.
Cricklewood
London NW2 6ON
Tel 181 450 0422
Tsing Tao (China).

World Imports
132 Sloane St.
Sloan Square
London SW1 9AX
Tel 171 730 2626
Fax 171 730 5705
Corona Extra, Modelo
Especial, Negro Modelo,
Pacifico Clara, Polar
(Mexico).

Cider

Biddenden Vineyards
Little Whatmans
Biddenden
Ashford
Kent TN27 8HD
Tel 1580 291726
Fax 1580 291933
Cider and English wines.

H P Bulmer Co.
Plough Ln.
Hereford
Hereford HR4 0LE
Tel 1432 352000
Fax 1432 352084
Cider, low-alcohol cider, perry.

Carr Taylor Vineyards
Westfield
Hastings
E Sussex TN35 4SG
Tel 1424 752501
Fax 1424 751716
Cider, English wines.

Cripple Cock Co.
St. Columb
Cornwall
Farmyard scrumpy.

Devon Organic Apples
Whitestone Farm
E Cornworthy
Totnes
Devon TQ9 7HF
Tel 180422 400
Fax 180422 253
Organic cider.

The Gaymer Group
Whitchurch Ln.
Bristol
Avon BS14 0JZ
Tel 1275 836100
Fax 1275 839905
Cider, Babycham (perry).

James White Cider
Cider Ho.
Friday St.
Brandeston
Suffolk IP13 7BP
Tel 1728 685537
Fax 1728 685892
Cider, apple juice.

Merrydown Wine Co.
Horam Manor
Horam
Heathfield
E Sussex TN21 0JA
Tel 14353 2254
Fax 14353 3218
Cider, mead, fruit wine,
ginger wine.

**Somerset Cider Brandy
Co.**
Burrow Hill
Kingsbury
Episcopi
Martock
Somerset TA12 5BU
Tel 1460 40782
Cider brandy.

Wootton Vineyard
North Wootton
Shepton Mallet
Somerset BA4 4AG
Tel 1749 890359
Cider, English wines, brandy.

Cider Museum
Pomona Pl.
21 Ryelands St.
Hereford
Hereford HR4 0LW
Tel 1432 354207
Story of cidermaking in an
old cider works. Includes King
Offa Distillery for cider
brandy. Gift shop.

Courses of Instruction

Brewers Laboratory
N London Poly
Holloway Rd.
London N7 8DB
Tel 171 607 2789
Training courses for brewers.

Brewlab Training Courses
Life Sciences Bldg.
Univ. of Sunderland
Chester Rd.
Sunderland
Tyne and Wear SR1 3SD
Tel 191 515 2535
Fax 191 515 2531
Brewing courses, tasting instruction.

Fundamentals of Mini-Brewing
Crown Hotel
Wheelgate
Malton
N Yorks YO17 0HP
Tel 1653 697580
Contact: Geoff Wollons

Three-day residential course run by and for independent brewers.

Pub Chains

Most large breweries also own pubs, called "tied houses." Some serve only the beers from the brewery that owns them, some serve "guest ales" from other breweries.

Allied Lyons Retailing
107 Station St.
Burton upon Trent
Staffs DE14 1BZ
Tel 1283 45320

Greenalls Inns
Egypt Rd.
New Basford
Nottingham
NG7 7GD
Tel 1602 785074

Mitchells & Butlers Taverns
60–61 Lionel St.
Birmingham
B3 1JE
Tel 121 233 9889

Pubmaster
Fairnine Ho.
Brunel Rd.
Wakefield
Yorks WR2 0XG
Tel 1924 825260

Trent Inns
Daybrook
Nottingham
NG5 6BU
Tel 1602 671717

Whitbread Pub Partnerships
Monson Avedon
Cheltenham
Gloucs GL50 4EL
Tel 1242 261166

Books

The Brewery Manual and Who's Who, 10 Belgrade Rd., Hampton, Middx TW12 2AZ. Tel 181 841 7750, Fax 181 941 7721. Annual listing of brewing companies, pub owners, importers, etc. around the world.

Good Pub Guide. Published by CAMRA.

The Incredibly Biased Beer Guide, by Ruth Herman. Published by Sigma Press (John Wiley in USA). About the brewers themselves, plus their choice of pubs. Not tasting notes.

Middle England Pub Guide. Available from British Tourist offices.

Real Ale Drinker's Almanac, by Roger Protz. A guide to over 150 UK breweries and their brews. Published by Lochar; available from CAMRA.

Suffolk Real Ale Guide, by Suffolk CAMRA. Over 900 pubs, etc. Order from Nigel Smith, 200 Back Hamlet, Ipswich, Suffolk IP3 8AR.

Technical Papers, The Grist, 2 Balfour Rd., London N5 2HB. Tel 171 359 8323, Fax 171 354 3962. Practical advice on brewing and brewery management.

Tetley's Good Food Pubs, P.O. Box 142, Leeds, W Yorks LS1 1QG. Tel 1532 435282. Free guide to over 70 Tetley's pubs in the north of England.

Traditional Pubs for Everyone. Guide to the independent family brewers' pubs of SE England. Free from British Tourist Authority offices.

Yorks & Humberside Pub Guide. Available from British Tourist offices.

Newspapers and Magazines

The Brewer, Brewers Guild, 8 Ely Pl., London EC1N 6SD. Tel 171 405 4565. 12/ year. Technical papers, etc.

Brewers Guardian, 10 Belgrade Rd., Hampton, Middx TW12 2AZ. Tel 181 941 7750. 12/year. Technical papers, etc.

Brewers & Distillers International, 63 Burton Rd., Burton upon Trent, Staffs DE14 3DP. Tel 1283 66784. Marketing and technical information for the industry.

Cheers, 41 Haddricks Mill Rd., S Gosforth, Newcastle upon Tyne, Tyne and Wear NE3 1QL. Tel 191 284 2742. 4/year. News of pubs and clubs.

Club & Pub News, Cumberland Ho., Lissadel St., Salford, Manchester M6 6GG. Tel 161 745 8845. Weekly. News of pubs and clubs.

Free House, 47 Church St., Barnsley, S Yorks S70 2AS. Tel 1226 734333.

The Grist International, 2 Balfour Rd., London N5 2HB. Tel 171 359 8323, Fax 171 354 3962. News and articles for the small independent brewer worldwide. Advisory service on brewplant, careers, business.

What's Brewing, CAMRA, 34 Alma Rd., St. Albans, Herts AL1 3BW. 12/year. Newspaper with reviews, news from the UK and around the world, interviews, calendar of events, etc.

Festivals

The Great British Beer Festival is run each year in early August by CAMRA, currently in the Grand Hall at Olympia, London. There are hundreds of varieties of beer and cider, plus pub games, organizations and publications, collectibles, and so on. CAMRA and its local branches also organize other festivals round the country. Details of these can be found in the monthly *What's Brewing.*

UK Listings By Area

AREA 1   London
AREA 2   Kent, Surrey, Sussex
AREA 3   Dorset, Hampshire, Isle of Wight, Wiltshire
AREA 4   Avon, Cornwall, Devon, Gloucestershire, Somerset
AREA 5   Bedfordshire, Berkshire. Buckinghamshire, Hertfordshire, Middlesex, Oxfordshire
AREA 6   Derbyshire, Herefordshire, Northamptonshire, Shropshire, Staffordshire, Warwickshire, West Midlands, Worcestershire
AREA 7   Cambridgeshire, Essex, Lincolnshire, Norfolk, Suffolk
AREA 8   Cheshire, Cumbria, Lancashire, Leicestershire, Greater Manchester, Merseyside
AREA 9   Humberside, Nottinghamshire, Yorkshire
AREA 10 Cleveland, County Durham, Northumberland, Tyne and Wear
AREA 11 Wales
AREA 12 Scotland
AREA 13 Northern Ireland
AREA 14 Isle of Man
AREA 15 Channel Isles, Scilly Isles

AREA 1. London

Brewers

Guinness Brewing International
Park Royal Brewery
London NW10 7RR
Tel 181 965 7700
Fax 181 453 0420

Orange Brewery
37–39 Pimlico Rd.
London SW1
Tel 171 730 5984

Stag Brewery
Lower Richmond Rd.
London SW14 7ET
Tel 181 876 3434
Fax 181 876 2039
Courage Group.

The Whitbread Beer Co.
Chiswell St.
London EC1Y 4SD
Tel 171 606 4455
Fax 171 615 1000
Head office.

Fuller, Smith & Turner
Griffin Brewery
Chiswick Ln. S
Chiswick
London W4 2QB
Tel 181 994 3691
Fax 181 995 9230
Contact: Anthony Fuller, chairman

Young & Co.
The Ram Brewery
Wandsworth
London SW18 4JD
Tel 181 870 0141
Fax 181 870 9444

Places to Enjoy Beer

Black Friar
174 Queen Victoria St.
London

City Pride
28 Farringdon Ln.
London

Country Arms
Hale End Rd.
London E4

The Old Farmhouse
291 Kentish Town Rd.
London N1
Tel 171 485 2802

Royal Oak
York St.
London W1

The Sun
63 Lambs Conduit St.
Bloomsbury
London WC1
Tel 171 405 8378

Ye Olde Bell
95 Fleet St.
London

Ye Olde Cheshire Cheese
145 Fleet St.
London

Half Moon
93 Lower Richmond Rd.
Putney
London SW5
Tel 181 788 2387
Fax 181 789 7863
Pub with live music most nights.

Lord Henniker
Stratford Grove
Stratford
London E15

Retail Outlets

Alan Greenwood's Beer Agency
17 Brumfield Rd.
Ewell
London
Tel 181 397 4763

Beer & Home Brew Shop
8 Pitfield St.
Shoreditch
London
Tel 171 7393701

AREA 2. Kent, Surrey, Sussex

Harvey Hopper
Brewery Shop
6 Cliffe High St.
Lewes
E Sussex BN7 2AH

Get a copy of the brewery handbook and pub guide, visit all 33 tied houses in Sussex and Kent, drinking a pint of ale in each, then claim your reward.

Brewers

Harvey & Son
Bridge Wharf Brewery
6 Cliffe High
Lewes
E Sussex BN7 2AH
Tel 1273 480209

Larkins Brewery
Larkins Farm
Chiddington
Edenbridge
Kent TN8 7BB
Tel 1892 870328

Shepherd Neame
17 Court St.
Faversham
Kent ME13 7AX
Tel 1795 532206

P & D J Goacher
5 Hayle Mill Cotts
Bockingford
Maidstone
Kent ME15 6DT
Tel 1622 682112

Pilgrim Brewery
West St.
Reigate
Surrey RH2 9BL
Tel 17372 22651

Hogs Back Brewery
Manor Farm
The Street
Tongham
Surrey GU10 1DE
Tel 1252 783000
Fax 1252 782328
Open Monday to Saturday,

tours Saturday by appointment. Gift shop, brewery shop, sales of beers from 60 independent and regional brewers and bottled beers from all over the world.

King & Barnes
18 Bishopric
Horsham
W Sussex RH12 1QP
Tel 1403 69344

Places to Enjoy Beer

The Evening Star
Surrey St.
Brighton
E Sussex
Tel 1273 328931

Anchor Inn
13 George St.
Hastings
E Sussex TN34 3EG
Tel 1424 424379

The Gardener's Arms
Cliffe High St.
Lewes
E Sussex
Tel 1273 474808

William the Conqueror
Rye Harbour
E Sussex TN31 7TU
Tel 1797 223315

Griffins Head
Chillenden
Canterbury
Kent
Tel 1304 840325
Built in 1286.

Royal Oak
Spital St.
Dartford
Kent DA1 2DR
Tel 1322 271703

The Bear Inn
Market Place
Faversham
Kent
Tel 1795 532688
*Closest pub to Shepherd
Neame Brewery.*

The Elephant Inn
31 The Mall
Faversham
Kent
Tel 1795 590157
Beer festival in early June.

Kings Head
117 High St.
Hythe
Kent
Tel 1303 266283

Dog & Bear
The Square
Lenham
Maidstone
Kent ME17 2PG
Tel 1622 858219
*Built in 1602 as a coaching
inn.*

**Bush, Blackbird &
 Thrush**
Bush Rd.
E Peckham
Tonbridge
Kent TN12 5LW
Tel 1622 817349
*Range of cask beers. Near
Whitbread Hop Farm.*

Cricketers Inn
South St.
Dorking
Surrey RH4 2JU
Tel 1306 889938

The Plough
Orestan Ln.
Effingham
Surrey
Tel 13724 58121

White Hart
1 High St.
Hampton Wick
Surrey KT1 4DA
Tel 181 977 1786

Fox & Pelican
Headley Rd.
Grayshott
Hindhead
Surrey GU26 6OG
Tel 1428 604757

Home Cottage
Redstone Hill
Redhill
Surrey RH1 4AN
Tel 1737 762771

Princes Head
28 The Green
Richmond
Surrey TW9 1LX
Tel 181 940 1572
C17 pub.

Woodman Arms
Hammerpot
Angmering on Sea
W Sussex
Tel 1906 74240

Park Tavern
11 Priory Rd.
Chichester
W Sussex PO19 1NS
Tel 1243 785057

Dorset Arms
22 Malling St.
Lewes
W Sussex BN7 2RD
Tel 1273 477110

James King
Old Brighton Rd.
Pease Pottage
W Sussex
Tel 1293 612261
*Named after the founder of
King and Barnes Brewery.*

The Bridge
87 High St.
Shoreham by Sea
W Sussex BN4 5DE
Tel 1273 452477

Of Historic Interest

**Fleur de Lis Heritage
 Center**
Preston St.
Faversham
Kent ME13 8NS
Tel 1795 534542
Housed in C15 inn.

**The Whitbread Hop
 Farm**
Beltring
Paddock Wood
Kent TN12 6PY
Tel 1622 872068
Fax 1622 872630
*Family park with history of
hop farming, Whitbread Shire
Horse Center, Animal Village,
hot air ballooning, restaurant,
gift shop, and special events.
Open year-round.*

**Tenterden & District
 Museum**
Station Rd.
Tenterden
Kent
Tel 158 06 3350
*Local history, including hop
gardens.*

AREA 3. Dorset, Hampshire, Isle of Wight, Wiltshire

Brewers

Hall & Woodhouse
The Brewery
Blandford Forum
Dorset DT11 9LS
Tel 1258 452141
Fax 1258 454700
Tours available.

J C & R H Palmer
The Old Brewery
Bridport
Dorset DT6 4JA
Tel 1308 22396

Eldridge Pope & Co.
Dorchester Brewery
Weymouth Ave.
Dorchester
Dorset DT1 1QT
Tel 1305 251251
Fax 1305 258300
Tours available.

Poole Brewery
The Brewhouse
68 High St.
Poole
Dorset BH15 1DA
Tel 1202 685288
Brewery and pub. Poole Bitter, Bosun Bitter.

Devenish
Trinity Ho.
Trinity St.
Weymouth
Dorset

Coopers of Wessex
P.O.B. 130
Business Pk.
Southcote Rd.
Bournemouth
Hants
Tel 1202 295640

Ballard's Brewery
Old Sawmill, #C
Nyewood
Rogate
Petersfield
Hants GU33 5HA
Tel 1730 821362

George Gale & Co.
The Hampshire Brewery
Horndean
Portsmouth
Hants PO8 0DA
Tel 1705 571212
Fax 1705 598641

Ringwood Brewery
138 Christchurch Rd.
Ringwood
Hants BH24 3AP
Tel 1425 471177

Wadworth & Co.
Northgate Brewery
Devizes
Wilts SN10 1JW
Tel 1380 723361

Mole's Brewery
5 Merlin Way
Bowerhill
Melksham
Wilts SN12 6TJ
Tel 1225 704734

Bunces Brewery
Old Mill
Netheravon
Wilts SP4 9QB
Tel 1980 70631

Gibbs Mew
Anchor Brewery
Netherhampton Rd.
Salisbury
Wilts SP2 8RA
Tel 1722 411911
Fax 1722 411486

Archer's Ales
London St.
Swindon
Wilts SN1 5DG
Tel 1793 496789

Arkell's Brewery
Kingsdown Brewery
Upper Stratton
Swindon
Wilts SN2 6RU
Tel 1793 823026

Wiltshire Brewing Co.
The Old Brewery
Church St.
Tisbury
Wilts SP3 6NH
Tel 1747 870666

Ushers Brewery
Parade Ho.
Fore St.
Trowbridge
Wilts BA14 8JY
Tel 1225 763171

Places to Enjoy Beer

Castle Tavern
7 Church St.
Christchurch
Dorset

The Tavern
Rossmore Rd.
Upper Parkstone
Poole
Dorset
Tel 1202 740688

Fountain Inn
Enmore Green
Shaftesbury
Dorset

The Stable
Albion St.
Brighton
E Sussex

The Kings Head
The Square
Wickham
Fareham
Hants PO17 5JN
Tel 1329 832123

Old House at Home
2 South St.
Havant
Hants
Tel 1705 483464

Still & West
2 Bath Square
Portsmouth
Hants PO1 2JL
Tel 1705 821567
C18 pub once used by press gangs, who pressed unsuspecting young men into the British Navy.

Alice Lisle
Rockford Green
Ringwood
Hants BB24 3NA
Tel 1425 474700
Named after one of the victims of Judge Jeffries, the Hanging Judge.

The White Horse
High St.
Whitwell
Ventnor
Isle of Wight PO38 2PY
Tel 1983 730375

Retail Outlets

Belgian Biere Co.
23 Monacrh Way
West End
Southampton
Hants SO3 3JQ
Tel 1703 470277
Large range of Belgian beers.

AREA 4. Avon, Cornwall, Devon, Gloucestershire, Somerset

Brewers

Oakhill
Old Brewery
High St.
Oakhill
Bath
Avon BA3 5AS
Tel 1749 840134

Bristol Brewery
Counterslip
Bristol
Avon BS1 6EX
Tel 1272 297222
Fax 1272 276150
Courage Group.

Butcombe Brewery
Butcombe
Blagdon
Bristol
Avon BS18 6XQ
Tel 1275 472240

Courage
Bristol Brewery
Counterslip
Bristol
Avon BS1 6EX
Tel 1272 279222

Smiles Brewing Co.
Colston Yard
Colston St.
Bristol
Avon BR1 5BD
Tel 1272 297350

Blue Anchor
Helston
Cornwall
Brewpub.

St. Austell Brewery Co.
63 Tre-varthian Rd.
St. Austell
Cornwall PL25 4BY
Tel 1726 74444

Thompsons
London Inn
11 West St.
Ashburton
Devon TQ13 7BD
Tel 1364 52478

Summerskills
15 Pomphlett Fm.
Broxston Dr.
Billacombe
Devon PL9 4BG
Tel 1752 481283

Exe Valley Brewery
Lan Farm
Silverton
Exeter
Devon EX5 4HF
Tel 1392 860406

Otter Brewery
Mathayes
Luppitt
Honiton
Devon EX14 0SA
Tel 1404 891285

Furgusons Plympton Brewery
Valley Rd.
Plympton
Plymouth
Devon PL7 3LQ
Tel 1752 330171

Blackawton Brewery
Washbourne
Totnes
Devon TQ9 7UF
Tel 180423 339

Whitbread
Monson Ave.
Cheltenham
Gloucs GL50 4EL
Tel 1452 331155

Uley Brewery
The Old Brewery
Uley
Dursley
Gloucs FL11 5TB
Tel 1453 860120

Donnington Brewery
Stow on the Wold
Gloucs GL54 1EP
Tel 1451 30603

Wickwar Brewing Co.
Old Cider Mill
Station Rd.
Wickwar
Gloucs GL12 8NB
Tel 1454 294168

Royal Clarence Hotel &
  Brewery
The Esplanade
Burnham on Sea
Somerset TA8 1BQ
Tel 1278 783138

Ash Vine Brewery
White Hart
Trudoxhill
Frome
Somerset BA11 5DP
Tel 1373 836344

Cotleigh Brewery
Ford Rd.
Wiveliscombe
Somerset TA4 2RE
Tel 1984 24086

Exmoor Ales
Golden Hill Brewery
Wiveliscombe
Somerset TA4 2NY
Tel 1984 23798

Places to Enjoy Beer
The Swan Inn
Pennsylvania
Bath
Avon

Albert Inn
West St.
Bedminster
Bristol
Avon

Garland Ox
Bodmin
Cornwall

Swann Inn
Kenwyn St.
Truro
Cornwall

Mill on the Exe
Bonhill Rd.
Exeter
Devon

Oxenham Arms
South Zeal
Devon
C13 coaching inn. Great food.

Bath Arms
Cheddar
Somerset

Of Historic Interest
North Cornwall Museum
The Clease
Camelford
Cornwall
*Cidermaking exhibit. Rural
life in North Cornwall.*

Chard & District
  Museum
High St.
Chard
Somerset
Tel 1460 65091

*Local history. Cidermaking
exhibit.*

AREA 5.
Bedfordshire,
Berkshire,
Buckinghamshire,
Hertfordshire,
Middlesex,
Oxfordshire

Brewers
Charles Wells
The Brewery
Havelock St.
Bedford
Beds MK40 4LU
Tel 1234 272766
Fax 1234 279000

Banks & Taylor Brewery
The Brewery
Shefford
Beds SG17 5DZ
Tel 1462 815080

Nix Wincott Brewery
Three Fyshes Inn
Bridge St.
Turvey
Beds MK43 8ER
Tel 1223 064264

Chiltern Brewery
Nash Lee Rd.
Terrick
Aylesbury
Bucks HP17 0TQ
Tel 1296 613647

The Griffin
Caversham Bridge
Reading
Berks

Swan Hotel
The Hythe
Staines
Middx TW18 3JB
Tel 1784 452494
C18 riverside inn with
conservatory overlooking the
river.

Load of Hay
Villiers St.
Uxbridge
Middx

McMullen & Sons
Hertford Brewery
26 Old Cross
Hertford
Herts SG14 1RD
Tel 1992 584911

Berkshire Brewery
Imperial Way
Reading
Herts RG2 0PN
Tel 1734 222988
Fax 1734 312005
Courage Group.

Courage Ltd.
Ashby Ho
1 Bridge St.
Staines
Middx TW18 4TP
Tel 1784 466199
Fax 1784 468131
Head office.

Morland & Co.
The Brewery
Ock St.
P.O. Box 5
Abingdon
Oxon OX 14 5DD
Tel 1235 553377

Hook Norton
  Brewery Co.
Brewery Ln.
Hook Norton
Banbury
Oxon
Tel 1608 737 210

W. H. Brakspear & Sons
The Brewery
New St.
Henley on Thames
Oxon RG 9 2BU
Tel: 0491 573636

Morrell's Brewery
Lion Brewery
St. Thomas St.
Oxford
Oxon OX 1 1LA
Tel 1864 792013

Glenny Brewery Co.
Two Rivers Brewery
Station Ln.
Witney
Oxon OX 8 6BH
Tel 1993 702574

Places to Enjoy Beer

Royal Oak
Peel Rd.
Wealdstone
Middx

The Eagle & Child
N Woodstock Rd.
Oxford
Oxon
Next to the Ashmolean.
Pleasant pub with a very
small garden at the back.
Once the hangout of the
Inklings (J.R.R. Tolkien, C. S.
Lewis, Charles Williams).

Queens Arms
Park End St.
Oxford
Oxon

Retail Outlets

The Beer Cellar
Business Center
Unit 10
Wenman Rd.
Thame
Oxon OX9 3XA
Tel 1844 26050
Fax 1844 260560
Mail order.

AREA 6. Derbyshire, Herefordshire, Northamptonshire, Shropshire, Staffordshire, Warwickshire, West Midlands, Worcestershire

Brewers

Wye Valley Brewery
69 St. Owen St.
Hereford
Hereford HR1 2JQ
Tel 1432 274968

Wood Brewery
Wistanstow
Craven Arms
Salop SY7 8DG
Tel 1588 672523

Hanby Ales
Unit C9
Wem Ind Estate
Wem
Salop SY4 5SG
Tel 1939 32432

Bass Brewers
137 High St.
Burton upon Trent
Staffs DE14 1JZ
Tel 1283 511000
Fax 1283 513578

Burton Bridge Brewery
23 Bridge St.
Burton upon Trent
Staffs DE14 1SY
Tel 1283 510573

Ind Coope Burton Brewery
107 Station St.
Burton upon Trent
Staffs DE14 1BZ
Tel 1283 31111
Guided tours, visitors' center, tastings, food. Burton Ale, Double Diamond, Skol, Ansell's Best Bitter, Castlemaine XXXX.

Marston
Thompson and Evershed
The Brewery
P.O. Box 26
Shobnall Rd.
Burton upon Trent
Staffs DE14 2BW
Tel 1283 31131

Banks's
Park Brewery
Lovatt St.
Wolverhampton
Staffs WV1 4NY
Tel 1902 711811

Daniel Batham & Son
Delph Brewery
The Delph
Brierley Hill
W Midlands DY5 2TN
Tel 1384 77229

Holden's Brewery
George St.
Woodsetton
Dudley
W Midlands DY1 4LN
Tel 1902 880051

Sarah Hughes Brewery
Beacon Hotel
Bilston St.
Sedgeley
Dudley
W Midlands DY3 1JE
Tel 1902 883380

Enville Brewery
Enville Hall
Stourton
Stourbridge
W Midlands

Highgate Brewery
Sandymount Rd.
Walsall
W Midlands WS1 3AR
Tel 1922 23168

Holt, Plant & Deakin
Dudley Rd.
Wolverhampton
W Midlands WV2 3AF
Tel 1902 450504

Aston Manor Brewery Co.
Thim-blemill Ln.
Aston
Birmingham
Warks B7 5HF
Tel 121 328 4336

Bass Brewing
Cape Hill Brewery
P.O. Box 27
Birmingham
Warks B16 0PQ
Tel 1271 448 1481
Fax 121 558 2515

Faithful City Brewery
32 Friar St.
Worcester
Worcs
Tel 1905 613177

Places to Enjoy Beer

Jonty Farmer
Kedleston Rd.
Derby
Derbs DE3 1FZ
Tel 1332 292312

The Newdigate Arms
High Rd. E
W Hallam
Derbs DE7 6HN
Tel 1602 320604

The George
Hardborough Rd.
Brixworth
Northants NN6 9BX
Tel 1604 881439

The Plume of Feathers
Harley
Much Wenlock
Salop
Tel 1952 727360

Seven Stars
Coleham
Shrewsbury
Salop

Horse & Jockey
15 Jockey Bank
Ironbridge
Telford
Salop TF8 7PD
Tel 1952 433798

The Meadow Inn
Buildwas Rd.
Ironbridge
Telford
Salop TF8 7BJ
Tel 1952 433193

Royal Oak
High St.
Eccleshall
Staffs

The Hollybush
Penn Rd
Wolverhampton
Staffs

The Vine
The Delph
Brierley Hill
W Midlands DY5 2TN
*Also known as the Bull &
Bladder.*

The Malt Shovel
Spon End
Coventry
W Midlands

Brunswick Arms
Malvern Rd.
St. John
Worcester
Worcs

Of Historic Interest

Revolution House
Old Whittington
Chesterfield
Derbs
Tel 1246 453554
*Originally an alehouse where
plotters met to plan the
revolution of 1688.*

Bass Museum
Horninglow St.
Burton upon Trent
Staffs
Tel 1283 511000
*7000 years of ales and beers,
plus the history of Bass ale
and the transport of beer.
Experimental brewhouse.
Free. Licensed bar, restaurant,
souvenir shop, Shire horse
stables.*

**Heritage Brewery
Museum**
Anglesey Rd.
Burton upon Trent
Staffs DE14 3PF
Tel 1283 69226
*Working brewery museum.
Open October to March,
Thursday to Saturday; April
to September, Monday to
Saturday. Admission includes
free beer sample.*

**Staffs County Museum &
Park Farm**
Milford
Stafford
Staffs
Tel 1889 881388
*C18 mansion, museum in
servants' quarters. Includes
working brewhouse, working
farm, and gardens.*

Black Country Museum
Tipton Rd.
Dudley
W Midlands
Tel 121 557 9643
*Living museum of local
history includes pub, local
crafts.*

AREA 7.
Cambridgeshire,
Essex, Lincolnshire,
Norfolk, Suffolk

Brewers

Elgood & Sons
North Brink Brewery
Wisbech
Cambs PE13 1LN
Tel 1945 583160

North Brink Brewery
Wisbech
Cambs PE13 1PN
Tel 1945 583160

Crouch Vale Brewery
12 Redhills Rd.
S Woodham Ferrers
Chelmsford
Essex CM3 5UP
Tel 1245 322744

T D Ridley & Sons
Hartford End Brewery
Chelmsford
Essex CM3 1JZ
Tel 1371 820316

George Bateman & Son
Salem Bridge Bry
Mill Ln.
Wainfleet
Skegness
Lincs PE24 4JE
Tel 1754 880317
Fax 1754 880939

Broadland Brewery
Woodbastwick
Norwich
Norfolk NR13 6SW
Tel 1603 720353

**Woodforde's Norfolk
Ales**
Broadland Brewery
Woodbastwick
Norwich
Norfolk NR13 6SW
Tel 1603 720353

Reepham Brewery
1 Collers Way
Reepham
Norfolk NR10 4SW
Tel 1603 871091

Greene King & Sons
Westgate Brewery
Bury St. Edmunds
Suffolk IP33 1QT
Tel 1284 763222

Tolly Cobbold
The Brewery
Cliff Rd.
Ipswich
Suffolk IP3 0AZ
Tel 1473 231723

Adnams & Co.
Sole Bay Brewery
Southwold
Suffolk IP18 6JW
Tel 1502 722424

Mauldons Brewery
7 Addison Rd.
Chilton Ind. Est.
Sudbury
Suffolk CO10 6YW
Tel 1787 311055

Nethergate Brewery Co.
11–13 High St.
Clare
Sudbury
Suffolk CO10 8NY
Tel 1787 277244

Places to Enjoy Beer

Star & Garter
Moulsham St.
Chelmsford
Essex

The Spreadeagle
Victoria Ave.
Southen on Sea
Essex

Hope & Anchor
Victoria St.
Grimsby
Lincs
*Three-time winner of local
CAMRA Pub of the Year
award.*

The Green Dragon
Waterside
Lincoln
Lincs
Tel 1522 524950

Denmark Arms
Sandringham Rd.
Norwich
Norfolk

Queens Head Freehouse
39 Churchgate St.
Bury St. Edmunds
Suffolk
Tel 1284 761554

The Chestnut Horse
Great Finborough
Suffolk
Tel 1449 612298

Lord Nelson
81 Fore St.
Ipswich
Suffolk
Tel 1473 254072

Retail Outlets

CPM Specialist Beers
Meads
500 London Rd.
Westcliff
Essex
Tel 1702 345474
*Over 150 Continental brews,
homebrew supplies, gifts.*

Of Historic Interest

**Cambridge & County
  Folk Museum**
2–3 Castle St.
Cambridge
Cambs
*Housed in the former White
Horse Inn. Three centuries of
county life.*

**Stamford Brewery
  Museum**
All Saints St.
Stamford
Lincs
Tel 1780 52186
*Complete Victorian steam
brewery. Displays include
cooperage, brewer's office,
home brewing. Souvenir shop.*

Bygones at Holkham
Holkham Park
Wells next the Sea
Norfolk
Tel 1328 710806
*Victorian life, including a
brewery exhibit.*

Lavenham Guildhall
Market Square
Lavenham
Suffolk
*Local history including
cooperage exhibit.*

AREA 8. Cheshire, Cumbria, Lancashire, Leicestershire, Greater Manchester, Merseyside

Brewers

Frederic Robinson
Unicorn Brewery
Stockport
Cheshire SK1 1JJ
Tel 161 480 6571

Burtonwood Brewery
Bold Ln.
Burtonwood Village
Warrington
Cheshire WA5 4PJ
Tel 1925 225131

Coach House Brewing Co.
Wharf St.
Warrington
Cheshire
Tel 1925 232800

Tetley Walker
The Brewery
Dallam Ln.
Warrington
Cheshire WA2 7NU
Tel 1925 31231

Jennings Bros.
Castle Brewery
Cockermouth
Cumbria CA13 9NE
Tel 1900 823214

Dent Brewery
Hollins
Cowgill
Dent
Cumbria LA10 5TQ
Tel 15875 326

Joseph Holt
Derby Brewery
Empire St.
Cheetham
Greater Manchester M3 1JD
Tel 161 834 3285

West Coast Brewery Co.
Kings Arms
Helmshaw Walk
Chorlton on Medlock
Greater Manchester M13 9TH
Tel 161 273 1053

Oak Brewing Co.
Phoenix Brewery
Green Ln.
Heywood
Greater Manchester OL10 2EP
Tel 1706 627009

Hydes Anvil Brewery
46 Moss Ln. W
Manchester
Greater Manchester M15 5PH
Tel 161 226 1317

J W Lees & Co.
Greetgate Brewery
Middleton Junction
Manchester
M24 2AX
Tel 161 643 2487

The Whitbread Beer Co.
Boddingtons Brewery
P.O.B. 23
Strangewys
Manchester
Greater Manchester M60 3WB
Tel 161 828 2000

Daniel Thwaites
Star Brewery
P.O. Box 50
Blackburn
Lancs BB1 5BU
Tel 1254 54431

Moorhouse's Brewery
4 Moorhouse St.
Burnley
Lancs BB11 5EN
Tel 1282 22864

Mitchell's of Lancaster
11 Moor Ln.
Lancaster
Lancs LA1 1QB
Tel 1524 63773
Fax 1524 843345

Mitchell's of Lancaster
11 Moor Ln.
Lancaster
Lancs LA1 1QB
Tel 1524 63773

The Whitbread Beer Co.
Cuerdale Ln.
Samlesbury
Preston
Lancs PR5 0XD
Tel 1772 877 671
Tours Monday to Thursday, start 7:30PM. Booking needed.

Everards Brewery Ltd.
Tiger Bry
Castle Acres
Narborough
Leicester
Leics LE9 5BY
Tel 1533 630900

Hoskins Brewery
Beaumanor Brewery
Beaumanor Rd.
Leicester
Leics LE4 5QE
Tel 1533 661122

Hoskins & Oldfield
North Mills
Frog Island
Leicester
Leics LE3 5DH
Tel 1533 532191

Grolsch-Ruddles Brewing Co.
Langham
Oakham
Leics LE15 7JD
Tel 1572 756911

Robert Cain Brewery
Stanhope St.
Liverpool
Merseyside L8 5XJ
Tel 151 709 8734

Places to Enjoy Beer

Queens Head
Main St.
Frodsham
Cheshire

— 224 —

Fox & Hounds
Tilston
Malpas
Cheshire

Tithe Barn Hotel
Station St.
Cockermouth
Cumbria

Blundell Arms
Upper Aughton Rd.
Birkdale
Lancs

Unicorn Hotel
North Rd.
Preston
Lancs

The White Horse
off Front St.
Birstall
Leics LE4 4EF
Tel 1533 674490

The Dove
Dwoning Dr.
Evington
Leics
Tel 1533 419037

Crown & Thistle
16 Loseby Ln.
Leicester
Leics LE5 5DR
Tel 1533 622480

The Maltings
Knightthorpe Rd.
Loughborough
Leics
Tel 1509 268587

The Coach & Horses
Field Head
Markfield
Leics
Tel 1530 242312

The Mill on the Soar
Coventry Rd.
Sutton in the Elms
Leics
Tel 1455 282419

The Rose & Crown
Main St.
Thurnby
Leics
Tel 1533 419075

The White Lion
Main St.
Whissendine
Leics
Tel 1664 79233

The Firs
202 Oadby Rd.
Wigston
Leics
Tel 1533 888517

Of Historic Interest

**Museum of Local Crafts
   & Industry**
Burnley
Lancs
Tel 1282 24213
Housed in old brewhouse.

Pilkington Glass Museum
Prescott Rd.
St. Helens
Lancs
Tel 1744 692014
*Evolution of glass-making
techniques.*

Wigan Pier
Wigan
Merseyside WN3 4EU
*Living history of 1900. Drink
in the pub, work down the
mine, more.*

AREA 9. Humberside, Nottinghamshire, Yorkshire

Brewers

Whitbread
P.O. Box 13
Castle Eden
Hartlepool
Cleveland TS27 4SX
Tel 1429 836007
*Tours Monday to Friday; 21
days' written notice needed.*

Old Mill Brewery
Mill St.
Snaith
Goole
Humberside DN14 9HS
Tel 1405 861813

Hull Brewery Co.
144–148 English St.
Hull
Humberside HU3 2BT
Tel 1482 586364

Malton Brewery Co.
Crown Hotel
Wheelgate
Malton
N Yorks YO17 0HP
Tel 1653 697580
*Small brewery supplying
about 20 pubs in N Yorkshire
with traditional ales. Tours by
arrangement. Double Chance
Bitter, Pickwick's Porter, Owd
Bob.*

Cropton Brewery
New Inn
Cropton
Pickering
N Yorks YO18 8HH
Tel 17515 330

T & R Theakston
The Brewery
Masham
Ripon
N Yorks HG4 4DX
Tel 1765 89544
Visitors' center, tours, and a
cooperage. Best Bitter, XB,
Old Peculier.

Bass Brewing
Tower Brewery
Wetherby Rd.
Tadcaster
N Yorks LS24 9SD
Tel 1937 732361

John Smith's
The Brewery
Tadcaster
N Yorks LS24 9SA
Tel 1937 832091
Fax 1937 833537
Courage Group. Yorkshire
Bitter, Magnet.

Samuel Smith Old
   Brewery H
High St.
Tadcaster
N Yorks LS24 9SB
Tel 1937 832225
Fax 1927 834673
Water for the beers is drawn
from 200-year-old well. Tours
available.

Marston Moor Brewery
Crown Inn
Kirk Hammerton
York
N Yorks YO5 8DD
Tel 1423 330341

Mansfield Brewery Co.
Littleworth
Mansfield
Notts NG18 1AB
Tel 1623 25691
Fax 1623 631062

Riding Traditional Bitter and
Mild, Old Baily Strong Bitter.

Hardy's & Hanson's
Kimberley Brewery
Kimberley
Nottingham
Notts NG16 2NS
Tel 1602 383611

Home Brewery
Mansfield Rd.
Daybrook
Nottingham
Notts NG5 6BU
Tel 1602 269741

Stocks Doncaster
   Brewery
The Hallcross
33 Hallgate
Doncaster
S Yorks DN1 3NL
Tel 1302 328213

S H Ward & Co.
Sheaf Brewery
Eccleshall Rd.
Sheffield
S Yorks S11 8HZ
Tel 1742 755155
Tours by arrangement.
Sheffield and Thorne Best
Bitter, Kirby Strong.

Trough Brewery
Louisa St.
Idle
Bradford
W Yorks BD10 8NE
Tel 1274 613450

Fountain Head Brewery
Ovendon Woods
Halifax
W Yorks HX2 0TL
Tel 1422 357188
Fax 1422 348937
Courage Group.

Samuel Webster &
   Wilsons
Fountainhead Brewery
Ovendon Wood
Halifax
W Yorks HX2 0TL
Tel 1422 357188
Wilsons Original Mild and
Bitter, Yorkshire Bitter.

Timothy Taylor & Co.
Knowle Spring Brewery
Keighley
W Yorks BD21 1AW
Tel 1535 603139

Joshua Tetley & Son
The Brewery
Hunslett Rd.
Leeds
W Yorks LS1 1QG
Tel 1532 435282
Tetley Mild and Bitter.

H B Clark & Co.
Westgate Brewery
Wakefield
W Yorks WF2 9SW
Tel 1924 373328

Places to Enjoy Beer

Rose & Crown
North Bar Without
Beverley
Humberside HU17 8DP
Tel 1482 862532

White Hart
20 Westgate
North Cave
Brough
Humberside HU15 2NJ
Tel 1430 422432
Built in 1773 as a coaching
house.

Nelsons Hotel
Cleveland St.
Doncaster
Humberside DN1 7RH
Tel 1302 344550

The Apollo
1082 Holderness High Rd.
Hull
Humberside HU9 4AH
Tel 1482 703365

Kingstown Arms
Kingstown Hotel
Hull Rd.
Hedon
Hull
Humberside HU12 9DJ
Tel 1482 890461

Ye Old Corn Exchange
North Church Side
Hull
Humberside HU1 1RP
Tel 1482 26366

Cayley Arms Hotel
Allerston
Pickering
N Yorks YO18 7PJ
Tel 1723 859338

Buck Inn
Thornton Watlass
Ripon
N Yorks HG4 4AH
Tel 1677 422461

Golden Ball
31 Sandside
Scarborough
N Yorks YO11 1NU
Tel 1723 353899
Small outdoor beer garden

Angel & White Horse
Bridge St.
Tadcaster
N Yorks LS24 9SB
Tel 1937 836470

Hole in the Wall
High Petergate
York
N Yorks YO1 2EH
Tel 1904 634468

Walkers Bar
Micklegate
York
N Yorks

Horse & Jockey
Front St.
Arnold
Notts

The Old Castle
1 Castle Rd.
Nottingham
Notts NG1 6AA
Tel 1602 413311

Ye Old Trip to Jerusalem
Brewhouse Yard
Nottingham
Notts NG1 6AD
Tel 1602 473171
*Reputedly the oldest pub in
the country.*

Griffin's Head
Moor Rd.
Papplewick
Notts NG15 8EN
Tel 1602 633672

Edmund Arms
25 Worsborough Village
Barnsley
S Yorks S70 5LW
Tel 1433 51380

Green Tree
Bearswood Grn.
Hatfield Woodhouse
Doncaster
S Yorks DN3 2QR
Tel 1302 840305
Meals, outdoor beer garden.

Devonshire Arms
Eccleshall Rd.
Sheffield
S Yorks S11 8JB
Tel 1742 72202

Coach & Horses
Eastgate
Honley
Huddersfield
W Yorks HD7 2PA
Tel 1484 661871

Liquorice Bush
Market Place
Pontefract
W Yorks WF8 1AX
Tel 1977 703843

Of Historic Interest

York Castle Museum
Eye of York
York
N Yorks YO1 1RY
Tel 1904 653611
*Museum of everyday life
including pub.*

W Yorks Folk Museum
Shibden Hall
Shibden Park
Halifax
W Yorks
*Regional folklife, including
brewhouse, reconstructed Old
Crispin Inn.*

Abbey House Museum
Kirkstall
Leeds
W Yorks
Tel 1532 755821
*Social history of Leeds,
including restored pub.*

AREA 10. Cleveland, County Durham, Northumberland, Tyne and Wear

Brewers

J W Cameron & Co.
Lion Brewery
P.O. Box 21
Hartlepool
Cleveland TS24 7QS
Tel 1429 266666
Traditional Bitter, Strongarm.

North Yorkshire Brewing Co.
84 N Ormesby Rd.
Middlesbrough
Cleveland TS24 2AG
Tel 1642 226224
Flying Herbert, Dizzy Dick, Samson Ale, Double Maxim.

Butterknowle Brewery
Lynesack
Butterknowle
Bishop Auckland
Co. Durham DL13 5QF
Tel 1388 710109

Northern Clubs Federation Brewery
Lancaster Rd.
Dunston
Gateshead
Tyne and Wear NE11 9JR
Tel 191 460 9023
Fax 191 460 1297

Big Lamp Brewery
1 Summerhill St.
Newcastle upon Tyne
Tyne and Wear NE4 6EJ
Tel 191 261 3227

Hadrian Brewery
Unit 7
Foundry Ln. Ind. Est.
Byker
Newcastle upon Tyne
Tyne and Wear NE6 1LH
Tel 191 276 5302

Newcastle Breweries
Tyne Brewery
Gallowgate
Newcastle upon Tyne
Tyne and Wear NE99 1RA
Tel 191 232 5091

Vaux Breweries
The Brewery
Sunderland
Tyne and Wear SR1 3AN
Tel 191 567 6277

Places to Enjoy Beer

The Zetland
High St.
Marske by the Sea
Cleveland

Tap & Barrel
near Bus Station
Middlesborough
Cleveland

Sun Inn
Knowle St.
Stockton
Cleveland

Colpitts Hotel
Hawthorne Terrace
Durham
Co. Durham

Red Lion
Trimdon Village
Hartlepool
Co. Durham

Bay Hotel
Sea Front
Cullercoats
Tyne and Wear

Bridge Hotel
Castle Garton
Newcastle upon Tyne
Tyne and Wear

Of Historic Interest

Open Air Museum
Off A693
Beamish
Co. Durham DH9 0RG
Tel 1207 231811
Living history museum with Victorian pub.

AREA 11. Wales

Brewers

Plassey Brewery
Eyton
Wrexham
Clwyd LL13 0SP
Tel 1978 780277

Felinfoel Brewery Co.
Farmers Row
Felinfoel
Llanelli
Dyfed SA14 8LB
Tel 1554 773357
Fax 1554 752452

The Whitbread Beer Co.
The Brewery
Magor
Gwent NP6 3DA
Tel 1633 880661
Tours Tuesday to Thursday, booking needed.

S A Brain & Co.
Old Brewery
St. Mary St.
P.O. Box 53
Cardiff
S Glam CF1 1SP
Tel 1222 399022

Bullmastiff
5 Anchor Way
Penarth
S Glam CF6 1SF
Tel 1222 702958

Places to Enjoy Beer

Bulkeley Arms
Beaumaris
Anglesey

Bee & Station Hotel
Rhyl
Clwyd

Ivy Bush Hotel
Brecon Rd.
Pontardawe
Glamorgan

Royal Hotel
Usk
Gwent

London Hotel
141 Mostyn St.
Llandudno
Gwynedd

The Bell Country Inn
Llanyre
Powys
Tel 1597 823959
Fax 1597 825899
Inn with good food, rooms.

AREA 12. Scotland

Brewers

Caledonian Brewing Co.
Slateford Rd.
Edinburgh
EH11 1P4
Tel 131 337 1286
Fax 131 313 2370

Maclay & Co.
Thistle Brewery
Alloa
Clackmannan FK10 1ED
Tel 1259 723387

Harviestoun Brewery
Dollar
Clackmannan FK14 7LX
Tel 12594 2141

Belhaven Brewery Co.
Spott Rd.
Dunbar
E Lothian EH42 1RS
Tel 1368 62734
Fax 1368 64450

Broughton Brewery
Broughton
Biggar
Lanark ML12 6HQ
Tel 18994 345
Fax 18994 474

Caledonian Brewery Co.
Slateford Rd.
Edinburgh
Lothian EH11 1PH
Tel 131 337 1286

McEwan & Younger
Fountain Brewery
Fountain Bridge
Edinburgh
Lothian EH3 9YY
Tel 131 229 9377
Scottish and Newcastle.

Orkney Brewery
Quoyloo
Sandwick
Orkney KW16 3LT
Tel 1856 84802

**Tranquair House
Brewery**
Innerleithen
Peebles EH44 6PW
Tel 1896 831370

Places to Enjoy Beer

Bow Bar
West Bow
Edinburgh
Lothian

Cadenhead
172 Canongate
Edinburgh
Lothian EH8 8DF
Tel 131 556 5864

The Guildford
W Register St.
Edinburgh
Lothian

Bon Accord
Charing Cross
Glasgow
Strathclyde

The Mercantile
Commercial St.
Dundee
Tayside

Of Historic Interest

**Buckie Maritime
Museum**
Cluny Pl.
Buckie
Grampian
Tel 1309 73701
*Local history including
coopering.*

**Hamilton District
Museum**
129 Muir St.
Hamilton
Strathclyde ML3 6BJ
Tel 1698 283981
*Local history in C17 coaching
inn.*

AREA 13. Northern Ireland

Brewers

Bass Ireland
Ulster Brewery
Glen Rd.
Belfast
BT11 8BY
Tel 1232 301301

Places to Enjoy Beer

The Station Bar
3 Lower English St.
Armagh
Tel 1861 523 731

McCarrol's
5 Ann St.
Ballycastle
Co. Antrim
Tel 12657 621 23

Jenny Watts
High St.
Bangor
Co. Down
Tel 1247 270 401

Crown Liquor Saloon
46 Gt. Victoria St.
Belfast
A National Trust monument.

Dan Magennis
May St.
Belfast

The Front Page
9 Ballymoney St.
Belfast
Tel 1232 324 924

Hannigan's
Fountain St.
Belfast

Kitchen Bar
Telfair St.
Belfast

Morning Star
Ann St.
Belfast

Morrison's
21 Bedford St.
Belfast 13
Tel 1232 248 458

Lurig Inn
5 Bridge St.
Cushenhall
Co. Antrim
Tel 12667 715 27

The Dungloe
41–43 Waterloo St.
Derry
Tel 1504 267 716

Anchor Bar
9 Bryansford Rd
Newcastle
Co. Down
Tel 13967 233 44

AREA 14. Isle of Man

Brewers

**Mount Murray
Brewing Co.**
Bushy's Brewery
Mt. Murray
Braddan
Isle of Man
Tel 1624 661244

Isle of Man Breweries
Falcon Brewery
Douglas
Isle of Man
Tel 1624 661140

AREA 15. Channel Isles, Scilly Isles

Brewers

Guernsey Brewery
S Esplanade
St. Peter Port
Guernsey CI
Tel 1481 720143
Fax 1481 710658

R W Randall
Vauxlaurens Brewery
St. Julians Ave.
St. Peter Port
Guernsey CI
Tel 1481 720134
Fax 1481 713233

Ann St. Brewery Co.
57 Ann St.
St. Helier
Jersey CI
Tel 1534 31561
Fax 1534 67033

Places to Enjoy Beer

Pomme d'Or Hotel
St. Helier
Jersey CI

About the Author

Heather Wood is English, but has lived in New York City for the last umpteen years.

In the late sixties, Wood was a professional folksinger. With her group, The Young Tradition, she toured extensively in the UK, the US, and Canada, singing traditional English folksongs a capella and made several records. She currently sings with David Jones (English) and Tom Gibney (American) in a group called Poor Old Horse.

Wood also worked in the professional audio industry for Dolby Laboratories (UK) and Eventide (USA). She has spent several years in publishing, with ABC Consumer Magazines *(High Fidelity, Musical America)* and Tor Books.

Wood is the author of a book entitled *101 Marvelous Money-Making Ideas for Kids 12 to 15*, published by Tor, and has also written short stories, poems, songs, articles, and reviews, mainly on folk topics. With Leslie Berman, she is co-editor of the *Grass Roots International Folk Resource Directory*, now in its third edition.

Her previous (and sometimes current) occupations include a short spell in the British Army (where she learned to drive a tank), kennelmaid, dress designer, various jobs in the hotel, catering, and retail trades, and working with Sheldon Landwehr, the columnist, critic, and dining editor, whose reviews appear regularly in the *New York Post*.

Hobbies include reading (mostly science fiction, fantasy, and historical romances), traveling, cooking, sewing, knitting, crocheting, collecting stamps, playing Scrabble, and doing English crossword puzzles.

While Wood enjoys the occasional glass of beer, she really prefers cider (the alcoholic variety), and is happy to note that it is beginning to catch on in America.

Other Storey/Garden Way Publishing Books on Beer and Brewing

Beer Across America: A Regional Guide to Brewpubs and Microbreweries by Marty Nachel

The Beer Enthusiast's Guide by Gregg Smith

Better Beer & How to Brew It by M.R. Reese

Brewing the World's Great Beers: A Step-by-Step Guide by Dave Miller

The Complete Handbook of Home Brewing by Dave Miller

Great Beer from Kits: Getting the Most from Kit Brewing by Joe Fisher and Dennis Fisher

Homebrew Favorites: A Coast-to-Coast Collection of more than 240 Beer and Ale Recipes by Karl F. Lutzen & Mark Stevens

Dave Miller's Homebrewing Guide: Everything You Need to Know to Make Great-Tasting Beer by Dave Miller

Secret Life of Beer: Legends, Lore, and Little-Known Facts by Alan D. Eames

A Taste for Beer by Stephen Beaumont

These books are available at your bookstore, homebrew supply shop, or directly from Storey Communications, Inc., Department WM, Schoolhouse Road, Pownal, Vermont 05261.

To order toll-free by phone, call 800-441-5700.